THE MAN-IN-SPACE DICTIONARY

BOOKS BY MARTIN CAIDIN

MAN-IN-SPACE DICTIONARY

BY APOLLO TO THE MOON

AVIATION AND SPACE MEDICINE

RENDEZVOUS IN SPACE

RED STAR IN SPACE

I AM EAGLE!

NEW WORLD FOR MEN

THIS IS MY LAND

THE POWER OF DECISION

AIR FORCE

GOLDEN WINGS

VANGUARD!

COUNTDOWN FOR TOMORROW

THE ASTRONAUTS

THUNDERBIRDS!

SAMURAI!

ZERO!

THUNDERBOLT!

THE SILKEN ANGELS

CROSS-COUNTRY FLYING

LET'S GO FLYING!

WORLDS IN SPACE

WAR FOR THE MOON

THE LONG NIGHT

SPACEPORT U.S.A.

BOEING 707

THE LONG, LONELY LEAP

BLACK THURSDAY

THE ZERO FIGHTER

THE NIGHT HAMBURG DIED

A TORCH TO THE ENEMY

MAN INTO SPACE

TEST PILOT

ROCKETS BEYOND THE EARTH

X-15: FIRST FLIGHT INTO SPACE

ROCKETS AND MISSILES

JETS, ROCKETS AND GUIDED MISSILES

OVERTURE TO SPACE

THE
MAN-IN-SPACE
DICTIONARY

A MODERN GLOSSARY

Written and Compiled by
Martin Caidin

New York
E. P. DUTTON & CO., INC.
1963

Published simultaneously in Canada by Clarke,
Irwin & Company Limited, Toronto and Vancouver

Library of Congress Catalog Card Number:
63–14274

This book is for
my fellow members of
The Canaveral Press Club
and to the "old days"
at the Cape

AUTHOR'S FOREWORD

As the age of the exploration of space grows into a maturity of years and we change from exploration to exploitation, there exists a growing need for a general dictionary of terms that relate to *man* in space. This book is the first such work directed specifically to this need.

Obviously, many of the terms included involve the discretion of the author. Terms concerned with the physiological aspects of aerospace medicine were clearly important. The decision was made to include many of the instrumented, unmanned satellites placed in orbit or sent on deep-space probes, since the data they return from their robot studies affect directly the conduct of manned expeditions to follow. The mechanics of space flight and of certain aspects of atmospheric flight also are included, as well as those terms of rocket engineering which the participant in any manned space venture encounters constantly in his activities. On the same basis, terms relating to astronomy, to lunar and planetary study, will also be found in this dictionary in view of their importance in relationship to manned space efforts.

In the long period of time necessary to produce this volume, the author received the closest co-operation from many groups directly engaged or active in astronautics research. I have been especially fortunate in the close work with and the assistance provided by the Department of the Air Force, especially those offices at the Air Force Missile Test Center,

Aerospace Medical Laboratories, School of Aerospace Medicine, Air University, and the Pentagon. The personnel of the National Aeronautics and Space Administration, especially of the Office of Public Information in Washington, the Manned Spacecraft Center in Houston, the Goddard Space Flight Center in Greenbelt, Maryland, and the Marshall Space Flight Center in Huntsville, Alabama, gave freely of their time and effort.

From such sources much material was compiled. A collection of Air Force glossaries relating to aerospace, medical, aviation, standardized and non-standardized terms was invaluable, as were the publications of NASA, which has begun a major effort in the definition of terms relating to manned space activities. These official publications included successive issues of the Air Force *Glossary of Standardized Terms;* the *Aerospace Glossary,* edited by Woodford Agee Heflin and issued by the Air University; NASA's *Short Glossary of Space Terms,* edited by William H. Allen and B. A. Mulcahy; and others.

A close friend and professional associate, Gilbert Edelman, provided a thorough final review of all material; Mr. Edelman's participation has been one of the strictest critical review, and constitutes a vital measure to the final product.

Despite the earnest attempts to be fully inclusive of terms bearing on this subject, it would be impossible to be so fortunate as to have accomplished the goal of complete coverage. Many terms, to be sure, must be missing. With the swift advance of astronautics, new terms, in the interim between completion of this book and its publication, will be created. These newly emerging terms in the most revolutionary field of science and technology of our time, the manned exploration of space, will, it is hoped, be embodied in future editions of *The Man-in-Space Dictionary.*

MARTIN CAIDIN

A

ABERRATION. The apparent displacement of the position of a particular celestial body due to the speed of the observer.

ABLATION SHIELDS. Ablation materials covering that portion of a spacecraft (or missile nose cone) that first penetrates the atmosphere during re-entry from space. The ablating materials are dissipated (vaporized, carried away) as the heat shield (such as laminated glass resin) reaches temperatures exceeding 2,000°F. In this fashion the tremendous heat of re-entry is carried away from the spacecraft, and the main structure of the vehicle is prevented from heating up to dangerous limits. See **heat shield; re-entry.**

ABORT. To cancel or to destroy a mission. In terms of rocket booster flights, an abort is accomplished when the Range Safety Officer sends a command signal by radio to the rocket. The command signal orders the rocket (1) to shut off the flow of fuel to the motors, thus ending powered operation, and (2) to set off explosive charges that destroy the rocket. See **abort system; ASIS; destruct; destruct button; destruct line; Range Safety Officer.**

ABORT RECOVERY ZONE. In any rocket-boosted, manned space-vehicle launch, that area specifically assigned for the recovery of the personnel involved should it be necessary to abort the mission at any point.

ABORT SYSTEM. Also: *Abort Sensing and Implementation System.* This is an electronic device installed aboard a rocket booster that can react to a dangerous situation 100 times faster than a trained astronaut. It is an "electronic watchdog" that looks for an emergency in the rocket during the liftoff, ascent, and complete flight. In terms of the Atlas-D booster of Project Mercury, the Abort Sensing and Implementation System weighs 36 lbs., is fully automatic, and it goes into full-time operation from the very instant that the Atlas rocket motors ignite. The ASIS monitors all the essential sub-

ABORT SYSTEM. Mercury spacecraft development test of abort system; escape rocket fires to lift boilerplate capsule from ground level

systems of the Atlas, including propulsion, pneumatic, electrical, hydraulic, and flight control. If any one or several of these subsystems fails to operate properly, the abort system "senses" the trouble. Immediately its control unit "flashes an abort command" that ignites the escape rocket atop the manned capsule. The rocket pulls the capsule up and to the side of the booster rocket before the failure of the rocket can damage the manned capsule.

ABSENCE OF CONVECTION. A major problem in spacecraft cabins under sustained zero *g*, solved by constantly using forced air draft and circulation. An example is the burning of a candle. A candle flame receives oxygen as a result of its own updraft of warm exhaust air which in turn draws in fresh air, a process based on the difference in weight of warm and cold air. Under zero-*g* (weightless) conditions, this difference no longer exists, since the air no longer has weight. Under zero-*g* conditions the process of convection ceases; the candle flame is deprived of its oxygen supply and is extinguished immediately. Without forced air circulation, exhaled respiratory gases could collect in the form of a mass or cloud in the immediate vicinity of an astronaut (without his pressure suit and helmet) and impede his oxygen intake. This affects other body processes as well as retarding the exchange of respiratory waste gases. Without convection, heat exchange is carried out solely by radiation between skin, clothing surfaces, and spacecraft interior walls. Under normal conditions in a 1*g* field, half of the body's heat is lost by evaporation and convection. Under zero *g* these processes no longer exist, and heat exchange must be carefully monitored.

ABSOLUTE ZERO. The point at which all molecular motion ceases. This temperature is minus 459.7°F., 273.2°C., or 0° Kelvin.

ACCELERATION. A rate of change in the velocity of a body, with respect to a given direction. *Negative Acceleration* is commonly referred to as *Deceleration*. Acceleration is experienced by a rocket as it moves from the position of rest, prior to the moment of launching, throughout the entire portion of its flight when its rocket engines are operating.

ACCELERATION PROFILE. A description of the variations and peaks of acceleration to which an astronaut is subjected throughout the various portions of a flight, including propulsion phase, atmospheric deceleration, and attitude control movements in free fall. The Acceleration Profile describes, as well, those periods of time during which the astronaut is subjected to the different peaks of gravity forces. During deceleration because of atmospheric resistance, for example, he might endure a force resulting from a deceleration of 8 times normal gravity for a period of 4 minutes.

ACCELERATION TOLERANCE. The maximum amount of *g* forces that a man can withstand during a space mission (1)

before he is unable effectively to control his spaceship, or (2) before he "blacks out" from the forces acting upon his body.

ACCELEROMETER. The "speedometer" of rocket boosters. This is a sensitive device in the control system of a rocket booster that senses and responds to different forces of acceleration. It measures the amount of acceleration, the rate at which the acceleration forces increase, the time of acceleration, and other factors. The accelerometer is linked to the electronic brain of the rocket's control system, and it feeds its information to the robot brain. The electronic brain translates all the different factors of acceleration into the speed of the rocket at any given time. Thus the accelerometer serves as a rocket's "speed indicator."

ACCESS DOORS. Also: *Access Panels.* Locked, hinged, or pressure-secure hatches, panels, or doors which, when removed, provide ready access to electronic, mechanical, control, or other equipment for ease of inspection, servicing, or replacement.

ACCESS ROAD. A road at any launching center, such as Cape Canaveral or Vandenberg Air Force Base, that provides a direct access for vehicles or personnel to a rocket's launch pad. Before any launch, all access roads are closed to all personnel.

ACCOMMODATION. In aerospace medicine, the functional adjustment of the body to environmental changes such as might be encountered under any conditions of aerospace missions.

ACCUMULATOR. A device or apparatus that accumulates or stores up, such as a contrivance in a hydraulic system that stores fluid under pressure. An accumulator is sometimes incorporated within the fuel system of a gas-turbine engine to store up and release fuel under pressure as an aid in starting, prior to the engine's buildup of pressure from its own operation.

ACCUSTOMIZATION. In aerospace medicine, the process of adapting with maximum possible ease and comfort, or with a minimum of discomfort, to an extreme or new environment such as sustained flight in a cramped space cabin or living within the limited confines of a minimal lunar installation.

ACID TRAILER. A trailer rig vehicle that hauls a tank car filled either with acid-based fuels or oxidizers, such as fuming nitric acid.

ACOUSTIC VELOCITY. The speed of propagation of sound waves. Also called "speed of sound." See **sonic.**

ACQUISITION. The process of locating the orbit of a satellite or trajectory of a vehicle in space so that tracking or telemetry data can be gathered. Also, the process of pointing an antenna or telescope so that it is properly oriented to allow gathering of tracking or telemetry data from a space vehicle. See **"locked on."**

ACQUISITION AND TRACKING RADAR. A radar set that locks onto a strong signal and tracks the object reflecting the signal. See **"locked on."**

ACTINIC. Pertaining to electromagnetic radiation capable of initiating photochemical reactions, as in photography or the fading of pigments. Especially pertinent to design of photographic equipment for space vehicles and probes.

ACTIVE SATELLITE. A satellite transmitting a signal, in contrast to a "passive satellite," which does not transmit or generate signals or radiations. An active satellite may transmit environmental data, photography, course data, etc. See **passive satellite.**

ACTUATING SYSTEM. A subsystem in a rocket booster vehicle or spacecraft module that, on a timed or transmitted "command," actuates a device or system by supplying and sustaining the energy for the operation over a specified period of time.

ADAPTER SKIRT. A flange or extension of a booster rocket stage or section that provides a ready means of fitting another stage or section to it. See **interstage section.**

ADHESION. Effect of attractive forces existing between dissimilar molecules.

ADIABATIC. Occurring without gain or loss of heat; a change in the properties—such as volume and pressure—of the contents of an enclosure, without a concomitant exchange of heat between the enclosure and its surroundings.

ADVANCED SATURN. The Saturn C-5. See **Saturn.**

ADVENT. An extensive research program to produce a 24-hour-orbit, instantaneous repeater communications satellite of 1,250 lbs. payload weight. In the summer of 1962, Advent was canceled and replaced with two new Air Force military satellite communications systems: a fully stabilized, 500-lb., high-altitude satellite; and a medium-altitude communications satellite system.

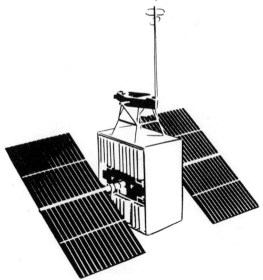

ADVENT military communications satellite; electronics protected against jamming by enemy

AEROASTHENIA. Flying fatigue; or flight fatigue.

AEROBALLISTIC VEHICLE. A wingless vehicle (i.e., missile) employing the boost-glide and continuous roll technique for flight at hypersonic speeds within the earth's atmosphere. The trajectory is ballistic to apogee, after which the vehicle assumes an angle of attack (10° to 20°) and descends partly ballistically and partly through aero-dynamic lift to an altitude of about 60,000 feet, thereafter resuming a ballistic descent to the surface. A slow continuous roll is imparted to the wingless vehicle during the aerodynamic portion of flight to distribute frictional heat evenly over the airframe so as to preserve the structural integrity.

AEROBALLISTICS. A term derived from aerodynamics and ballistics and dealing pri-marily with the motion of bodies such as a guided rocket, whose flight path is deter-mined by applying the principles of both sciences to different portions of the path.

AEROBIOLOGY. The study of the distribu-tion of living organisms freely suspended in the atmosphere.

AERODONTALGIA. Toothache resulting from changes in barometric pressure during flight in unpressurized or pressurized air-craft or spacecraft, but in which there is a decreased barometric pressure. The first signs of pain usually occur at pressure alti-tudes between 5,000 and 15,000 feet, and the problem is more frequent in ascent than descent. Common sources of aerodontalgia are mechanically imperfect fillings, inade-quately filled root canals, and pulpitis due to poor choice of filling materials. One of the most frequent sources of toothaches, in aircraft or decompression chambers, is an amalgam filling which was not properly con-solidated or well packed into the prepared cavity, or in which the cement base beneath the amalgam was not heavy enough.

AERODONTIA. The branch of dentistry concerned with the peculiar dental problems of personnel subjected to flight under lowered ambient air pressure conditions.

AERODUCT. Highly advanced type of ramjet engine, designed for flight up to 6,000 mph at outer edges of atmosphere, where it will scoop up ions and electrons freely available and then, by a metachemi-cal process within the duct of the engine, expel these particles in a propulsive jet stream. Under advanced study, and being considered for use, with liquid-rocket en-gines, in aerospace vehicle capable of flight within and beyond the atmosphere.

AERODYNAMIC HEATING. The heat-ing of a vehicle caused by friction of that vehicle's surface with atmospheric mole-cules. See **re-entry.**

AERODYNAMICS. The field of dynamics concerned with the motion of air and other gaseous fluids, or of the forces acting on bodies in motion relative to such fluids. As such, all spacecraft are the product of aero-dynamic engineering as well as astronautics engineering.

AEROELASTICITY. The study of the effect of aerodynamic forces on elastic bodies. See **aerodynamics.**

AEROEMBOLISM. The formation of gas bubbles (principally nitrogen) in body tissue, blood, and spinal fluid after exposure to low atmospheric pressure as in high-alti-tude flying without benefit of a pressure suit or pressurized cabin; characterized by rash or other irritating sensations of the skin, pain in the joints and chest, and/or neuritis.

AEROEMPHYSEMA. An altitude de-compression sickness brought on by the formation of gas bubbles in the connective tissues, as under sustained exposure to low ambient air pressures without a protective pressurized cabin or suit.

AEROLITE. A meteorite composed princi-pally of stony material. See **meteor.**

AEROMEDICAL. Pertaining to the science and practice of aviation medicine.

AEROMEDICS. Popular term for doctors of aviation and space medicine.

AERONEUROSIS. As commonly used by pilots and crew members—*flight fatigue.* Aeroneurosis is a functional nervous dis-order, caused when a pilot flies an excessive number of hours or is under severe strain for a long period of time. A pilot who suffers from aeroneurosis often has severe stomach pains, is nervous and irritable, has insom-nia, and becomes emotionally unstable. He must be relieved from flying duty until he no longer has these symptoms.

AERONOMY. The science concerned with the atmosphere of the earth or another planetary body, in respect to its chemical characteristics, physical properties, relative motion, and reactions to radiation bombardment from outer space.

AERO-OTITIS MEDIA. Acute or chronic traumatic inflammation of the middle ear, caused by a difference of pressure between the air outside and inside the eardrum. It is characterized by congestion, inflammation, discomfort, and pain in the middle ear, and may be followed by temporary or permanent impairment of hearing, usually the former. See **middle ear.**

AEROPAUSE. A region high above the earth generally accepted as the boundary or the transition region between the earth's atmosphere and outer space. Because the terms *atmosphere* and *space* may be defined in many ways, the aeropause is considered a region of undefined limits above the earth, but one in which functional effects of the atmosphere on man and aircraft cease to exist.

AEROPHYSICS. The science of the effects of upper atmospheric and extraterrestrial environments on space vehicle materials, structures, and passengers. Aerophysics studies include physical chemistry, high-altitude gas dynamics, physics, and energy transfer.

AEROS. An advanced meteorological satellite system, with the first launchings planned in 1964 or 1965. The satellite is to be placed in a 24-hour orbit, stabilized to face the earth, carrying television cameras of variable focus.

AEROSINUSITIS. The sinuses are air-filled, relatively rigid, bony cavities in the skull, lined with mucous membrane. Two of these sinuses are situated within the bones of the forehead, one within each cheekbone, and two in the bones just back of the root of the nose. They communicate with the nose by small openings. If these openings are normal rapid pressure changes in ascent or descent are accomplished without difficulty

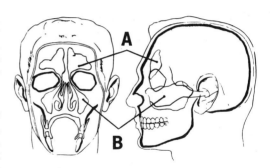

Some of the SINUSES. A, Frontal sinus. B, Maxillary sinus.

due to adequate equalization of pressure at all times. If the openings of the sinuses are obstructed by the swelling of the mucous membrane lining (caused by infection, a cold, an allergy), then quick pressure equalization becomes impossible. Change of altitude produces a pressure differential between the ear inside and outside and causes severe pain, a condition known as aerosinusitis. Unlike the ears, the sinuses are almost equally affected by ascent and descent. Pain from aerosinusitis can become so intense as to incapacitate an individual.

AEROSOL. A mixture of fine liquid or solid particles and the gas or air in which the particles are suspended; a potential spacecraft cabin danger.

AEROSPACE. A term that came into common usage by 1960. It designates the complete area of flight operations for unmanned satellites and for manned spacecraft. It was coined specifically to meet a need for explaining the areas or zones where space vehicles operate. The concept of aerospace, including both the atmosphere and space, is based on the premise that there is no sharp dividing line between the atmosphere and space. Since airplanes fly high enough to leave that part of the atmosphere where their wings affect their flight, they are considered *aerospace vehicles*. Similarly, the Mercury manned capsule is not considered a "true spaceship," because it too operates in both the atmosphere and space. A "true spaceship" would be a vehicle that operates *only* in space, and never makes planetfall.

AEROSPACE POWER. The entire aeronautical and astronautical capacity of a nation, including military, scientific, civilian, industrial, laboratory, and private resources of the sciences.

AEROSPACE VEHICLE. Any vehicle capable of controlled flight in both the atmosphere and in space.

AEROTHERMODYNAMIC BORDER. A zone lying about 90–100 miles above the earth. At this altitude there no longer is sufficient atmosphere, no matter how tenuous, to create any significant heat from friction on the surface of a spacecraft moving at a speed great enough to achieve orbit about the earth. At this altitude—on the edge of the aerothermodynamic border —a spacecraft may achieve successful orbit. However, because there still remains some measurable gaseous density, the time of orbiting is limited. The Atlas-D shell, for example, will orbit only 2 to 4 times before re-entry.

AEROTHERMODYNAMICS. The study of the aerodynamic and thermodynamic problems connected with aerodynamic heating. See **re-entry profile.**

AFFTC. Air Force Flight Test Center. Its operating headquarters is Edwards Air Force Base, located in the California desert northeast of Los Angeles. This is the major flight test center for high-performance jet aircraft and rocket research aircraft like the X-15. AFFTC is also the command and trained headquarters for the Dyna-Soar manned spaceship program.

AFMTC. Air Force Missile Test Center. The administrative and technical command headquarters, with offices at Patrick Air Force Base, Florida, that operates the Atlantic Missile Range. See **AMR.**

AFSSD. Air Force Space Systems Division. The organization within the U.S. Air Force that supplies modified intercontinental ballistic missiles to the National Aeronautics and Space Administration, for use as rocket boosters for space flight, such as **Atlas** and **Titan.**

AFTERBODY. A companion body that trails a satellite in orbit; this may be a clamp ring that has been discarded, a protective nose fairing jettisoned from the payload, or the booster rocket or rockets.

AFTERBURNING. Irregular burning of fuel that remains after fuel cutoff in the combustion chamber of a rocket booster.

AGENA A. An upper-stage rocket vehicle used with a first-stage Thor or Atlas booster rocket. In the Air Force Discoverer satellite program, the Agena A has enjoyed tremendous reliability and success. Many of the satellites launched into orbit by Agena A have figured prominently in man-in-space programs, by testing equipment and exposing human factors materials to the forces of rocket booster flight, weightlessness, cosmic radiation, and re-entry. As used in the Discoverer program, the Agena A is 19.5 feet long and 5 feet in diameter. It weighs 8,600 lbs. fueled, with an empty weight (not including payload) of 2,000 lbs. The single Hustler 8048 motor burns with 15,500 lbs. thrust for 120 seconds. Burnout speed is approximately 18,000 mph. The success of Agena A led directly to the more versatile and powerful Agena B, which will be used as a robot rendezvous mission vehicle with the Gemini 2-man capsule.

AGENA B. A direct development of the Agena A upper-stage rocket used with outstanding success atop Thor and Atlas first-stage boosters. Agena B is an orbital rendezvous rocket that will be used for orbital rendezvous missions with 2-man Gemini Mark II spacecraft. Agena B is 28 feet long and 5 feet in diameter. It weighs 15,000 lbs. fueled, with an empty weight of 2,500 lbs. not including payload. The single Hustler 8081 motor burns with 16,000 lbs. thrust for 240 seconds. Payload capacity is from 2,500 to 4,000 lbs. Agena B models in the Mark II program may have slightly different specifications.

ATLAS–AGENA B two-stage booster for Midas and Samos satellites, Ranger and Mariner space probes. Cutaway atop Agena B shows Ranger lunar probe vehicle

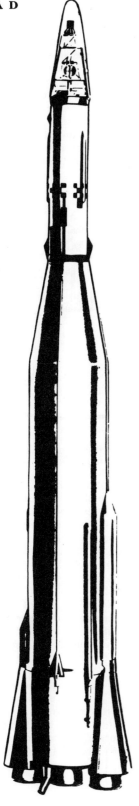

AGENA D. Essentially the Agena B vehicle, but with a special adapter section capable of mounting any scientific or other payload of NASA. Agena D will be used for a maximum variety of space missions with different payloads.

AGRAVIC. A condition where gravity does not exist. It is a theoretical condition only; absolute agravic conditions (under present knowledge) cannot possibly exist anywhere in the known universe. The term is possibly confusing with zero-gravity. See **free fall; weightlessness.**

AIR BREAKUP. The disintegration of a vehicle in the air, usually due to extreme aerodynamic stresses and loads imposed by high-speed flight. Also the breakup of a vehicle that re-enters the atmosphere from space and is subjected to sudden and extreme deceleration and aerodynamic loads.

AIR-BREATHING. Said of any flight vehicle that depends for its combustion upon free oxygen in the atmosphere by ingesting ambient air during flight; i.e., vehicle powered with a reciprocating, turbo-jet, or ramjet engine.

AIR DRAG. The totality of all forces, due to the interaction of a vehicle with the air mass, acting in a direction opposite to the flight velocity. Air drag is a convenient way for dissipating the high velocity of a satellite body re-entering the atmosphere, so that a surface landing may be made at a desirable and safe impact speed. This convenience, however, is not available on an airless planetary body such as the moon, in which air drag is totally absent. In order to achieve a safe landing here at a desirable velocity, a serious penalty in payload for deceleration rockets is required.

AIRGLOW. Luminescence of the sky during hours of darkness, caused by the release of energy absorbed by upper atmospheric atoms during daytime exposure to solar radiation. Also known as **nightglow.**

AIRGLOW FILTER. Used in the manned orbital missions of Project Mercury. A device which filters out all light except the 5,577-

angstrom wavelength, one of the bright lines of the airglow spectrum. It is intended as an aid in studying the patterning of the airglow layer. See **airglow.**

AIR LOAD. The aerodynamic load or force imposed upon a body moving through the sensible atmosphere.

AIRLOCK

AIRLOCK. An airtight transfer compartment through which entry or exit may be made from a sealed cabin, module, or base facilities installation such as a lunar base camp. An airlock must have the capacity for pressure regulation to any desired value, from vacuum conditions to an excess of 14.7 psi. In space-flight operations, spacecraft airlocks will permit the movement of personnel from the sealed interior to the airlock. Here the passage between spacecraft and airlock will be sealed. The airlock pres-

sure will then be vented to space until vacuum conditions prevail, permitting egress from the spacecraft while sustaining integrity of the pressure environment of the spaceship itself. The opposite procedure will be followed for entry. The astronauts will enter the airlock and seal the outer door. Pressure will build up until the airlock pressure is equal to that of the spacecraft, permitting safe opening of the interior door or hatch to the cabin.

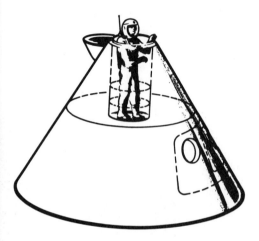

AIRLOCK system of Apollo Command Module, showing position for entry and egress

AIR PLOT. A continuous plot of the position of an airborne object represented graphically to show true headings steered and distances flown; an air plot would also be made of the operations of the search and recovery aircraft of a recovery force searching for a satellite vehicle returned to the earth's surface. See **recovery forces.**

AIR SOUNDING. The act of measuring atmospheric phenomena or determining atmospheric conditions at altitude, especially by means of apparatus carried by balloons or rockets.

ALBEDO. The reflecting power of any object in space. It is expressed as the ratio of light that is reflected from an object, to the total amount falling on it. The earth has an albedo of 0.39. The brightest planet is Venus, with an albedo of 0.76. The albedo of a manned spacecraft is vital to the performance of that vehicle, since its reflective power determines in great part the internal temperatures caused by the radiations of the sun.

ALFA TRAINER. Air Lubricated Free Axis Trainer. A training device permitting extensive simulation of orbital flight attitudes for Mercury and Gemini spacecraft control requirements. The trainer utilizes a periscope display and a window with a simulated earth horizon for controlling actual Mercury capsule attitudes and rates during orbit and retrorocket firing. Pilot control is exercised by a Reaction Control System consisting of pressurized air reaction control nozzles.

ALGAE. Tiny green or brown plant substances, often seen on ponds or on wet, dripping rocks. Algae (singular *alga*) have been studied for years as a vital part of a closed-cycle manned system for space flight. Algae are excellent for absorbing carbon dioxide from the air, and in return give off fresh oxygen. Until recently scientists planned that algae would also be used as part of a food supply for spacemen on extended flights. However, algae have an excess of *carotene* (the substance that gives carrots color), and if a man ate quantities of algae for any extended period, he would turn a bright yellow color.

ALKALI METAL HYDROXIDES. Chemical compounds with the ability to absorb carbon dioxide from the air, and of especial value to sealed spacecraft cabins. They include potassium hydroxide, sodium hydroxide or caustic soda, calcium hydroxide, lithium hydroxide, etc.; many of these chemical compounds are known by trade names, such as Baralyme (a mixture of calcium hydroxide and barium hydroxide).

ALFA TRAINER, with Astronaut Wally Schirra

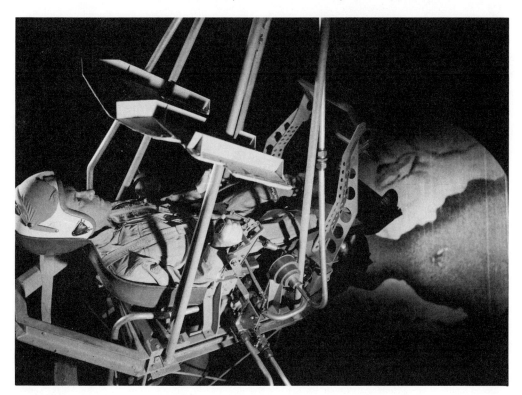

"ALL SYSTEMS GO." Pilot's report that all systems and equipment of his spacecraft are operating normally, that he has instrument indications that these systems are operating normally, and perfectly. Also used as **"A-OK,"** "All-OK," and **"in the green."**

ALPHA CENTAURI. A star in the constellation Centaurus, seen in the southern hemisphere. About 4.3 light years distant. See **Proxima Centauri.**

ALTIMETER. Pressure instrument to measure atmospheric pressure and translate readings into feet of altitude above sea level. The altimeter contains an aneroid—a closed, hollow, metal disc from which air has been removed (a bellows containing a vacuum). Atmospheric pressure flattens the bellows; pressure reduction causes its expansion. The accordionlike action operates a lever that turns dials on the altimeter face. The reading is in *indicated pressure* (or *density altitude*) above sea level.

ALTITUDE ACCLIMATIZATION. A slow physiological adaptation to significantly reduced atmospheric pressure, resulting from prolonged exposure.

ALTITUDE ALKALOSIS. A condition of increased alkalinity in the blood and tissues brought on by exposure to lowered ambient air pressure. This particular condition results from increased loss of carbon dioxide from the blood when rapid breathing to obtain oxygen increases ventilation. See **breathing, control of; hyperventilation.**

ALTITUDE ALKALURIA. A symptom of altitude alkalosis indicated by the urine becoming alkaline.

ALTITUDE CHAMBER. A steel-walled tank which may be completely sealed and from which the air is exhausted in order to simulate flight at extreme altitudes above the earth. Altitude chambers are used for "flights" at altitudes from 3 to 500 miles above the earth—or at any height lower than

ALTITUDE CHAMBER, or pressure chamber. The chamber operator is at the controls

this. Also known in the aviation and space-medicine field as **decompression chamber; flight chamber; pressure chamber.**

ALTITUDE SICKNESS. The syndrome of depression, anorexia, nausea, vomiting, and collapse, due to decreased atmospheric pressure, occurring in an individual exposed to an altitude beyond that to which acclimatization has occurred. See **dysbarism.**

ALTITUDE TETANY. Tetany, a disease marked by muscular spasms, especially of the extremities, brought on by exposure to low ambient air pressure. See **dysbarism.**

ALVEOLAR AIR. The air deep in the lungs, in the alveoli, resulting from the process of respiration. This air consists of oxygen, nitrogen, carbon dioxide, and water vapor. The alveoli are tiny air sacs, with walls 1/50,000th of an inch thick, through which fresh inspired oxygen is passed on to the blood stream, and carbon dioxide is expelled to be exhaled from the lungs. The alveoli, of which there are millions within the lungs, are moist and porous to facilitate the respiratory process. See **alveoli; breathing, process of; respiration.**

ALVEOLAR EQUATION. A specified relationship between the component gas and moisture fractions in the air cells of the lungs and the barometric pressure at a given altitude. As the barometric pressure decreases, the proportion of water vapor in the air cells increases.

ALVEOLI. Millions of tiny air sacs in the lungs through which the body's "exchange of gases" of the respiration process takes place. The walls of these sacs are 1/50,000th of an inch thick, are moist and porous, and permit air to pass through. Each sac is surrounded by blood capillaries, where the red blood cells take on fresh oxygen and give off carbon dioxide. The total area of the alveoli in the lungs, if spread out flat, would be about 800 square feet. See **alveolar air; breathing, process of; respiration.**

AMBIENT. Surrounding, encompassing, as in ambient air, ambient temperature, etc.

AMBIENT AIR. Atmospheric air at any given altitude. A pilot flying in a pressurized cabin may be at a cabin altitude (density altitude) of 40,000 feet; the pressure of the outside or ambient air might be 72,000 feet.

AMR. Atlantic Missile Range. The national missile and space-vehicle launching and testing range that is operated and maintained by the U.S. Air Force for the country's military, space, and scientific agencies. Its headquarters is the Air Force Missile Test Center, with offices at Patrick Air Force Base, Florida. AMR is one of the two long-range national missile ranges; the second is the Pacific Missile Range (PMR) that is operated and maintained by the U.S. Navy, with launching installations on the West Coast of the United States. In their numerical order, the following are the stations of the Atlantic Missile Range:

    (1) Cape Canaveral Missile Test Annex
    (2) Jupiter Inlet (Florida coast)
    (3) Grand Bahama
    (4) Eleuthera
    (5) San Salvador
    (6) Mayaguana
    (7) Grand Turk
    (8) Dominican Republic
    (9) Mayaguez
    (9a) Antigua
    (10) St. Lucia
    (11) Ferando de Noronha
    (12) Ascension

ANACOUSTIC ZONE. The zone of "eternal silence" in space. This becomes an absolute condition at 100 miles above the surface of the earth. Here the remaining air molecules are so widely dispersed that sound waves cannot be propagated, and it is impossible to have any conditions of sound. See **aerothermodynamic border.**

ANALEPTIC DRUGS. Emergency drugs carried in spacecraft that, when used in times of physical injury or loss of strength, have a helpful and invigorating effect. The drugs stimulate the central nervous system of the body.

ANALOGUE COMPUTER. An "electronic brain" or computing machine that works on the principle of measuring (as distinguished from counting). The measurements obtained, such as voltage, electrical resistance, etc., are then translated into data which can be used immediately for tracking and controlling rocket boosters and space vehicles. Analogue computers comprise the "black box" type of electronic brain produced in small sizes, which are used for automatic operation of spacecraft guidance and control systems. See **digital computer.**

ANECHOIC CHAMBER. A room especially designed so as completely to absorb all sound—a room without echoes. It is used for isolation research on human subjects. The anechoic chamber is so quiet that a man can hear the beating of his heart as though it were the "thudding of a triphammer."

ANECHOIC CHAMBER

ANEMIC HYPOXIA. See **hypoxia.**

ANEROID. Also used in aneroid switch, etc. The aneroid is an instrument that is sensitive to any changes in atmospheric pressure. It is designed to note changing atmospheric pressures, and at certain altitudes selected beforehand, it may switch on different items of equipment in a spacecraft. Aneroid also refers to the control unit in an automatic parachute, which opens the parachute at a preselected altitude. A man who bails out at 25,000 feet, for example, falls freely without opening his parachute. As he falls, the aneroid notes that moment when the outside pressure shows the jumper is at an altitude of 14,000 feet. The aneroid then closes a switch that springs open the parachute pack, to release the parachute into the air.

ANGEL. A radar echo caused by a physical phenomenon that is undiscernible by the unaided vision.

"ANGELS SEVENTY." Cryptic command or code for pilots, radar controllers, ground and air communications personnel, that tells a pilot or other personnel of unidentified or known enemy vehicles at 70,000 feet, and requiring the pilot of an intercepting aircraft to proceed with all possible speed to this altitude. The reference may be to any given altitude. Usually employed in air-defense operations and in using chase planes for research activities.

ANGSTROM UNIT. An expression of the length of light waves; it represents a minute unit of length equal to 1/10,000 of a micron, or 1/100,000,000 of a centimeter.

ANGULAR ACCELERATION. The acceleration of a spacecraft around an axis, such as pitch, roll, or yaw. For example, a spacecraft in orbit may start rolling around its longitudinal axis. The spacecraft undergoes an angular acceleration around its longitudinal axis when it begins to roll and when it increases the speed of its roll. See **acceleration.**

ANHYDRONE. The commercial name for a chemical compound (magnesium perchlorate) that may be used in a closed-cycle spacecraft system to absorb excessive water vapor from the air. Anhydrone is an efficient compound for this process, but has not found acceptance because of its explosive tendencies.

ANNA. A geodetic satellite and satellite program the name of which stands for the program participants—Army, Navy, NASA, and Air Force. ANNA is a 355-lb., 36-inch satellite with a band of solar cells around its center. Its purpose in a planned 600-mile circular orbit is to establish a triangulation point in space in order to determine precise distances and positions on earth. Included in the payload are sets of xenon flash tubes to produce light flashes in space for study and triangulation from the ground.

ANNULAR ECLIPSE. An eclipse in which a thin ring of the source of light appears around the obscuring body.

ANOMALISTIC PERIOD. The interval between two successive arrivals at perigee of a satellite in orbit about a primary. Also called "perigee-to-perigee period."

ANOXIA. A condition existing when the tissues within the human body are completely starved of oxygen. This condition may exist at any altitude above 50,000 feet. A pilot breathing 100% oxygen at this altitude or above will still have complete oxygen starvation if his lungs and body lack the necessary pressurization. See **hypoxia.**

ANTHROPOMETRIC ADAPTATION. The adaptation—modifying—of any control lever, cockpit, cabin, instrument panel, switch, or other device, in order to meet the specific requirements of the individual human pilot, crew, or passenger. Example: The contour couch of the Mercury space capsule is molded to the specific contours of each individual astronaut. See **contour couch.**

ANTHROPOMETRIC ADAPTATION. A spacecraft cabin mockup being used to test the location of controls and the pilot's ability to reach all of them

ANTHROPOMETRIC ENGINEERING. The engineering of any aviation or space-flight equipment, devices, controls, etc., that takes into account as the primary consideration the comfort, safety, and efficiency of the individual or crewmen who operate that equipment. See, for example, **contour couch; Mercury capsule.**

ANTHROPOMORPHIC DUMMIES. Special dummies made to the weight, distribution of mass, height, and proportions of a human being, with articulated limbs. The dummies are elaborately engineered, fitted out with instrumentation to register forces, loads, and other effects of flight on the human body. They are used for tests of flight and survival equipment, and on simulated flight and space missions to determine the forces that will be exerted upon a human being. If these forces exceed the tolerance limits of the human, changes in equipment or in the mission profiles can be made prior to committing a human being to the rigors of actual flight.

ANTHROPOMORPHIC DUMMY

ANTI-BLACKOUT SUIT. A suit with a system of air-pressurized bladders worn around the abdomen, thighs, and legs to help a pilot resist g forces (acceleration) and increase his ability to remain conscious under these forces. See **g-suit.**

ANTI-EXPOSURE SUIT

ANTI-EXPOSURE SUIT. Also called exposure suit, immersion suit, survival suit. Strictly, a special waterproof coverall that is worn over flying clothing, regular clothing, or pressure suits. It is designed to protect the wearer against exposure, most particularly to the dangers of immersion in extremely cold water. As such, it will become standard equipment aboard manned spacecraft, which may descend on any part of the planet.

ANTI-*g* SUIT. See **anti-blackout suit, g-suit.**

ANTIPODAL BOMBER. Advanced aerospace design bomber vehicle that ascends beyond the sensible atmosphere, and while out of the atmosphere releases a directed bomb or missile along its trajectory, and then lands at the antipode of its launching point (the place on the planet diametrically opposite its launching point). A boostglide vehicle.

ANTIRADIATION DRUG. A long-term research project of the Walter Reed Army Institute of Research is to provide chemical protection through oral doses of an anti-radiation drug which can be taken before exposure to reduce the biological effect of ionizing radiation. Such a drug would be of direct value in traversing the Van Allen radiation belts and in withstanding severe radiation storms in space. Toxicity problems have been the greatest obstacles to development of the drug in acceptable form, though the toxic-reactive problems are now considered to be largely if not completely solved. (One group of test dogs was exposed to far more than the minimum radiation dosage necessary to cause a mortality rate of 100%. Two of the dogs in the group were administered the antiradiation drug. One week after exposure to the radiation, every animal but the two treated dogs were dead. Years later, the two treated dogs were still completely healthy.)

"A-OK." A voice communication that means "everything is working perfectly." Most people believe that Astronaut Alan B. Shepard, Jr., used the term "A-OK" during his suborbital space mission of May 5, 1961. Actually, Astronaut Shepard at no time during that mission ever said "A-OK." At a press conference on July 22, 1961, Astronaut Shepard explained that if he had used the term "A-OK," he would have pronounced it AWK, as in *awk*ward.

APENNINE MOUNTAIN RANGE. See **lunar mountains.**

APHELION. That point on a planet's, comet's, or spacecraft's orbit most distant from the sun. (The earth's aphelion is about 94,500,000 miles from the sun.)

APNEA. Literally, a cessation of breathing, but denoting a temporary cessation only. See **anoxia; hypoxia.**

APOGEE. The highest point above the surface of the earth reached during the orbit of a ballistic missile or a space vehicle or a natural satellite. Most orbits are not circular, but are elliptical. A satellite may have an apogee of 155 miles, with a perigee —the lowest point of the orbit—of 110 miles.

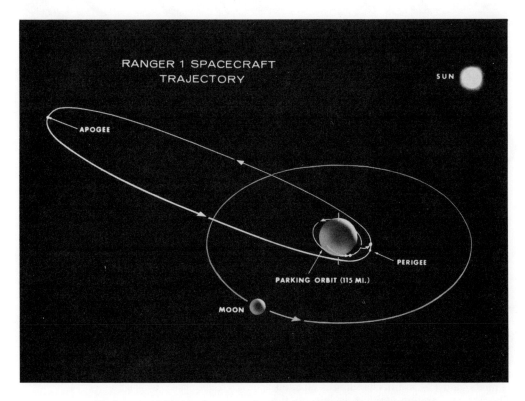

RANGER 1 SPACECRAFT TRAJECTORY

SUN

APOGEE

PERIGEE

PARKING ORBIT (115 MI.)

MOON

Trajectory of Ranger 1 spacecraft, showing APOGEE and PERIGEE

APOGEE ROCKET. A rocket attached to a satellite or spacecraft designed to fire when the craft is at apogee, the point farthest from the earth in orbit. The effect of the apogee rocket is to establish a new orbit farther from the earth or to allow the craft to escape from earth orbit. See **kick rocket.**

APPARENT SOLAR SIZE. To an observer located at a distance from the sun equal to that of the orbit of the planet Mercury, the diameter of the solar disc would appear twice as large as when seen from the earth. Seen from Mars, the sun would have a diameter of two-thirds the size as seen from earth. At the distance of the Jupiter orbit, the diameter is only one-fifth as large as seen from the earth; at the distance of the Pluto orbit, the sun appears about three times larger than the planet Venus appears to an observer on the surface of the earth.

APOLLO. A three-man spaceship approximately 12 x 13 feet in a "flattened cone" capsule shape; as the command module of a multi-modular spacecraft system, the Apollo weighs 10,000 pounds. It accommodates a three-man astronaut crew, and is intended to function as a three-man earth orbiter; a three-man earth research station for two to four weeks' orbiting; a six-man training and indoctrination flight training vehicle; a lunar survey vehicle; a lunar landing-vehicle command module; and a lunar-orbiter command module which will dispatch a two-man excursion vehicle to the lunar surface. The Apollo program has considered for the lunar mission three specific modes. These are (1) earth rendezvous, (2) direct ascent, and (3) lunar orbit rendezvous. The first mode, earth rendezvous, calls for the launching within a brief timespan of two Saturn C-5 boosters, each of 3,000 tons launch weight. The Apollo

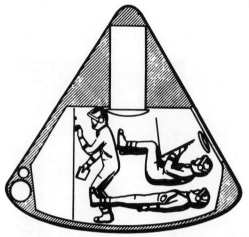

APOLLO. Crew positions within Command Module. Man at left adjusts equipment. Man at upper right operates controls. Man at lower right is "off duty" and has contour couch set for sleeping position

APOLLO Command Module re-enters atmosphere after lunar flight; re-entry speed is 25,000 mph

Command Module, Service Module, and Lunar Landing Vehicle are orbited as a single spacecraft by one C-5 booster. The second C-5 booster orbits for rendezvous and docking a fueled propulsion system which is then used to boost the 150,000-lb. lunar spacecraft out of earth orbit toward the moon, where (1) a lunar survey orbit is made, and (2) a lunar landing is effected. The Lunar Landing Vehicle is left on the lunar surface, and the Service Module used as the lunar ascent booster. Prior to re-entry of the Command Module into the earth's atmosphere, the Service Module is jettisoned, to be consumed on re-entry at 25,000 mph.

The second mode, direct ascent, calls for a Nova booster of 12,000,000 lbs. first-stage thrust, 4,800,000 lbs. second-stage thrust, and 200,000 lbs. third-stage thrust to boost the 150,000-lb. spacecraft directly from the earth's surface to the lunar landing.

The third mode, lunar orbital rendezvous, has supplanted the earth-rendezvous technique and has occasioned a stretchout in the development of the direct-ascent mode. The U.S. has committed itself to **lunar orbital rendezvous** (LOR) in its program for manned landings on the moon in the late 1960's. A single C-5 booster will be used as the propulsion system at launch. The Apollo LOR and Saturn C-5 will be 325 feet tall and weigh 3,000 tons at launch. Diameter

Deployment sequence (*right to left*) of parachute landing system of APOLLO Command Module. Drogue chute stabilizes module, then is ejected as triple-parachute landing system deploys. Illustration at far left shows the canopies streaming out just before full deployment

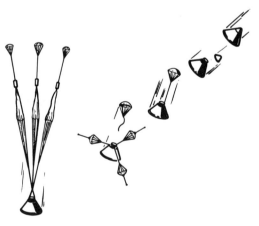

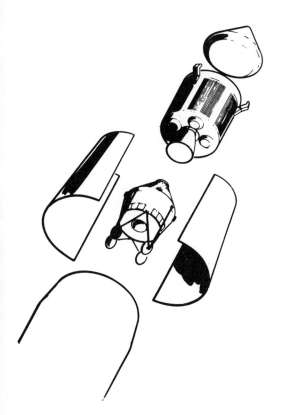

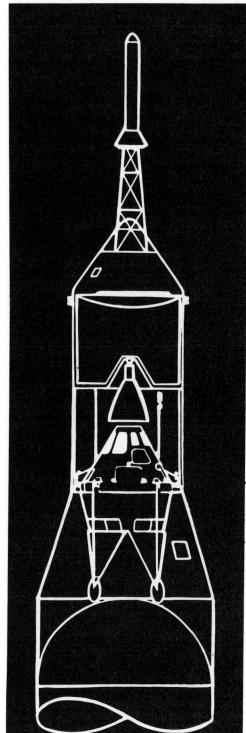

Exploded view of APOLLO spaceship system
into (*from top*) Command Module, Service
Module, LEM, and the top of the booster
rocket. Sections about LEM are jettisoned after
injection into translunar orbit

APOLLO. Launch configuration of three-
module Apollo spacecraft system. At top is
escape rocket and tower, attached to Apollo
Command Module. Directly below Command
Module is Service Module, with inflight propulsion systems and life support systems; trail-
ing this is Lunar Excursion Module (LEM).
During ascent, escape rocket and tower are
jettisoned. After injection into translunar orbit,
LEM is swung around nose-to-nose with Command Module, and connected at the airlocks
of both

of the C-5 booster will be 33 feet; diameter of the 3-module Apollo LOR will be 13 feet. The LOR spacecraft will include the 5-ton Apollo Command Module housing the crew and re-entry vehicle; a 23-ton, 23-foot tall Service Module providing mid-course correction and return-to-earth propulsion; and a 15-ton, 20-foot-tall Lunar Excursion Module (LEM). The Apollo LOR spacecraft will be placed into a 100-mile lunar orbit. Two astronauts will transfer to the LEM and descend to the moon while the Apollo Command-Service Modules remain in lunar orbit with one astronaut. After an exploration period of up to 4 days, the two astronauts will ascend from the moon in the LEM to Apollo LOR for rendezvous and transfer of the men back to the Command Module. After such transfer, the LEM will be jettisoned in its lunar orbit. The Apollo will be boosted by a 20,000-lb. thrust engine in the Service Module for its return to earth.

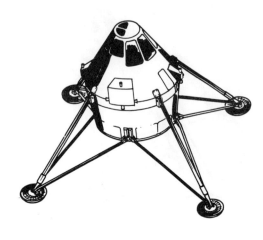

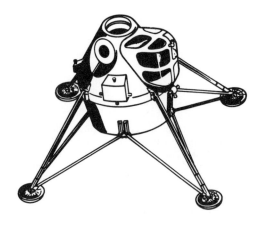

APOLLO Lunar Excursion Module (LEM). *Above:* Early NASA design for vehicle to land on the moon. *Below:* A later design in the development of the LEM vehicle

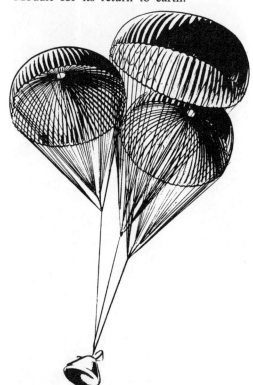

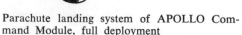

Parachute landing system of APOLLO Command Module, full deployment

APOLLO LEM-type spacecraft decelerating for landing on lunar surface

APOLLO ORBITING LABORATORY MODULE. An extended earth-orbit Apollo vehicle modification under advanced design study. The AOLM will be required and placed on active status only if unexpected sustained zero-*g* problems occur with 18-orbit Mercury and 2-week Gemini space flights. The AOLM would be designed to accommodate three astronauts and would be equipped extensively for study of sustained zero-*g* reactions. See **equilibrium and orientation; rotating room.**

APU. Auxiliary Power Unit.

ARC-JET ENGINE. A type of electrical rocket engine in which the propellant gas is heated by passing through an electric arc. See **electrical engine.**

ARENTS. A research program to place satellites in orbit at distances of approximately 22,000 miles from the earth, to carry out extensive radiation environment investigations and to study the behavior of equipment and components under the specific orbital conditions.

ARIEL. A satellite produced by scientists of the United Kingdom and launched by the United States with the Thor-Delta booster. Ariel, one of a series of many satellites to be launched in a mutual cooperation effort, weighs 132 lbs., is a cylinder with rounded ends, and has elaborate booms and antennas for special equipment for space experiments. Essentially its purpose is to study, through a series of 6 experiments, the ionosphere, solar radiations, and cosmic radiation.

ARIEL, first United States-British satellite

ARIS. Attitude and Rate Indicating System. A sensitive "flight attitude sensor" in a spacecraft, such as the Mercury capsule, that enables the pilot to control the attitude of his craft. A system of gyroscopes in the ARIS uses optical devices to study the earth's horizon, and compares what it sees with the attitude of the capsule. An instrument dial in front of the pilot shows him his attitude in terms of pitch-yaw-roll. By visually studying this ARIS instrument, the pilot is able manually to change the attitude of the capsule as he desires. The closest comparison to ARIS in aircraft instruments would be the **artificial horizon** or gyro horizon. This instrument also uses gyroscopes for its reference. It presents to the pilot a visual picture of his horizon and a small model airplane. As the actual airplane moves in flight and changes its attitude, the model airplane duplicates this movement. A pilot flying under "blind conditions" thus always has a visual reference of the attitude of the airplane in terms of whether it is flying straight and level, diving, climbing, turning, or performing simultaneously several of these maneuvers.

ARM. To activate the explosive units of a rocket vehicle destruct system; i.e., to activate the igniting circuitry of the destruct system.

ARPA. Advanced Research Projects Agency. A division of the Department of Defense responsible for over-all military planning and direction of unmanned and manned military space-flight projects.

ARTIFICIAL FEEL. A response experienced by the pilot of an aircraft or spacecraft upon activation of a control surface or system moved by a servo-mechanism; the response or feel results from an artificial pressure fed into the cockpit control that simulates the pressure of the actual movement.

ARTIFICIAL GRAVITY. A condition of simulated gravity that is established within a space vehicle orbiting the earth or in orbit about another planetary body. The cabin is rotated about the longitudinal axis of the spacecraft, and the centrifugal force generated is similar to the force of gravity. Serious physiological and balance problems have arisen, however, in experiments of this type.

ARTIFICIAL HORIZON. A gyroscopic device with a visual presentation for an aircraft or spacecraft pilot, especially to permit safe and controlled operation under conditions when the pilot cannot see outside of his cabin. It shows the pitching and banking motions of an aircraft, and is adaptable to spacecraft. See **ARIS.**

ARTIFICIAL SATELLITE. Any satellite, spacecraft, rocket booster, or other equipment injected into orbit about the earth.

ASCS. Attitude Stabilization and Control System. A spacecraft control system that uses gyroscopes to give a capsule or spaceship its "sense of balance." It is used for automatic stabilization and control. If a specific attitude in orbit is desired—such as a space capsule moving with its heat shield in the direction of flight, tilted 34° upward above a horizontal line—the ASCS then maintains this attitude. The gyroscopic system senses any movement of the capsule away from the desired attitude. Immediately an electronic brain sends command signals to the small reaction control jets. The jets fire automatically to bring the capsule back to the attitude desired. The closest comparison to ASCS in the control system of an airplane would be the automatic pilot, which uses a gyroscope-reference system that senses any change of the airplane from flying straight-and-level. In military aircraft, these are known as the AFCE—Automatic Flight Control Equipment. In the spacecraft, as in the airplane, the pilot can manually override the automatic system at any time. See **Mercury capsule control system.**

ASIS. Abort Sensing and Implementation System. The "electronic watchdog" in the Atlas-D booster rocket of Project Mercury that senses danger, and then triggers the escape rocket to pull the manned capsule up and away from the booster. It is an electronic device that weighs 36 lbs. and monitors all essential subsystems (propulsion, electrical, etc.) of the Atlas-D for any trouble or failures. See **abort system.**

ASKANIA. A high-precision optical instrument; a *cine-theodolite*. It combines a motion-picture camera and a powerful telescope, and is used singly or in pairs for tracking rocket boosters and space vehicles. It determines and records the history of any object in flight in terms of position-time. The filmed record specifies time, azimuth and elevation, and the position of the vehicle with respect to cross-hairs in the telescope. It is one of the most valuable instruments for tracking and flight-information recording purposes.

ASP. Aerospace Plane. A concept of an advanced vehicle capable of takeoff, ascent to orbital altitude and velocity, deceleration from orbit, re-entry, and descent and landing entirely under its own power systems, and from conventional-sized airfields—the latter defined as having runways of 10,000-foot length.

ASPECT-STABILIZED. Said of a spacecraft in earth orbit (unmanned or manned) which has been orbited under orbital flight control so that the same part of the vehicle always points toward the earth or away from the earth. This is a necessary stabilization mode for many astronomical and geophysical observations, especially from unmanned satellite vehicles.

ASPHYXIA. A cessation of breathing due to lack of oxygen, with or without an excess of carbon dioxide.

ASTEROID. One of many thousands of small planets that revolve about the sun in an "asteroid belt" or "asteroid zone" between the orbits of Mars and Jupiter. Ceres, with a diameter of 488 miles, is the largest asteroid. Also, in *artificial asteroid,* a space probe sent into solar orbit, such as Lunik I, Pioneer IV, Ranger III, etc.

ASTRIONICS: The science of electronics as applied especially to astronautics; *avionics* is the science of electronics as applied especially to aeronautics (or aviation).

ASTROASTHENIA. Fatigue of astronauts due to prolonged flight in space. See **aeroneurosis.**

ASTROBALLISTICS. The study of the phenomena arising out of the motion of a solid through a gas at speeds high enough to cause ablation; for example, the interaction of a meteoroid with the atmosphere. Astroballistics uses the data and methods of astronomy, aerodynamics, ballistics, and physical chemistry. See **ablation shields; re-entry profile.**

ASTROBIOLOGY. The science that studies the problem of indigenous life on celestial bodies other than the planet earth. Also see **planetary biology.**

ASTRODOME. A plastic, plexiglas, or glass dome. In an aircraft it is located somewhere along the top of the fuselage. A navigator sights through the astrodome for star references for celestial navigation. It is employed in the same manner for spacecraft. See **astrogation.**

ASTRODYNAMICS. A field of dynamics that deals with the motions of spatial bodies, including artificial satellites and deep-space probes, or with the forces that act upon these bodies in motion.

ASTROGATION. The science of navigation as applied to flight through space. Almost all astrogation procedures are combinations of man-machine systems. A hard foundation for astrogation is the science of celestial navigation (navigating by the stars) as applied to ships and aircraft.

ASTRONAUT. One who flies through space; an aeronaut is one who flies through the air.

ASTRONAUTICS. The science, technology, and art of flight in space. It includes such flights with unmanned vehicles or manned spacecraft. Astronautics is to space flight what aeronautics is to aviation.

ASTRONAUTS. The popular term to describe the pilots of the National Aeronautics and Space Administration (NASA) who will be aboard manned spacecraft as (1) passengers, (2) pilots, and (3) crew. The term "astronauts" derives from the earliest designation of men who flew through the air, i.e., "aeronauts," who were balloonists. Many space crewmen, such as the space pilots of the U.S. Air Force's Dyna-Soar space program, do not use the term "astronauts." "Astronauts" is most commonly identified with the seven test pilots of the Air Force, Navy, and Marine Corps who volunteered for the Project Mercury program and who were notified in April 1958 of their selection as Mercury pilots. All seven have participated equally in the Mercury program, and each man has been assigned a particular subsystem or specialty area on which to concentrate; the team of seven have then closely co-ordinated their activities. Their names and their Mercury assignments are:

Malcolm Scott Carpenter
Communications and navigation

Leroy Gordon Cooper, Jr.
Redstone booster and escape systems

John Herschel Glenn, Jr.
Cockpit layout

Virgil Ivan Grissom
Control system

Walter Marty Schirra, Jr.
Life-support system

Alan Bartlett Shepard, Jr.
Tracking and recovery

Donald Kent Slayton
Atlas booster

NASA's Gemini two-man spaceship is scheduled for its first manned flights in early 1964. Nine additional astronauts were selected in September 1962. To accommodate the space pilots of NASA and the Air Force, Cape Canaveral is being equipped to provide facilities for as many as 50 to 60 space pilots at any one time.

ASTRONETTE. Popular term to represent female astronaut.

ASTRONOMICAL TWILIGHT. That period of twilight that occurs, for computation purposes, when the sun is between the horizon and a point about 18° below the horizon, the latter measured at the middle of the sun. Astronomical twilight is the light diffused during this period, and suggests the time when the stars make their full appearance or begin to disappear.

ASTRONOMICAL UNIT (AU). In the astronomical system of measures, a unit of length usually defined as the mean distance of the earth from the sun, approximately 92,907,000 miles or 149,600,000 kilometers.

THE PROJECT MERCURY ASTRONAUTS. *Front row, left to right:* Walter M. Schirra, Jr., Donald K. Slayton, John H. Glenn, Jr., and M. Scott Carpenter. *Back row, left to right:* Alan B. Shepard, Jr., Virgil I. Grissom, and L. Gordon Cooper, Jr.

ASTRONOMY. The science of the study of the celestial bodies, their magnitudes, constitution, motion, location. The oldest of the known sciences.

ASTROPHYSICS. Application of laws and principles of physics to all aspects of stellar astronomy.

ASTROPLANE. An aerospace vehicle under study. According to Air Force specifications it will be capable of taking off and landing from runways no more than 10,000 feet in length; able to sustain flight within the extremely high atmosphere, scoop in gases and convert these gases to liquid propellants, and utilize the liquid propellants for flight at orbital speeds in space; and capable of then returning to the atmosphere and descending under pilot control, with return of powered flight within the atmosphere.

ATAXIA TEST. A study and evaluation of an individual's balance mechanism determined by the ability to walk (usually barefoot) along a narrow board.

ATELECTASIS. Partial collapse of the lung.

ATLAS. The popular name assigned to the Strategic Missile 65 (SM-65) of the U.S. Air Force. SM-65 is an intercontinental ballistic missile (ICBM) now on operational duty in combat-launching sites. Originally, the Atlas ICBM was designed in 1946 as a 250-ton giant with 5 main booster engines and several smaller control engines developing 750,000 lbs. thrust. The Atlas military designation as part of the over-all national military force is Weapon System 107A-1 (WS-107A-1), which includes all the equipment necessary to transport, service, fuel, arm, aim, and launch the SM-65. There have been 6 major Atlas models in the development program, from Atlas-A through Atlas-F, the latest combat model. Many Atlas missiles have been modified to serve as rocket boosters for different space shots, including earth satellites, lunar probes, and, in the Atlas-D model, as the booster for the one-man Project Mercury space capsule. See other **Atlas** and **Atlas-D** listings.

ATLAS-D. An Air Force intercontinental ballistic missile, model D (fourth major

Launch of ATLAS 15D

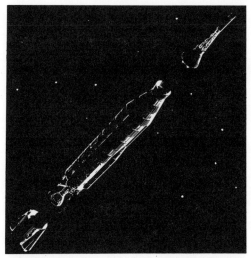

MERCURY–ATLAS booster, spacecraft, and escape system

modification in the development series), modified for use as a rocket booster for manned spacecraft and unmanned space vehicles. Atlas-D vehicles are supplied by the Air Force to NASA for its space missions.

ATLAS-D FLIGHT PLAN. This mission refers to the Atlas-D flight to boost into orbit the one-man Project Mercury spacecraft. The Atlas-D launches from Cape Canaveral on a heading of about 70°—just north of east from Canaveral. The internal programmer (automatic pilot) guides the rocket from liftoff until the first staging occurs (when the two main booster engines are jettisoned, or staged). Following is the specific flight plan of the Mercury-Atlas V mission to be used as a guideline:

Exactly 131 seconds after they were ignited, the two main rocket booster engines of the Atlas stopped firing. At that moment the Atlas-D was at an altitude of 39 miles, and 52 miles downrange from Canaveral. It was moving with a forward velocity of 10,300 feet per second. As the booster engines were jettisoned, the single sustainer engine and two small vernier engines continued to accelerate the Atlas-D. Exactly 154 seconds after launch, the escape tower of the Mercury capsule was jettisoned by firing a small rocket. Then, 304 seconds after the moment of launch, the Atlas-D reached the desired speed and height for orbit. A ground-command signal radioed from the ground shut down the sustainer and the vernier engines. All power of the Atlas-D at that instant stopped. The Atlas-D was then in orbit, moving with a velocity of 26,700 feet per second. This was within 5 feet per second of that planned. One second after the engines were cut off, the capsule separated from the now-inert Atlas-D shell. The capsule had been placed into an earth orbit with a perigee of 99 miles and an apogee of 146 miles. The time period required for a complete orbit of the earth was 88.5 minutes. Speed was approximately 17,500 mph at the time the first orbit started. The empty Atlas-D, weighing just over 5 tons, orbited the earth several times, then re-entered the atmosphere and burned.

ATLAS-D GUIDANCE SYSTEM.

The Atlas-D used for boosting manned capsules into earth orbit is controlled by a "radio-inertial guidance system," which is a refinement of Azusa guidance (see **Azusa**). Radio signals are broadcast from a transponder (amplifier for radio or radar messages) aboard the rocket as it climbs. The signals are measured by a powerful ground-based radar system. The flight data as determined by the radar-system controls are fed into an electronic computer. The computer immediately checks all the information it receives against the flight plan that was made before the flight. The computer notes any deviations from this plan. At once it transmits by radio signal flight corrections to the climbing rocket. These signals are picked up by a robot brain within the Atlas-D. The robot brain (also called "internal programmer," or "automatic pilot") moves the main booster engines and the smaller vernier engines of the Atlas to change its course as it climbs. This is the *radio portion* of the radio-inertial system. To complete the guidance system are the *inertial elements*—the gyroscopes that react to any changes of the Atlas-D through the three fundamental axes of flight: pitch, yaw, and roll. Any deviations from the flight path that was programmed before launching are noted and corrected. In addition, there is an accelerometer to measure the rate of acceleration of the Atlas in terms of *g*-forces and time—a measure of the continuing increase in the speed of the Atlas. "Reading" the guidance system and the

performance of the Atlas-D at all times from the ground is the impact-prediction system. See **impact predictor.**

ATLAS-D PROPULSION SYSTEM.

Atlas-D has five rocket engines. The main booster is in the form of a flared chamber skirt that surrounds the entire lower end of the vehicle. The booster consists of two engines that develop 150,000 lbs. thrust each at sea level for a launch power rating of 300,000 lbs. thrust (thrust increases as the rocket climbs and air pressure diminishes). A single sustainer engine in the center-line of the Atlas-D develops a sea-level rating of 60,000 lbs. thrust (in space the engine produces 80,000 lbs. thrust). There are also two small vernier engines for sensitive roll control and for very fine adjustments of velocity; each vernier develops 1,000 lbs. thrust. The Atlas-D sea-level thrust rating is 362,000 lbs. Atlas-F combat models develop approximately 400,000 lbs. thrust at sea level. The burning time of the Atlas-D booster is approximately 300 seconds, depending upon the mission to be flown.

ATLAS-D SPECIFICATIONS.

The Atlas-D booster vehicle for the Mercury-Atlas V (MA-5) space shot in November 1961 to orbit a chimpanzee is used as the standard for Atlas-D specifications:

Height of the Atlas-D from the base of the booster to the adapter section for the Mercury capsule is 65 feet. Height of the entire Mercury-Atlas system from the base of the booster to the top of the capsule escape tower is 93 feet. Atlas-D diameter through the tank section is 10 feet. The MA-5 vehicle at launch weighed 264,700 lbs. Weight of the Atlas-D vehicle after it entered orbit (after jettisoning the capsule escape tower, capsule, booster section) was 10,400 lbs.

ATLAS VEHICLES, HEIGHT *:

Atlas ICBM, blunt nose cone	75'10"
Atlas ICBM, ablation nose cone	82'6"
Atlas-D Mercury booster	93'0"
Atlas-Able space probe	99'4"
Atlas-Agena orbiter and space probe	88'2"
Atlas-Centaur orbiter and space probe	107'8"

* Exact heights vary with different missions and equipment; these are the basic standards.

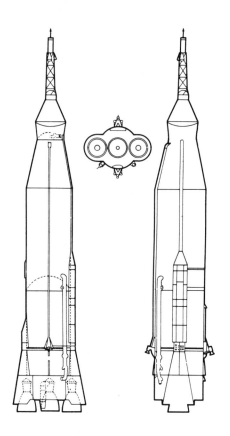

MERCURY–ATLAS SYSTEM

ATMOSPHERE. The ocean of air that surrounds the earth. It is composed of all the air surrounding the earth, with a pressure at sea level of 14.7 lbs. per square inch. The atmosphere is made up of about 21% oxygen, 78% nitrogen, and 1% of other gases, such as helium, hydrogen, etc. There is usually about 1% to 5% water vapor in the air, reducing accordingly the percentages of oxygen and nitrogen. According to their different characteristics, the atmosphere is generally broken up into vertically separated zones such as the **troposphere,** which extends to about 35,000 feet; the **stratosphere,** which continues beyond the troposphere to about 60 or 70 miles; the **ionosphere,** a region of intense electrical activity and which is itself broken up into four separate smaller layers of electrically charged particles; and, finally, the **exosphere,** where the upper limits of the atmosphere merge with the lower limits of space. There are many conflicting interpretations of the atmosphere, and especially as to where the atmosphere is said to end and space to begin. The atmosphere is compressible, and approximately one-half of the entire atmosphere density lies below 18,000 feet. At a height of 20 miles, the atmospheric pressure is only 1/95th that of sea level. We measure the **pressure** of the atmosphere with the barometer, made in terms of "inches of mercury." At standard sea-level pressure—with a temperature of 59° Fahrenheit—the atmospheric pressure is 29.92 inches of mercury. This is 14.7 lbs. per square inch. The latest guideline to the problem of defining atmosphere and space is the international agreement of the altitude necessary for a pilot to claim an "official space flight." This has been established as 100 kilometers, or 62 miles. Any flight above this altitude is accepted internationally as an official space flight. See also **aeropause; aerospace; aerothermodynamic border; atmospheric braking; atmospheric pressure.**

ATMOSPHERIC BRAKING. A maneuver of a spacecraft that employs both the friction drag and pressure drag of a vehicle to reduce its speed during atmospheric re-entry, so that it may descend and impact safely with the earth's surface—or the surface of another planetary body possessing an atmosphere of density sufficient to permit this maneuver. As the spacecraft drops lower and lower from its orbit, it encounters an increasing density of atmospheric molecules. The speed of the capsule is so great that tremendous heat is generated from the friction of the capsule's outer covering with the molecules of air. By adjusting the angle of descent, and the time the re-entry process is allowed to last, the heat caused by this friction is carefully controlled. The atmosphere serves as a "brake" to slow down, or decelerate, the descending capsule. See **re-entry.**

ATMOSPHERIC PRESSURE. At sea level one square inch of surface has an air pressure exerted upon it of 14.7 lbs. per square inch (psi). This is (technically speaking) the pressure of a column of air one inch square and 100 miles high. This is the approximate thickness of the layer of free air—atmosphere—covering the earth. At 10,000 feet, the air pressure is down from 14.7 to 10.11 psi. At 18,000 feet it is 7.34 psi; at 20,000 feet it is 6.75 psi; at 30,000 feet it is 4.36 psi; at 40,000 feet it is 2.7 psi; at 63,000 feet it is less than 1 psi. At 100,000 feet, or about 20 miles up, there is less than one-sixth of a pound per square inch. This is a pressure of about 1/95th that of sea level.

ATMOSPHERIC REFRACTION. Refraction by the atmosphere of light from a distant point, caused by the light passing obliquely through varying air densities.

ATTENUATION. The diminution (or fading out) of an emission of radiant energy; applies especially to radio communications signals.

ATTITUDE. The *attitude in flight* or the *attitude in orbit* of any space vehicle has no relation of any kind to the *flight path in space* of that vehicle. Since a space vehicle or manned spacecraft is moving through a vacuum, there is no atmosphere to act upon the surface or any fixed control surfaces of the spacecraft, such as the wings or tail of an airplane. The vehicle in space lacks *arrow stability*—such as an arrow achieves from the effect of wind upon its vanes. Thus a spacecraft in orbit can move sideways, nose up, or tumble end-over-end, without affecting the path of its flight in orbit. For purposes of control, scientific measurements, and re-entry, the capsule's *attitude* as it moves along its flight path (or orbital path) is carefully controlled. For example, the Mercury space capsule moves in orbit with the blunt heat shield facing in the direction of flight. The capsule is tilted with the heat shield pointing 34° above a horizontal line—the reference being the surface of the earth. From that point on during the orbits, the attitude control system is activated when necessary to maintain this or any other desired attitude, with reference to the surface of the earth. See **ARIS** and **ASCS.**

ATTITUDE CONTROL MOVEMENTS.

    Pitch. Up-and-down, like the bow of a boat pitching up and down in choppy water.

    Yaw. Side-to-side, like an airplane yawing its nose from side to side while keeping its wings level and continuing along a straight course.
    Roll. Rolling around and around, like an airplane flying a straight course, not losing or gaining altitude, with the wings rolling around and around.

ATTITUDE CONTROL SYSTEM. The control system of a rocket research aircraft, space capsule, or any vehicle traveling in thin atmosphere or in space, which uses the force of action and reaction to control the attitude of the vehicle in flight. In the Project Mercury capsule, small steam jets fire with a low thrust to change the capsule attitude as desired. This type of control system is entirely different from that of control surfaces, such as wings, ailerons, propellers, rudders, etc., which are used with aircraft within the lower atmosphere.

AUDIO FREQUENCY. Any frequency of sound that affects the human ear, ranging from 15 to 20,000 vibrations every second. The most audible range is between 500 and 4,000 vibrations per second.

"AUGER IN." To crash in any manned aircraft or spacecraft. As used by pilots and aircrews, it usually means that the crash has been fatal.

AURAL SIGNAL. A signal which must be heard by the ear and be interpreted without benefit or aid of visual instruments.

AURORA. Brilliant displays of light in the electrical atmosphere regions above the earth, caused by the agitation of electrical particles in the atmosphere by different types and intensities of radiation from the sun. The Auroras appear in many different colors, in bands, curtains, straight lines, banners, etc. They appear most frequently along the boundaries of the polar regions, and can be seen for many thousands of miles.

AURORA 7. Name assigned to Mercury capsule flown in three earth orbits on May 24, 1962, by Astronaut Malcolm Scott Carpenter.

AUTARK CLOSED ECOLOGICAL SYS-TEM. A completely sealed system, capable of minimum necessary ecological requirements, that is independent of the sun for thermal or photosynthetic needs; a sun-independent closed ecological system. See **algae; closed ecological system; photosynthesis.**

AUTOKINETIC MOVEMENT. An illusion common to night flying, when a pilot or airman stares uninterruptedly at a light. If the light is stationary it may seem to move and swing in wide arcs. If the light is moving, it may seem to move to the side when it is actually moving straight ahead. Trying to follow a light's apparent movement, pilots have been known to go into curving dives and to continue their dive into the ground. To prevent autokinetic movement—also known as *stare vision*—the pilot is warned not to stare for any extended period, but to keep shifting his gaze from point to point. Doctors feel this problem will be encountered in similar fashion in orbital rendezvous and docking maneuvers. See **size-distance illusion.**

AUTOMATIC OPENING PARACHUTE. A parachute equipped with a device that opens the parachute automatically when triggered by (1) an aneroid, which is responsive to a preset pressure altitude, such as 15,000 feet above sea level, or (2) a timer; if the airman bails out below 15,000 feet when the aneroid is set for that altitude, the timer cuts in and opens the parachute after a brief delay. Action on the part of the airman is unnecessary.

AUTOMATIC PILOT. A control mechanism incorporating a gyroscope; in an aircraft the autopilot initiates corrections on the control surfaces of the aircraft to maintain a steady and preset course and altitude without assistance from a human pilot. In the strict sense of the term, this is the three-axis automatic pilot which maintains a preset and steady altitude and heading by co-ordinating automatically the use of ailerons, elevators, and rudder, and presupposes a constant power setting. In a

spacecraft in orbit, the automatic pilot maintains spacecraft attitude according to pitch, yaw, and roll. See **ASCS.**

AUTOMATIC SEQUENCER. A timing device that starts and stops certain control equipment or instruments, and operates on a schedule that was programmed before the activity begins. For example, the final 27 seconds of the countdown of the Atlas rocket are fully automatic. At T-minus 27 seconds an automatic sequencer takes over the remaining operations to be accomplished before the countdown reaches "zero," and the Atlas begins the sequence that will launch it from its launch stand. The automatic sequencer is, in essence, an elaborate timing device with built-in control steps to occur at specific intervals of time.

AUTONOMIC NERVOUS FUNCTIONS. Those nervous functions which automatically or unconsciously control heartbeat, respiration, digestion, bowel and bladder function, touch, sight, balance, orientation. These areas of specific and vital physiological reaction are especially important in relation to conditions of acceleration and weightlessness.

AVERTED VISION. The central part of the eye is insensitive to starlight illumination levels. To see things clearly at night on the earth, in flight, or under conditions of darkside orbit, the individual must not look directly at them. Improved visual resolution and identification of objects at night result from averted—or off-center—vision. To see an object straight ahead, the observer actually looks slightly to the side of the object.

AVIATION MEDICAL ACCELERATION LABORATORY. The U.S. Navy facility which centers around the operation of the world's largest known human centrifuge. Operation of this centrifuge is co-ordinated with a major computer facility to establish a capability for dynamic flight simulation. Thus the occupant of the centrifuge gondola can fly exact replicas of flight patterns for both aircraft and space vehicles, such as

Mercury, Gemini, Apollo, X-15, X-20, etc., through use of exact cockpit and spacecraft cabin replicas. Many ancillary studies at the laboratory are conducted in the fields of instrumentation, equipment design, bio-pack development, performance under stress, biochemical stress indicators, etc.

AVIATOR'S DEAFNESS. A nerve-type deafness with permanent impairment of hearing due to repeated exposure to fatigu-ing noises; the hearing losses begin in the frequency range above that necessary to hear normal speech, becoming progressively worse with continued exposure to fatiguing noises. Formerly this condition was com-mon among open-cockpit pilots, then among pilots of powerful piston-engine airplanes such as the B-25, with high cockpit noise levels. In more recent times it is being en-countered by ground crews working around jet and rocket engine test cells, static test stands, gas generator equipment, airbases, and launch sites. It affects the hearing of frequencies of about 4,000 cycles per second.

AXIS. A straight line about which a body rotates, or around which a plane figure may rotate to produce a solid; a line of sym-metry. Also: one of a set of reference lines for certain systems of co-ordinates.

AZIMUTH. The bearing of an object measured in degrees from a fixed point, usually true north. Azimuth is horizontal bearing or direction.

AZUSA. An electronic tracking system that continuously collects precision data on the positions of a rocket booster in flight at any given moment. The Azusa system at Cape Canaveral includes 8 ground antennas laid out in a giant cross, linked to a trans-ponder in the rocket vehicle. In addition to its use for collecting precision data, the Cape's Azusa system also provides vital in-formation for range safety operations. Azusa is an integral part of the Atlas-D control, tracking, and safety systems. See **impact predictor; Range Safety Officer; transponder.**

B

B-52. An 8-jet engine bomber of approxi-mately 450,000 lbs. gross weight used as a "mother plane" to carry the X-15 and other manned aerospace vehicles to the lower stratosphere for air drops, after which the areospace vehicle, already above 40,000 feet and moving at a speed of approximately 450 miles per hour, commences its own powered flight.

BACKOUT. Reversing a countdown se-quence because of the failure of a component in a booster vehicle or payload, or because of a hold of unacceptable duration. See **countdown.**

BACKUP VEHICLE. A rocket booster kept in reserve to be used in the shortest possible time to "back up" a space mission if the primary booster vehicle fails to accomplish the planned mission. In terms of satellites, a backup satellite, an exact duplicate of the one to be orbited, is kept in reserve. If there is a failure prior to launch of the first satellite, the backup is immediately sub-stituted for it.

BAIKONUR. Cosmodrome in the USSR employed for the launch of manned orbital flights and major space missions, usually along an orbital inclination of approxi-mately 65° to the equator. The Baikonur Cosmodrome lies at 47° 22 minutes north latitude, 65° 25 minutes east longitude.

BAILLY. The largest crater on the side of the moon facing earth; has a measured diameter of over 180 miles. Not to be con-fused with Baily, with a diameter of ap-proximately 20 miles.

BAILOUT. Pilot's term for an emergency evacuation of an aircraft; i.e., bailing out—resorting to the personal parachute to aban-don a burning or uncontrollable aircraft. "Bailout" is inclusive, and covers any means of such evacuation, such as ejection.

BAILOUT BOTTLE. A small portable oxygen cylinder under very high pressure, worn attached to the flying suit or pressure suit of a pilot who ascends to great heights. In an emergency bailout, the pilot activates the bottle which provides pressure to the suit and oxygen flow to the pilot. Its use permits a pilot to bail out as high as 20 miles above the earth and fall free to 14,000 feet or lower, receiving pressurization and oxygen from the bailout bottle.

BAKER-NUNN CAMERA. A large camera used in tracking satellites orbiting the earth.

BALLISTICS. The science that deals with the motion, behavior, and effects of projectiles, especially bullets, aerial bombs, rockets, missiles, or the like; the science or art of designing and hurling projectiles so as to achieve a desired performance.

BALLISTIC TRAJECTORY. That part of a missile or booster trajectory that is traced after the cutoff of all propulsion and guidance; the missile or booster then reacts only to the force of gravity, its own momentum, and the conditions and properties of the atmosphere through which it passes.

BALLOON-TYPE BOOSTER. A rocket booster, or missile, that requires the pressure of its propellants, or substitute gases, within it to give it structural integrity. See **Atlas.**

BAMBI. Part of the Advanced Research Projects Agency (ARPA) Defender program concerned with the broad spectrum of ballistic missile defense. BAMBI—Ballistic Missile Boost Intercept—is a project to determine the feasibility of a multi-satellite system to identify and destroy ICBMs.

BARALYME. A mixture of calcium hydroxide and barium hydroxide. It is used to absorb carbon dioxide from the air, and has been tested for possible use in the closed-cycle environment control systems of manned spacecraft.

BARANY CHAIR. A revolving chair used to test a person's equilibrium.

BARBER CHAIR. An adjustable type of manned aerospace vehicle seat that can quickly shift the occupant from an up-

right seated position to a supine or semi-supine position to increase his tolerance to high acceleration.

BARIUM OXIDE. A chemical compound that is used in a closed cabin environment to absorb water vapor from the air.

BAROMETRIC PRESSURE. Atmospheric pressure as shown by the barometer. Of critical importance to all personnel who ascend to high altitudes is the fact that all criteria for the use of oxygen equipment and the possibility of dysbarism effects (see **dysbarism**) depend on the actual reading of the barometric pressure within the aircraft or aerospace vehicle and *not* on the corrected altimeter reading. Distinguishing between pressure and density altitude is vital to the aerospace physiologist and flight surgeon in the range of 35,000 to 50,000 feet. In this range, the physiological response of the human body changes rapidly with slight changes in altitude. The following facts are the critical guidelines:

(1) Aerodynamically, airplane performance is measured in terms of *density altitude,* which is the altitude corresponding to a given density in a standard atmosphere.

(2) Physiologically, human performance is measured by the *pressure altitude* which is shown by the actual reading on the altimeter not corrected for temperature. Thus, in the physiological sense, the physical property of the upper atmosphere most important to the airman is the *actual pressure* of the air in which he flies. (At sea level, the atmospheric pressure exerts a force of 14.7 psi, or 2,117 lbs. per square foot, and causes a column of mercury in an evacuated tube to rise approximately 29.92 inches, or 760 millimeters.)

BAROSTAT. A barometric-pressure sensing device that is set to be activated by the pressure level of a specific barometric pressure altitude; for example, a barostat that is set to a barometric pressure reading of 10,000 feet, at which altitude the barostat triggers a parachute-release system. See **aneroid.**

BARRIER REEFS. Test-pilot nomenclature for the individual and combined "danger areas" of flight that include extreme aerodynamic forces, atmospheric friction and excessive thermal heating, buffeting, compressibility, etc. So-called because of their characteristics, severe enough to destroy the strongest aircraft and space vehicles passing through the "reefs."

BASIC ASTRONAUTIC SCIENCES. Essentially an academic educational program (part of astronaut training program, Projects Mercury, Gemini, Apollo), this area of instruction in astronautics particularly includes ballistics, trajectories, fuels, guidance, and other aspects of missile operations, basic aviation medicine and orbital flight hygiene, the space environment, astronomy, meteorology, astrophysics, and geography, including the techniques for making scientific observations in these areas.

BASIC MEDICAL SCIENCES (ASTRONAUTICS).

(1) **Respiratory Physiology.** Includes the control of mechanics and physical chemistry of mammalian respiration; gaseous diffusion and exchange; effects of alterations in ambient conditions of pressure and temperature.
(2) **Circulatory physiology.** Includes the circulatory reflexes, the control of the circulation, its response to gravitational and accelerative stress, to alterations in oxygen and carbon-dioxide tensions, and to temperature change.
(3) **Metabolism.** Includes energetics, nutrition, hibernation, digestion, excretion.
(4) **Neurophysiology.** Includes postural and righting reflexes, physiology of vision, audition, proprioception, and orientation; central control of metabolism, temperature, endocrines, circulation, and respiration; circulation and metabolism of brain.
(5) **Behavioral Science.** Includes perception, motivation, and performance under stress, emotional stability, fatigue, social and sensory isolation, psychological assessment and training for special missions.

BATTLESHIP TANK TEST. A "hot" propulsion test system that uses propellant tanks with the thickness and strength approximating that of a battleship fuel tank, in order to permit repeated pressurization of the tanks to simulate the acceleration pressures and "hot" engine runs of a propulsion system in flight.

BAT WING. See flexwing.

BAY. A cubicle specifically designed to receive equipment of an exact shape and weight, with facilities for electrical plug-ins so that the equipment may be installed and activated immediately.

BEACON. As used in rocket and spacecraft vehicles, a device that contains an automatic radar receiver *and* transmitter. It is most often used in tracking, guidance, and warning systems. Its most common usage is as **transponder.**

BEAM. A ray or collection of focused rays of radiated energy. Radio waves used as a navigation aid comprise a radio beam.

BEAM-RIDER. A craft following a beam, particularly one which does so automatically, the beam providing the guidance.

BEARING. The horizontal angle at a given point measured clockwise from a specific reference datum to a second point.

BEAST. Term commonly used to refer to booster rocket vehicles.

BEAUPRE CHUTE. A multi-stage parachute developed by Francis Beaupre and the team of the Air Force's Project Excelsior. The Beaupre parachute deploys at great heights and serves to stabilize in free fall a pilot or airman who has been forced to bail out of his aircraft at altitudes in the stratosphere. An unstabilized free-falling human body has a tendency to go into a very rapid flat spin with a rotation speed up to 240 revolutions per minute. The Beaupre Chute, tested in jumps by Captain Joseph W. Kittinger, Jr., from altitudes up to 102,800 feet, prevents the flat spin. The flat spin has directly killed several airmen. The Beaupre Chute is worn as a conventional parachute. When it is deployed from the pack, the chute opens to a diameter of 6 feet. In the descent it slows the man down only slightly, but permits outstanding feet-first falling stability. At a preset altitude of 14,000 to 19,000 feet, an automatic timer operated by an aneroid releases the main parachute. A modified Beaupre parachute is standard equipment in the two-man Gemini spacecraft. See **aneroid; flat spin.**

BEAUPRE CHUTE. Full-jump equipment with Beaupre chute, worn by Captain Joseph W. Kittinger, Jr., USAF, for Project Excelsior

BELCO. Booster Engine Cutoff. In Project Mercury, the moment in the Atlas booster ascent when the two main booster engines are shut down. Immediately afterward the booster engines and booster skirt are jettisoned; thrust is continued by sustainer and verniers. See **Atlas-D flight plan; Atlas-D propulsion system.**

BEHAVIORAL SCIENCE. See **basic medical sciences.**

BENDS. The often acute pain and discomfort in the arms, legs, and joints resulting from the formation of nitrogen bubbles, together with other biological gases, in body tissues and fluids, caused by exposure to reduced barometric pressure (lowered density altitude). Bends, the pain of which may be mild but is often deep and gnawing, most frequently occur in the larger joints,

such as knee, shoulder, and ankle, but the small joints of the hands and wrists are often affected. Tissues having the highest content of fat are most likely to form bends bubbles. Fat dissolves five or six times as much nitrogen as an equal mass of blood. See **aeroembolism; decompression sickness; dysbarism.**

BIG JOE. Popular name given to Atlas-D booster rocket used in early flight tests of Project Mercury manned capsule. Atlas 10-D fired on September 9, 1959, made tests of ablative heat shield, afterbody heating, entry dynamics, attitude control, sequencing, recovery operations of capsule, over a range of 1,500 miles.

BINARY STAR. Two stars revolving around a common center of gravity.

BINOCULAR VISION. See **depth perception.**

BIOASTRONAUTICS. The medical science of manned flight in space.

BIODYNAMICS. The science of the motions of bodies and of the forces acting upon bodies in motion, or in the process of changing motion, *as these motions or forces affect life.*

BIO-INSTRUMENTS. Physiological sensors attached to the human body to record and to transmit functional physiological data of the individual.

BIOKINEMATICS. Generally, a study of individual strength, or strength-in-action. More specifically, the maximum possible yield limits of muscle effort and bone in a man's efforts to generate and to apply power. It establishes parameters of pilot-control force under any condition. Individual strength parameters are established on the basis of man's ability to raise an object of a specified weight from ground level under 1 g to an infinite number of levels, as measured in terms of acceleration and strain.

BIOMEDICINE. The combined disciplines of biology and medicine directed toward analyzing the human tolerances to different environmental variances, and providing protection over a sustained period whenever such tolerances may be exceeded.

BIONICS. The study of systems which function after the manner of, in a manner characteristic of, or resembling living systems.

BIOPACK. A sealed unit, in which are maintained minimum required levels of pressurization, oxygen, heating, refrigeration, and power supplies for biological and/or biomedical research flights in the space environment. Usually carried in balloons, aircraft, satellite vehicles, and vertically fired rockets.

BIOPROPELLANT. A liquid rocket propellant that consists of a mixture in the combustion chamber of a liquid fuel and a liquid oxidizer; also, either the fuel or the oxidizer before being brought together in the combustion chamber. Example: the liquid propellant of the Atlas booster, consisting of kerosene and liquid oxygen.

BIOSATELLITE. An orbiting satellite that carries animal or plant life for space-environment research.

BIOSPHERE. That part of the earth and its atmospheric envelope in which plant and animal life are sustained.

BIOTECHNOLOGY. Generally, the complete science of biology as it is applied toward solving the physiological and psychological problems of manned space flight. More specifically, the major activities and approaches of biotechnology as pursued by NASA include: (1) man-machine integration and instrumentation; (2) environmental stress tolerance and adaptation; (3) protective equipment, including escape devices and radiation shielding; (4) life support systems; (5) crew performance; and (6) the public health problems relating to ground crews and general areas. Supporting this biotechnological work are the basic space medical and behavioral sciences, which are: (1) cardiovascular physiology; (2) respiratory physiology; (3) metabolism and nutri-

tion; and (4) neurophysiology and psychology.

BI-PROPELLANT HYPERGOLIC. In Project Gemini, monomethyl hydrazine is the fuel, and mixed oxides of nitrogen the oxidizer, for the attitude and maneuvering reaction system of the Gemini capsule. See **hypergolic fuel.**

BIRD. Any rocket vehicle, missile, booster, spacecraft, satellite.

BIRDWATCHER. A relatively new species now common to the Cape Canaveral area; an enthusiastic observer of "birds" that rise from the Cape. To be found on beaches, rooftops, roads, or any good position from where birds may be seen ascending from Canaveral. Always present during a countdown. An extremely hardy species.

BIT. From BInary digiT—a unit of information.

BLACK BODY. An ideal body in space which absorbs totally all radiation that falls on it, and reflects none. In the specific sense, a totally black body does not and cannot exist.

BLACK BOX. Any automatic control or assisting unit, such as an automatic pilot or radar unit, that may be mounted in or removed from an aircraft, missile, booster, or spacecraft as a single package.

BLACK-BOX OPERATION. A maintenance procedure that consists of replacing a malfunctioning black box with a second unit that functions properly.

BLACKOUT (1). A condition of unconsciousness; most commonly applied to a blackout caused by the steady application of high g forces. A man in a sitting position reacts specifically under increasing g forces. Between 3.5 and 5 g positive (head to foot application of the g force) a man's eyesight dims out (grayout). At 4 to 5.5 g, his vision blacks out. He is still conscious, but he cannot see. A force of 4.5 to 6 g maintained for 3 to 5 seconds (depending upon the individual) means complete unconsciousness. The blackout caused by 5*g* force for more than 5 seconds results from the fact that the retina (or photographic film) of each eye is sensitive to a lack of oxygen, more so than any other part of the body. Between the heart and the brain is a column of arterial blood roughly 12 inches in height. At 5*g*, the downward pull of the blood column equals the upward push of the blood that comes from blood pressure. The continued *g* force in the meantime "pools" the blood in the legs to about 240 blood pressure. The result of the shift in pressure distribution is impaired circulation. Blood cannot go up to the brain and any return of blood to the heart from below the heart is difficult. If the *g* force continues, the heart finally pumps itself dry as blood accumulates in the lower part of the body. At 4*g* too little blood (i.e., oxygen) reaches the retina and the oxygen already there is used up in 3 seconds. Result—vision blacks out even though the man is still conscious. If the *g* force continues, he becomes completely unconscious because blood and oxygen no longer reach the brain. The function of time in relation to *g* is a vital factor in withstanding *g* forces. A pilot can take 10*g* for 3 seconds, for example, without blacking out. A pilot who builds up his *g* forces very gradually assists his body, because the arteries in the lower part of his body will constrict in a few seconds in compensation for the fall in blood pressure in the upper part of the body; in this fashion he gains an added tolerance of 1*g*, and can take 6*g* before blacking out. Other factors are involved. Increasing the blood pressure by tensing up the body helps, as do certain flight garments, such as the *g*-suit, to squeeze the body and build up blood pressure. Changing the position of the body is the single most important factor in resisting *g* forces. A man lying in a semisupine position (as in the Mercury capsule) takes the *g* forces while his eyes are level with his heart, making it easier for his body to continue pumping blood between the heart and the eyes and brain. A man in this position can take up to 12*g* and still remain in control of his senses and his equipment. See **g-suit; g-tolerance; positive-*g* tolerance.**

BLACKOUT (2). A fadeout of radio communications due to environmental factors such as ionospheric disturbances or a plasma sheath surrounding a re-entry vehicle. See **ionized layer; re-entry profile.**

BLANKETING. The process of having a desired signal blanketed, or eliminated from reception, by the presence of an overriding, undesired signal.

BLASTOFF. The moment of ascent of a rocket from its launch stand. Also **liftoff; takeoff.**

BLEED. Also *bleedoff*. To remove all or part of the fuel or fluid content of a tank or fuel line by bypassing the normal use of that fuel or fluid, as in "to bleed off excess fuel from a tank."

BLIP. A single spot of light that appears on a radarscope or radar viewscreen and indicates radar "acquisition of the target," such as an aircraft, missile, booster, or space vehicle.

BLOCKHOUSE. Master control center for direct control of launch operations. Example: Atlas blockhouse. Located 750 feet from Atlas launch stand. Blockhouse is of thick steel walls, reinforced concrete, thick layer of sand, the latter with gunite to maintain curving layer of sand in place. Blockhouse is staffed by approximately 40 people for a launch operation. Has closed-circuit TV monitors and periscopes for outside visual operations; radio and telephone linkage to other control centers, to central control, etc. Prior to actual ignition of the rocket the blockhouse is sealed and internal air supply is used.

BLOOD, BOILING OF. At an average height of 63,000 feet pressure altitude, the blood and fluids of the unprotected pilot begin to bubble and boil. At this altitude the boiling temperature of water is 98–99°F. Acting as a heat engine, the body provides enough heat to boil the pilot's blood and fluids within the body. Explosive decompression—a sudden exposure to near-space or vacuum conditions—results in an explosive boiling of the blood and body fluids. For this reason space flights to date have been made with a backup protective system—both a sealed cabin environment and a full-pressure suit. Any loss of cabin pressure results in automatic inflation and pressurization of the suit about the entire body.

Protected by his pressure suit, Air Force pilot uncovers beaker of warm water at pressure altitude of 93,000 feet. Human BLOOD would react the same way as the water without pressure suit or cabin protection

BLOOD, SATURATION LEVEL. The percentage of oxygen saturation within the blood. Under ordinary conditions at ground level, the blood is approximately 95% saturated with oxygen. An increased rate of breathing or the breathing of pure oxygen increases the saturation; in the latter case it is raised to approximately 100%. If saturation levels decrease to much less than 95%, unfavorable physiological reactions result. At 10,000 feet pressure altitude, arterial oxygen saturation drops to 90%. At 15,000 feet the saturation averages 84%; at 18,000 feet the saturation level is 70%, with attendant serious effects on the individual. A saturation level of 80% produces moderate hy-

poxia—dimming of vision, tremor of the hands, errors of judgment, and clouding of thought and memory. See **anoxia; hypoxia.**

BLOWOFF. The separation of a payload (i.e., satellite, probe, capsule) from its booster rocket, as accomplished by an explosive bolt or other explosive device. Some payloads are separated by springs under tension, which are released by timer or radio signal.

BLOWOUT. The explosive loss of cabin pressure in a pressurized aircraft or spacecraft. Caused by the puncture or rupture of a cabin wall, resulting in the explosive escape of gases under higher internal pressure to lower external pressure. Blowout also includes the puncturing or rupturing of a pressure suit, resulting in the same conditions. See **explosive decompression.**

BOATTAIL. The rear section of a ballistic rocket booster vehicle, sometimes tapered but squared off at the end, which serves also as the base of the missile during launch.

"BODACIOUS AFTERBURNER." Astronaut expression for Atlas-D booster vehicle.

BOGIE. Enemy aircraft or spacecraft.

BOILERMAKER'S DEAFNESS. A nerve-type deafness induced by repeated exposure to fatiguing noises. See **aviator's deafness.**

BOILERPLATE. As in "boilerplate capsule." A metal copy of the flight vehicle, built to the same external dimensions and configuration, but with structure and/or components which are heavier than the flight model. Boilerplate models are air-dropped from planes, cranes, fired on rocket sleds, flight-boosted by rockets, etc.

BOILING. The bubbling of body fluids in an unpressurized environment that occurs when the atmospheric pressure drops to 47 millimeters of mercury or less. See **blood, boiling of.**

BOILOFF. The vaporization of liquid oxygen in a rocket vehicle that uses liquid oxygen as its oxidizer. See **liquid oxygen; goxing.**

BOILERPLATE. Mercury boilerplate capsule in water-drop test

BOOSTGLIDE VEHICLE. A design proposal for an aerospace vehicle that would fly powered by air-breathing engines to the limits of the sensible atmosphere, then would be boosted by rockets into space so as to orbit the earth one or more times, and would be aided in remaining aloft by skip-gliding at hypersonic speeds along the edges of the atmosphere, and then would return under manned aerodynamic control to the earth's surface.

BOOSTER. Any rocket vehicle used to boost upper rocket stages, satellites, probes, manned spacecraft or payloads to specific altitudes and velocities.

"BOOSTER ON INTERNAL DC." A phrase ("sequence") in the countdown to signify that the rocket booster is now drawing power from its internal power sources; outside power no longer is being used. Occurs shortly before ignition.

BOOTSTRAP. To lift off from a launch platform and climb at maximum possible speed.

BOSS-WEDGE. Code identification of an extensive Air Force study for a manned military space-bombing and reconnaissance system; an extension of the X-20 Dyna-Soar program. BOSS-WEDGE stands for Bomb Orbital Strategic System—WEapon Development Glide Entry.

"BOUGHT THE FARM." Pilot's expression denoting that an airman has crashed with fatal results.

BOW WAVE. A powerful shock wave preceding the descending flight of a vehicle re-entering the earth's atmosphere from space. See **shock wave.**

BOYLE'S LAW. (After Robert Boyle, Irish physicist.) The law that the volume of gas changes in inverse proportion to the amount of pressure exerted upon it under constant temperature. See **aeroembolism.**

BRADYHEMARRHEA. A local or general stagnation or slowing down of the blood flow to a rate insufficient to meet physiological requirements; may be caused by stagnant hypoxia. See **hypoxia.**

BRAIN. Generally refers to a navigational device, or an electronic data processing system; any electronic computer.

BRAIN BUCKET. A crash helmet; also, a jet-pilot or spacesuit helmet.

BRAKING ELLIPSES. A series of orbital approaches to a planetary atmosphere for the purpose of slowing up a vehicle preparatory to landing, in order to avoid the extreme heat of friction which would be caused by excessively fast and sustained re-entry or entry into a planetary atmosphere. Each ellipse decreases in size because of the planetary drag, and effects a reduction in velocity.

BRAKING ROCKETS. Another term for **retro-rockets.** Auxiliary rockets, either liquid- or solid-propellant, fired in the direction of flight and used to "brake" or decelerate a space vehicle in its orbital flight, to begin the descent back to the earth's atmosphere. "Braking rocket," however, as an inclusive term, can be applied to any rocket power system used to decelerate a vehicle.

BRAKING STAGE. A rocket stage intended specifically for vertical descent and landing on a spatial body, as distinguished from a retrostage, which is intended primarily to provide orbital deceleration for re-entry from an orbit.

BREAKOFF FEELING. A sensation experienced by some pilots at extreme altitudes —in aircraft and balloons—of being suddenly separated and detached from the earth and human society; a feeling so deeply intense that a number of these pilots doubted they would ever return to the earth's surface again.

"BREAK POINT." In sustained manned flight through space: that time at which the personnel of a space vehicle on an extended space flight must shift from *stored sustenance* to *regenerated supplies*. Estimated at from 15 to 30 man-days of flight. See **closed ecological system.**

BREATHING, CONTROL OF. Normal breathing, although to a certain extent under voluntary control, is essentially an involuntary act. At low altitudes, regulation of respiratory movements is accomplished by responses of the nervous system to the concentration of carbon dioxide in the blood— *not* to that of oxygen. Nerve impulses affecting frequency and depth of respiration originate in the respiratory center of the medulla oblongata. When the content of carbon dioxide in the blood increases, as it does during exercise, the respiratory center is stimulated and the rate and depth of respiration increase. When the content of oxygen in the blood is decreased, an increase in the rate and depth of respiration occurs through stimulation of chemically sensitive nerve centers located in the aorta and carotid artery. The increase in pulmonary ventilation that can be achieved by this mechanism, however, is considerably less than the maximum resulting from an increase in the carbon dioxide content of the blood. Under ordinary circumstances and at ground level, this relative insensitivity of the respiratory control mechanism to reduced oxygen tension in inspired air imposes no undue hardship. As the need for oxygen in the cells of the body becomes greater during exercise,

for example, the output of carbon dioxide by the cells likewise increases. The amount of carbon dioxide carried by the blood is larger, the central respiratory control mechanism is stimulated, and the ventilation rate is increased to accomplish elimination of the carbon dioxide. The more rapid rate of ventilation increases the amount of oxygen brought into the alveoli of the lungs and thus more oxygen is made available for absorption by the blood. It is only because of the close parallel between the rate of production of carbon dioxide and the need for oxygen by the tissues of the body that various oxygen requirements are so well met at ground level. At high altitudes (pressure altitude) the situation is very different. The amount of oxygen reaching the tissues is lowered without any corresponding increase in production of carbon dioxide. Therefore, the body fails to make the response required, namely, an adequately increased ventilation rate. At altitudes of between 12,000 and 15,000 feet, the oxygen tension in the blood falls low enough to stimulate the chemoreceptors, producing a reflex rise in ventilation rate. Actually, this increase is inadequate. Under such circumstances, more rapid breathing produces a greater loss of carbon dioxide. Excessive loss of carbon dioxide (hyperventilation) produces dizziness, tingling of the extremities, and if continued long enough, tetanic spasms of the limbs, and finally unconsciousness. See **alveolar air; alveoli; breathing, process of; respiration.**

BREATHING, PROCESS OF. The respiration process involves inhaling, in which the individual exerts slight muscular effort to pull the chest wall and diaphragm away from the lungs. This action reduces the pressure within the lungs. Atmospheric pressure (ambient air, pressure suit, pressurized cabin) then forces air into and fills the lungs. Involuntary relaxing of the muscles that expand the chest produces exhalation; this requires no effort. The average individual under conditions of normal working activity breathes 12 to 16 times a minute (less while resting, more under strenuous exercise). He inhales about one pint of air at a time, or from 6 to 8 quarts a minute. Under conditions of intense psychological, emotional, or physical stress (conditions encountered in test or experimental aerospace work) or any combination of these, the breathing rate increases to as high as 60 quarts per minute. The *purpose of the respiratory process* is essentially to bring oxygen into the bloodstream and to eliminate carbon dioxide. This vital *exchange of gases* is made through the walls of millions of tiny sacs and blood vessels in the lungs. Normal functioning of the exchange of gases is dependent upon ambient air pressure; lowered air pressure interferes with the process. The volume of air inhaled and exhaled with each breath is called the *tidal* volume. *Vital capacity* is the volume of air which can be exhaled after the deepest possible inhalation, and represents the maximum in tidal volume. *Pulmonary minute volume,* or pulmonary ventilation, is the volume of air respired per minute, and can be determined by multiplying the tidal volume by the number of breaths per minute. See **alveolar air; alveoli; breathing, control of; respiration.**

BRENNSCHLUSS. German for *combustion termination,* a term commonly used in U.S. rocket programs. The cessation of burning in a rocket, resulting from (1) consumption of propellants, (2) deliberate cutoff or shutdown, or (3) any other cause. The moment at which propulsion ends, no matter what the cause.

BUFFETING. The random and uncontrolled motions—sometimes violent—sustained by an aircraft or spacecraft when turbulence is encountered, especially under conditions of compressibility arising from very high airspeeds. The irregular oscillations that occur from this circumstance.

BUG (1). Unidentified problem in any complicated device such as a booster vehicle, aircraft, or spacecraft that causes malfunctions or failures or, if encountered in a checkout such as a countdown, seriously interferes with the continuation of the countdown or causes a scrub.

BUG (2). The popular name for the two-man lunar landing vehicle of Project Apollo that will descend from a 100-mile lunar orbit to the lunar surface. The Bug will weigh 30,000 lbs. and will be approximately 20 feet in height. See **Apollo.**

BULLHORN. Loudspeakers placed throughout launch, control, and support areas for information and commands to all personnel.

BURNOUT. That moment when a rocket exhausts all available propellant.

BURNOUT VELOCITY. The exact velocity of a rocket at the instant of burnout.

BUTTON UP. To seal completely any unit, equipment, or vehicle; i.e., to "button up the capsule," to close, lock, and seal all hatches and openings. A final preparation for a mission.

C

CABLE REELS. In the atmospheric descent of the Gemini or Apollo spacecraft beneath an inflatable flexwing (see **flexwing**), maneuverability and change of angle of attack of flight path will be accomplished by shifting the center of gravity of the spacecraft and the center of pressure of the flexwing. This will be carried out by pilot control through a cable reel system. Moving a hand control within the spacecraft actuates gas-operated cable reels, causing them slightly to extend or shorten in order to achieve pressure and/or center of gravity changes. Two cables (as in Gemini) are used to vary pitch and two cables are used for roll control.

CANARD. An aircraft or aerospace vehicle (such as the RS-70) with its elevators forward of the main wing. Also: an aerodynamic control surface on the nose of a missile, booster, aerospace vehicle, or satellite for re-entry control purposes.

CANOPY. The plexiglas covering of a cockpit or cabin. See **greenhouse.**

CAPCOM. Designation for individual in Mercury Control at Cape Canaveral, or at any communications station around the world, who is assigned to communications with an astronaut in a space capsule.

CAPE CANAVERAL. Launching site for Air Force Missile Test Center, Atlantic Missile Range, located on the east coast of Florida. Also identified as Cape Canaveral Missile Test Annex and Cape Canaveral Auxiliary Air Force Base. Launching site for missiles, test rockets, research rockets, unmanned satellites, manned satellites, deep-space probes.

CAPILLARY ACTION. Tendency of liquids to rise or fall in narrow tubes; an area of special study under zero-*g* conditions, in relationship to the storage of liquids within spacecraft cabins and to the action of liquid fuels in tanks and pipelines.

CAP PISTOL. A space-vehicle control system intended to maneuver spacecraft in attitude control with unusual precision and reliability. The device is cylindrical and squat, and is small enough to be cupped within the hand. Known officially as the Encapsulated Solid-Propellant Pulse Engine, and devised under an Air Force program for control of advanced space-vehicle systems under research/development contract to Curtiss-Wright, the Cap Pistol supplies thrust in levels comparable to the human breath at its lower range. Tiny bits of solid propellant are imbedded in plastic tape. Each bit is installed in the tape with its own self-contained, shaped firing nozzle. The system eliminates nozzle clogging for fine-thrust devices. The low impulse rating makes possible precision corrections for vernier accuracy in pitch, yaw, and roll attitudes. The tiny rocket "engines" in the tape can be fired individually or on a rapid-fire basis; the number of "engines" fired is determined by a direct-action digital computer. The rocket propellant is temperature insensitive, and can be stored for many years.

CAPSTANS. See **pressure suit—partial.**

CAPSULE. Manned or unmanned spacecraft in capsule shape. The Mercury capsule is a manned vehicle; the recovery capsule of the USAF Discoverer program is an unmanned capsule. The capsule shape is usually blunt at its leading surface, is non-airlifting, and has very high aerodynamic drag. It is non-controllable in directional flight.

CAPTIVE TEST. A test under partial or maximum power of any aircraft, booster vehicle, or propulsion system in which the vehicle or system is restrained by holddown clamps or shackles. Designed to prove out reliability and integrity of the system prior to flight test. See **static test.**

CARBON DIOXIDE. A colorless gas which under normal surface atmospheric conditions forms 0.03% of the air. Carbon dioxide (CO_2) is produced when carbon is consumed in the presence of oxygen—a normal energy-producing process which in human beings produces carbon dioxide as a waste respiratory gas. See **breathing, control of; hyperventilation.**

CARBON-DIOXIDE CHAMBER. A sealed atmospheric environmental chamber in which the carbon-dioxide content is gradually increased from a normal 0.05% to approximately 4% over a period of 3 hours. Used for pilots and astronauts for hyperventilation and other danger-situation training. The effects as described by Astronaut Alan Shepard: "We were able to note the physiological effects such as increased breathing, pulse rate, flushing, and, in some cases, a slight headache."

CARDIOVASCULAR REACTIVITY. The response and behavior of the heart and blood vessels to various types of inflight stress, such as exercise, extreme heat or cold, and acceleration.

CARRIER VEHICLE. A complete booster rocket, including all stages. Examples: Atlas-D, Atlas-Agena, Atlas-Able, Atlas-Centaur, Scout, Juno II, Jupiter-C, Thor-Delta, Thor-Agena, Saturn, Nova, Vanguard, etc.

CASCADE SHOWER. A group occurrence of cosmic rays. Also called "air shower." See **cosmic radiation.**

CAT. The cat is of especial value in zero-gravity experiments because of the animal's unique vestibular apparatus, which provides it with exceptional ability in orienting itself. The labyrinthine righting reflex of the cat is such that, under normal conditions, if a cat is held upside down and then released, the animal immediately assumes a normal posture so that it lands—always—on its feet. This reflex condition functions under blindfolded as well as normal visual conditions. But under full weightless conditions the animal's otoliths do not receive any stimulation at all. When released to float about in the zero-*g* condition, test animals became confused, panicky, and completely disoriented—providing detailed reactions of an animal with a superb "normal" righting reflex to zero-*g* conditions when this reflex is eliminated entirely.

CAVITATION. The rapid formation and collapse of vapor pockets in a flowing liquid under very low pressures—a frequent cause of serious structural damage to rocket components.

CCMTA. Cape Canaveral Missile Test Annex. Official designation for launching site of Atlantic Missile Range and/or Air Force Test Center. Formerly identified as *Range Station One* of Atlantic Missile Range. See **Cape Canaveral.**

CELESTIAL BODY. Generally, a body in space such as the sun, stars, moon, planets, meteors, and so forth. In its restrictive sense, any body in space exclusive of an artificial space vehicle.

CELESTIAL EQUATOR. See **spatial references.**

CELESTIAL GUIDANCE. See **celestial navigation.**

CELESTIAL MECHANICS. The study of the theory of the motions of celestial bodies under the influence of gravitational fields.

CELESTIAL NAVIGATION. The science of plotting the position and the course of a moving vehicle, and the directing of the vehicle from within the vehicle by means of sightings on celestial bodies. See **astrogation; star tracker.**

CELESTIAL SPHERE. Imaginary sphere of infinite radius, assumed for navigational purposes. Its center coincides with the center of the earth.

CENTAUR. Space-booster system. First stage is "sawed-off" Atlas-D booster vehicle. Second stage is Atlas body with two engines that burn "high energy" fuel combination of liquid hydrogen/liquid oxygen.

CENTER OF MASS. That point in a given body, or in two or more bodies that act together in respect to another body, which represents the mean position of the matter in the body or bodies. For example, the earth-moon system involves revolution of the two bodies about the earth-moon system center of mass, which lies about 1,000 miles under the earth's surface on a line connecting the center of the moon with the center of the earth.

CENTRAL CONTROL BUILDING. Located on Cape Canaveral at intersection of Cape and Heavy Launch Roads. From here all range functions concerning launch and flight of space missions or missile flights are co-ordinated and controlled. It is the "nerve center" of Atlantic Missile Range.

CENTRAL FORCE FIELD. An electromagnetic or gravitational field attracting and limiting the behavior of surrounding objects or particles, such as the gravitational field of the earth.

CENTRIFUGAL FORCE. The apparent force tending to carry an object away from the center of rotation.

CENTRIFUGE. Training device used to simulate high acceleration forces of rocket ascent and re-entry; often used by pilots and/or astronauts with complete spaceship control and cabin systems mockups or simulators for most realistic simulation of acceleration profiles of flight. (Illustrations, page 48.)

CENTRIPETAL ACCELERATION. Acceleration caused by centripetal force. See **gravity simulation.**

CENTRIPETAL FORCE. The force that pulls a moving body inward toward the center of rotation.

CENTRIFUGES. *Left:* Naval facility at Johnsville, Pennsylvania, used for simulated Mercury missions under high *g*-load conditions. *Right:* Centrifuge at Wright Aeromedical Laboratory, Dayton, Ohio

Astronaut John Glenn preparing for high-*g* run in CENTRIFUGE

CHAFF. Also: **window.** A cloud of radar-reflective metal foil strips used to facilitate radar pickup of descending space vehicles. In Mercury program, chaff is ejected at 21,000 feet when drogue parachute deploys.

CHAMBER FLIGHT. A simulated flight to varying levels of "high altitude" in a decompression chamber. See **altitude chamber.**

CHAMBER OF SILENCE. A modified anechoic (echoless) chamber for extended isolation and sensory deprivation tests of cosmonauts in the USSR manned spaceflight program. The chamber is a large metal shell suspended on rubber shock absorbers and mounted in the center of a large laboratory. The mounting and shock absorbers assure absolute silence within the chamber when sealed. The metal walls are 16 inches in thickness; two small viewports of the same thickness in glass are provided for study of the occupant. A replica of the spaceship cabin seat and equipment for extensive medical-psychological tests are installed in the chamber, which is occupied for periods of from several hours to as long as one to two weeks. See **sensory deprivation.**

CHAMBER PRESSURE. (1) The high pressure of the gases that exists within the combustion chamber of an operating rocket engine. (2) The atmospheric pressure level of an altitude or decompression chamber.

CHAMBER SKIRT. The complete main booster assembly of the Atlas vehicle. Contains the two outboard engines each of 150,-000 lbs. thrust. The outer covering and two engines are jettisoned from the vehicle at first staging, approximately 131 seconds after liftoff. Single sustainer engine and two verniers continue flight propulsion.

CHARACTERISTIC. The disposition inherent in any piece or unit of equipment, or integration of equipment into a single body, that tends to make it perform in a certain way. For example, the Mercury capsule is inherently—characteristically—aerodynamically unstable because of its blunt shape, as compared to the arrow stability of a vehicle employing airfoils and fins for such stability.

CHARACTERISTIC VELOCITY. In a rocket vehicle, the theoretical change in speed which would be achieved by that vehicle in the absence of gravity or air resistance. It is one measure of the inherent performance capability of the rocket.

CHASE. In "chase plane," "chase pilot": A chase pilot flies in an escort airplane advising a pilot who is making a check, training, or research flight in another aircraft or spacecraft.

CHATTER. A low-speed vibration which can be heard or felt in any machinery or equipment.

CHECKOUT. The process and sequence of actions that is taken to test, examine, and establish the integrity and readiness of a system—such as a booster vehicle, for example—to function properly, by testing all components and the unit as a whole. Also: an astronaut will go through a *checkout* of a spacecraft's systems to familiarize himself thoroughly with all equipment and procedures.

CHECKOUT. Engineers inspect retropack system before mating Mercury capsule with Atlas booster

CHEMACON BACKPACK. An individual atmosphere control unit, strapped for support as a personnel backpack, for oxygen and pressure supply in space environment, entirely separate from any spacecraft oxygen and/or pressure supply system.

CHEMICAL FUEL. A fuel that depends upon an oxidizer for combustion or for development of thrust, such as liquid or solid rocket fuel, jet fuel, or fuel for an internal combustion engine. Also: an exotic fuel that uses special chemicals, such as boron, to achieve greater power.

CHEMOSPHERE. A zone or stratum of the atmosphere that is considered to begin at about 100,000 feet above the earth's surface and to extend to 50 miles above the surface. It is noted for its photochemical activity. In meteorology, the chemosphere is often considered as an extension of the stratosphere. See **atmosphere.**

CHERRY PICKER. A small platform at the end of a movable crane arm, employed during prelaunch operations of Mercury-Redstone suborbital flights. Until shortly before ignition, the cherry-picker platform was kept near the capsule hatch to permit emergency escape from the capsule of the astronaut to the platform, which swung away from the rocket.

CHERRY PICKER during test of pilot-abort system for Mercury-Redstone shots

CHICKEN SWITCH. Emergency or abort handle in a space vehicle used to initiate escape mechanisms. In Mercury capsule, the switch that ignites the escape rocket to lift the capsule away from its booster.

CHILLDOWN. The process of cooling down the plumbing (fueling) system of a launch pad prior to the loading and feeding of cryogenic propellants to prevent excessive reaction of supercold liquids with normal-temperature plumbing, where the temperature variation may be as great as 500°F.

CHLORATE CANDLE. Usually, a mixture of solid chemical compounds which, when ignited, liberates free oxygen into the air.

CHLORELLA. A type of unicellular green algae, considered useful in converting carbon dioxide into oxygen in a closed ecological system. See **algae; closed ecological system.**

CHOKES. Pain and irritation in the chest and throat as a result of reduced ambient pressure. See **aeroembolism; decompression sickness; dysbarism.**

CHROMOSPHERE. An atmospheric "shell" of the sun that lies beyond the photosphere and is best visible during a time of total eclipse. It may also be observed spectroscopically.

CHUFFING. See **chugging.**

CHUGGING. One of several forms of combustion instability in a liquid-rocket engine system, characterized by a pulsing operation at a fairly low frequency, sometimes defined as occurring between particular frequency limits; the noise made in this kind of combustion. Also called "chuffing."

CINE-THEODOLITE. An optical tracking instrument. See **askania.**

CIRCUITRY. The system of electrical or electronic circuits used in a space vehicle and booster system.

CIRCULAR VELOCITY. The velocity required to maintain an object in a circular orbit.

CIRCULATORY PHYSIOLOGY. See **basic medical sciences.**

CIRCUMLUNAR FLIGHT. A flight that launches from the surface of the earth, or from orbit around the earth, into an orbital flight around the moon.

CIRCUMPLANETARY SPACE. The area of space in the close vicinity of a planetary body; especially the space close by the earth that includes also the upper edges of the atmosphere. See **aerothermodynamic border; atmosphere.**

CISLUNAR FLIGHT. A flight that launches from the surface of the earth, or from orbit around the earth, into a flight in the space between the earth and the moon; specifically, not to the surface of the moon or an orbit around the far side of the moon (circumlunar).

CISLUNAR SPACE. The space between the earth and the moon, which is shaped like a frustum (truncated cone), with its base a great circle of the earth equal in diameter to the earth's diameter, and moving like the hand of a clock as the moon revolves about the earth. Also: specifically, the space between the earth and the orbit of the moon.

CLAMP RING. A circular metal ring that clamps together a rocket booster and the payload. The ring provides a structural member and external aerodynamic fairing as well, and usually is released by explosive bolts that snap the ring away from the booster-spacecraft combination, releasing the spacecraft for its own orbital flight.

"CLEAR THE PAD." Also: "clear the launch area." Blockhouse command in launch complex for all personnel to clear the outside area, either to enter blockhouse or to leave the area completely and go to a designated safe distance from the launch area.

CLIFF HANGER. An unusually hazardous and potentially lethal mission; the part of any mission in which danger and the possibility of fatal results are extreme.

CLIMATIC HANGAR. A closed hangar within which various climatic conditions are simulated for the realistic testing of personnel and equipment.

CLOSED ECOLOGICAL SYSTEM. Distillation apparatus for purifying human waste matter

CLOSED ECOLOGICAL SYSTEM. A spacecraft system that provides for the body's metabolism in the cabin by means of a cycle wherein exhaled carbon dioxide, urine, and other waste matter are converted chemically or by photosynthesis into oxygen, potable water, and edible food. Also: *closed cycle system, closed system.*

CLOSED LOOP. A family of automatic control units linked together within a system to form an endless chain. The effects of control action are constantly measured so that if the controlled quantity departs from the norm, the control units act to bring it back.

CLOSED RESPIRATORY GAS SYSTEM. A completely self-contained system within a sealed cabin, capsule, or spacecraft, which will provide adequate oxygen for breathing, maintain adequate cabin pressure, and absorb the exhaled carbon dioxide and water vapor. See **closed ecological system.**

CLUNGE. Popular expression at Cape Canaveral for complicated and crowded grouping of electronic equipment. Also: **rat's nest.**

CLUSTER. Two or more rocket engines that are grouped together and that fire simultaneously as a single propulsion unit. Example: Saturn C-1, with 8 H.1 engines of 188,000 lbs. thrust each to produce a total of approximately 1,500,000 lbs. thrust at launch.

COASTING FLIGHT. The flight of a booster vehicle between burnout and jettison of one stage, prior to igniting the next stage. Also: the time between when a rocket engine is shut down in flight and when it is again ignited, as during a mission to achieve a parking orbit, where the engine is shut down and then restarted to continue to greater velocity or refinement of orbit.

COCKPIT VERTIGO. A condition in which a pilot in flight refuses to believe the reading of his flight instruments, especially in terms of aircraft attitude. For example, the instruments indicate the airplane is in a steep left diving turn, but pulling a steady $1g$ force through the maneuver. "Sensing" only the $1g$ force, the pilot refuses to believe the instrument readings—there is a sharp disagreement, so to speak, between what his body senses tell him and what the instruments indicate. Under these conditions, a pilot can easily enter into flight maneuvers (such as continuing the diving turn) that become fatal. The pilot, suffering from cockpit vertigo, flies by his body senses which do not impart to him the correct actions of his aircraft. See **equilibrium and orientation; vertigo.**

COHERENT. Coherent, as applied to radiation, means that all of the quanta (i.e., photons) are in phase with one another. Radio waves are coherent. Light from an incandescent source is not. A laser is unique in that it is the only existing coherent source of visible light. See **laser.**

COHESION. Forces of attraction holding molecules of a body together.

COLD-FLOW TEST. A test of a liquid rocket without firing the rocket, in order to check or verify the efficiency of a propulsion subsystem, providing for the conditioning and flow of propellants (including tank pressurization, propellant loading, and propellant feeding).

COLD-PRESSOR TEST. A measurement of the response of heart and blood pressure to the stress of plunging an extremity (foot or hand) into ice water. A normal response is a definite increase in both heart rate and blood pressure.

COLORLESS SPACE. Below a certain level of solar illumination (photometric brightness) it is impossible for the human eye to detect color. At the mean distance of the orbit of Pluto from the sun, color discrimination is still possible. At a distance of about three times that of the Pluto orbit—approximately 10 billion miles—solar illumination becomes so low that color vision is no longer possible. At this distance there begins the "colorless world of interstellar space," in respect to its relationship with the illuminating power of the sun. As seen by the human interstellar traveler, this will be the point at which the sun gradually falls within the conventional scale of stellar magnitudes.

COMBUSTION CHAMBER. Bell-shaped chamber where fuel and oxidizer of rocket booster, or missile, mix, are ignited, and burn. Temperature within the combustion chamber usually exceeds 5,000°F. Atlas-D booster has three major combustion chambers for its propulsion system; Thor and Jupiter have one; Centaur has three chambers for Atlas section and four chambers for Centaur section.

COMET. A luminous member of the solar system composed of a head or coma, at the center of which a presumably solid nucleus is sometimes situated, and often with a spectacular gaseous tail extending a great distance from the head. The orbits of comets are highly elliptical, and when nearing the earth, they are visible in the skies.

COMMAND. An electronic or electrical signal that activates a control device or mechanism in a guidance system to initiate a control maneuver; also, a signal to initiate an event or sequence of events in a spacecraft's instruments or other devices.

COMMAND DESTRUCT SIGNAL. Radio signal transmitted by Range Safety Officer at any launching range. The signal detonates explosive charges in a rocket vehicle to destroy the vehicle.

COMMAND GUIDANCE. The remote control guidance of a booster rocket, a missile, or an orbiting vehicle by radio command.

COMMAND LINK. A ground transmitting station that can transmit radio signals to an orbiting satellite vehicle to "command" certain actions, such as turning on instruments, firing retrorockets, etc.

COMMAND RECEIVER. Any radio receiver device in a rocket vehicle or spacecraft that actuates an event or sequence of events upon receipt of a specific radio transmission command; specifically, a receiver in the destruct system of a rocket vehicle. This receiver is activated by a destruct transmission signal to detonate the explosive charges in the vehicle. See **ASIS; command destruct signal; Range Safety Officer.**

COMPANION BODY. A part of a rocket assembly or booster-payload assembly that remains in orbit with a primary satellite, such as a protective nose cone, empty rocket casing, clamp ring, side fairings, etc.

COMPARATOR. An electronic processing instrument that compares one set of data with another.

COMPLEX BEHAVIOR SIMULATOR. A physiological stress test device in which the subject is placed before a panel with 14 different signals, each requiring a different response. The signals appear in random order at increasing rate of speed. Since the test produces a maximum of confusion and frustration, it measures the ability to organize behavior and to maintain emotional equilibrium under stress.

COMPONENT. The term loosely applied to any part, subassembly, system, or subsystem when considered as part of a larger assembly or system.

COMPONENT OF FORCE. That portion of the total force acting on a body which acts in a particular direction. The sum of all the components is the total force.

COMPOSITE MATERIALS. Structural materials of metal alloys or plastics with built-in strengthening agents which may be in the form of filaments, foils, or flakes of a stronger material.

COMPOSITE PROPELLANT. A solid rocket propellant consisting of a fuel and an oxidizer.

COMPOSITE SATELLITES. The technique of launching into orbit several separated satellites with a single booster vehicle; this technique was pioneered with the U.S. Navy's Transit satellite program in which 2, 3, and 5 payloads were launched with one vehicle. Composite I, for example, attempted to orbit the **Greb 4, Injun 2, Lofti 2, Secor,** and **Surcal** satellites.

COMPRESSIBILITY. One of the so-called *"barrier reef"* obstacles to high-supersonic and hypersonic flight in the upper atmosphere; a problem especially encountered in rocket aircraft and winged re-entry vehicles. Aerodynamics defines the capacity of air to be compressed by the movement of a vehicle through that air, as compressibility. Unlike **flutter** (q.v.), which may occur at any speed, undesirable compression occurs with each individual type of vehicle only at a definitely established speed. An aircraft by its movement transmits sound in the form of shock waves. Normally this moves ahead of the vehicle. At transonic and plus-sonic speeds the sonic shock wave remains with the vehicle. The effect is that of air piling up around the vehicle. Separation of this

air into a supersonic shock wave under certain conditions can apply dangerous forces to the vehicle structure. The point of impact—or area of impact—of the shock flow can hammer and bludgeon metal out of shape and snap the structures free of the major vehicular body.

COMPRESSION CHAMBER. A powerful steel-walled, sealed chamber in which air pressure can be increased to two or more atmospheres, i.e., 30 psi or more.

CONCURRENCY. The carrying on of research and development activities on many different aspects of a major project, all performed within the same time span but at different locations.

CONDENSATION. Change from gas to vapor or liquid; vapor is a collection of liquid droplets. See **condensation trail.**

CONDENSATION TRAIL. Also: *contrail* or *vapor trail.* A visible cloud streak, usually brilliant white, which under certain atmospheric conditions trails behind an ascending booster rocket or aircraft. It is caused by the formation of water droplets or sometimes ice crystals due to the sudden compression, then expansive cooling of the air through which the vehicle passes.

CONDITION AMBER. Designates the period of time, at a launch complex or pad, when a live countdown is under way for a launching; also that the countdown has not yet progressed to the point where there is handling or use of explosive fuels or other materials that pose a specific "explosive" danger.

CONDITION RED. Designates the period of time, at a launch complex or pad, when a live countdown has progressed to the point where the booster and/or spacecraft vehicle has received its explosive mixtures of fuel or explosive destruct charges, that a specific danger exists in the area, and that all but the most essential personnel must immediately clear the area. The final phase of a live countdown.

CONDENSATION TRAILS. Boeing 707 airliner with contrails

CONFETTI. Quarter-inch diameter mylar plastic discs of different colors released by an orbiting Mercury spacecraft for visual tests and experiments by the pilot.

CONIC SECTION. A curve formed by the intersection of a plane and a right circular cone. Usually called "conic." The conic sections are the ellipse, the parabola, and the hyperbola—curves that are used to describe the paths of bodies moving in space. (The circle is a special case of the ellipse: an ellipse with an eccentricity of zero.)

CONSOLE. Instrument panel or group of panels in blockhouse, control center, etc., from which the control of a booster, spacecraft, or other vehicle system is carried out.

Blockhouse CONSOLES for Discoverer satellite program

CONTOUR COUCH. Fitting a pilot for his own personal contour couch by taking body-mold measurements

CONSTANT–VOLUME BALLOONS. High-altitude research balloons made of extremely thin plastic, in which automatic controls adjust volume and load so that the balloon may be sent to a given preselected altitude and sustained at that altitude for many hours or days. These balloons are considered extremely important for high-altitude cosmic radiation and similar tests of biological specimens and test animals, by exposing them for long periods to near-space conditions.

CONSTELLATION. Stars which for purposes of identification and reference are considered as belonging to arbitrary groups. In most stellar constellations there is actually no relation between the member stars; they appear close together only as a result of perspective.

CONSUMABLE STORES. Those stores for any spacecraft mission intended to be consumed directly by the astronaut or in otherwise meeting the astronaut's physiological needs as provided by the life-support system.

CONTOUR COUCH. A spacecraft-installed couch which supports an astronaut in a semi-supine position (reclining face-up position with the legs elevated to a position

slightly higher than the torso) and is molded to the specific contours of the individual astronaut's body.

CONTOUROMETER. A modified camera with an open lens installed in a cubicle of lightproof black cloth, with strip-covered stroboscopic speed lights. By special camera techniques of multiple film exposures, an individual subject is pictured with a series of zebra-like stripes that vary in thickness to indicate the relationships of changing form of contour. It is used for personally tailored helmets, masks, suits, seats, couches, etc.

CONTRAORBIT MISSILE. Missile sent backward along the calculated orbit of an approaching spacecraft, satellite, or aerospace vehicle or weapon for the purpose of destroying it in a head-on collision with an explosive warhead or by missile. Contraorbit attacks are considered much easier to accomplish than orbital attacks.

CONTROLLED ENVIRONMENT. The environment of any object—a spacecraft cabin, simulator, aircraft or instrument, or a man—in which environmental conditions such as temperature, pressure, humidity, etc., are controlled either automatically or remotely.

CONTROLLED LEAKAGE SYSTEM. A system that provides for the body's metabolism in a flight or space vehicle cabin by a controlled escape of carbon dioxide and other waste from the cabin, with replenishment provided by stored oxygen and food. See **closed ecological system.**

CONTROLLER. A device which receives (usually electronically) a measured value of a variable from a sensor, then compares that value with some specific reference value, and transmits a control signal to a control element to maintain the value of the variable within a specified range about the reference value. See **sensor.**

CONTROL PANEL. A surface or panel on which switches, rheostats, indicators, and the like are located for controlling and supervising electrical equipment. Generally, any panel that is used for the remote monitoring and control of control surfaces, remote equipment, etc.

CONTROL ROCKET. A vernier engine, retrorocket, or other such rocket, used to guide or make small changes in the velocity of a rocket, spacecraft, or the like.

CONVERSION FACTORS: LENGTH.

Length	Multiply by	To Obtain
Centimeters	0.3937	Inches
	0.03281	Feet
Kilometers	3281	Feet
	0.6214	Miles
	0.5396	Nautical Miles
	1093.6	Yards
Meters	39.37	Inches
	3.281	Feet
	1.0936	Yards
Miles	5280	Feet
	0.8684	Nautical Miles
	1760	Yards
Nautical Miles	6080.2	Feet

CONVERSION FACTORS: VELOCITY.

Velocity	Multiply by	To Obtain
Feet per minute	0.01136	Miles per hour
	0.01829	Kilometers per hour
	0.01667	Feet per second
Feet per second	0.6818	Miles per hour
	1.097	Kilometers per hour
	0.5921	Knots
Knots	1.0	Nautical miles per hour
	1.6889	Feet per second
	1.1515	Miles per hour
	1.8532	Kilometers per hour
Miles per hour	1.467	Feet per second
	1.609	Kilometers per hour
	0.8684	Knots

COPPER CLAUDE. An anthropomorphic dummy used extensively in investigating reactions to special environmental conditions. The dummy is carefully balanced to approximate the weight distribution of the average male pilot, and is equipped with a "nervous system" designed especially to respond to environmental factors—especially heat, cold, and ultraviolet factors. Copper Claude is exposed to boiling and freezing water, high and low temperatures, extreme aridity and humidity, ultraviolet and infrared radiations, and variables of these extremes. The tests are carried out to determine adaptability to man of protective clothing and equipment, and to establish the limits of safe protection and operation under the worst possible conditions.

CORIOLIS EFFECT. The deflection of a body in motion due to the earth's rotation, diverting horizontal motions to the right of the direction of rotation in the northern hemisphere and to the left in the southern hemisphere.

CORONA. The faintly luminous outer envelope of the sun. Also called "solar corona." The corona can be observed at the earth's surface only at solar eclipse or with the coronagraph, a photographic instrument which artificially blocks out the image of the body of the sun.

CORPUSCLE. A minute particle of radiation, e.g., corpuscular radiation from the sun.

CORPUSCULAR COSMIC RAYS. Primary cosmic rays from outer space which consist of particles, 86% nuclei of hydrogen (protons), 13% nuclei of helium (alpha particles), and 1% nuclei of elements of higher atomic number than helium. See **cosmic radiation.**

CORPUSCULAR RADIATION. Emission and propagation of elementary material particles (corpuscles). Those particles that are radiated.

CORTICAL ACTIVITY. The activity of the brain in the areas that control consciousness and awareness in response to sensory excitation.

CORTICAL REST. A somnolent state of the cortex of the brain (the areas of consciousness and awareness) resulting from diminution or absence of sensory input. Considered a research problem in sensory deprivation, such as might be encountered under extended space-flight conditions.

COSMIC DUST. Small meteoroids of a size similar to dust.

COSMIC FLIGHT. Flight through space; *cosmic flight* is a term used especially by Soviet authors.

COSMIC RADIATION. Atomic nuclei moving with near light velocity in space, showering down in constant streams into earth's upper atmosphere. *Primary cosmic radiation* is measured prior to penetration into earth's atmosphere; *secondary cosmic radiation* is associated with radiation levels at earth's surface. Interstellar source is unknown. Once believed to be exceedingly dangerous to manned space flight.

COSMODROME. Soviet name for rocket-launching center for space-flight operations. See **Baikonur.**

COSMOGRAPHY. Mapping of the solar system; embraces the sciences of planetography and spatiography. See **planetography; spatiography.**

COSMONAUT. Soviet term for astronaut.

COSMOS. The totality of the observed and postulated physical whole, conceived as an orderly and harmonious system.

COTAR. COrrelation Tracking and Ranging. COTAR is an electronic tracking system using omnidirectional antennas and a transponder in the space or booster vehicle to measure positions of the vehicle in flight.

COUCH, CONTOUR. Couch molded to contours of individual astronaut's body for maximum comfort and protection against acceleration forces. Mercury capsule contour couch is made of crushable honeycombed aluminum bonded to a fiberglas shell and padded with rubber.

COUNTDOWN. Passage of time in which a specific sequence of events is carried out toward launching rocket booster with capsule. Countdown proceeds from a specific set time, counting backward, to zero. Engineers wryly explain countdown as a "mathematically perfect method of reaching final goal of zero."

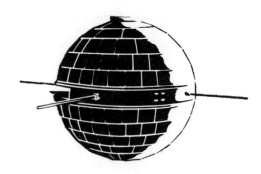

COURIER 1B, military communications satellite with "jamproof" message capabilities

COURIER. A delayed-repeater communications satellite carrying miniature tape recorders. The spherical 475-lb. satellite has the capacity to receive and record messages from an earth station over which it passes and later, over another station distant from the first, to transmit to earth the originally recorded messages. Courier 1A failed in its orbital attempt on August 18, 1960; Courier 1B went into orbit on October 4, 1960, and then functioned successfully.

CRATERLETS. See **lunar craters.**

CRATERS. See **lunar craters.**

CREEP. The property of a metal which allows it to be permanently deformed when subjected to a stress. Creep is accelerated at elevated temperatures.

CREEPS. Hot or cold sensations or itching of the skin, annoying but rarely dangerous; a result of exposure to reduced ambient pressure. See **decompression sickness.**

CRITICAL MALFUNCTION. The failure of any equipment, system, or systems that creates a specific and immediate danger, or causes an extremely dangerous and possibly fatal malfunction, and requiring immediate cessation of the mission and/or immediate correction of the failure.

CRYHOCYCLE. A cryogenically fueled, fully integrated power-generation and thermal control system. Powered by hydrogen and oxygen, the cryohocycle recovers normally wasted heat from energy conversion inefficiencies as well as metabolic heat from the crew; the heat is recovered by the coolant loop and returned to the power cycle by interstage reheaters between each of four stages of a single-disc turbine. Power levels are from one to 50 kilowatts for several weeks' duration; designed specifically for Air Force manned space-flight missions.

CRYOGENIC FUEL. A rocket fuel that either is itself kept at very low temperatures or is combined with an oxidizer kept at very low temperatures. Cryogenic fuels are usually non-hypergolic fuels. See **cryogenic temperature; hypergolic fuel; liquid hydrogen; liquid oxygen.**

CRYOGENIC TEMPERATURE. In general, a temperature range below about −50°C.; more particularly, temperatures within a few degrees of absolute zero.

CSAR. A communications satellite study system adopted by the Air Force to investigate the efficiency of high-gain passive reflectors on the satellites.

CUTOFF POINT. That moment in a countdown when for reasons of time and/or weather the count must be terminated without a launch. In Atlas-boosted manned flights of Mercury from Canaveral, several hours of daylight are required following capsule landing in water, to aid in recovery operations. If countdown is unduly delayed, the cutoff point may be reached and the mission for that day is scrubbed.

CUTTING SCORE. A critical test score or level of achievement especially in relation to astronaut selection tests; it is used to divide a group of subjects into subgroups having specified predicted characteristics, such as the likelihood of success in a given (critical or emergency) situation.

CYANOSIS. Physical evidence of hypoxia in that the fingertips and lips become a definitely recognizable blue color.

CYBERNETICS. A field of comparative study concerned with the controls inherent in the nervous system and the controls of certain mechanical or electronic machines, such as digital computers.

CYBORGS. Cybernetic Organisms. Men who would be surgically altered so that parts of their vital life systems are replaced with mechanical aids and organs; a semi-artificial human created by medical science with the human being as the basis. A proposal to adapt men to withstand space and extraterrestrial environments without cumbersome artificial protection.

CYCLIC _g_. Alternating positive _g_ (head-to-foot) and negative _g_ (foot-to-head). See **negative-_g_ tolerance; positive-_g_ tolerance.**

CYCLIC TESTING. The repeated testing of a device or unit at regular intervals to maintain assurance of its reliability. Cyclic testing usually is conducted on such items as combustion chambers, guidance systems, electron tubes, etc.

D

DAILY METABOLIC TURNOVER. The _daily metabolic requirement_ as specified for a man of 154 lbs.: 2 lbs. oxygen; 5 lbs. water; approximately 1 lb. solid food. A man weighing 154 lbs. eats the equivalent of his weight once every 20 days. This is his _input_. The metabolic _output_ consists of about 2 lbs. carbon dioxide, about 6 lbs. water, and a small amount of solids, urea, and minerals. In less than one year, the 154-lb. man consumes about 2,000 lbs. of oxygen, food, and water. It is because of this metabolic requirement that regeneration of human waste products is indispensable for sustained or long-range manned space flights.

DAISY DECELERATOR. A rail-mounted sled powered by rockets, upon which a man is accelerated to speeds of several hundred miles per hour, and then slammed into a water barrier to achieve high onset rates and peaks of decelerative _g_ forces; deceleration rates, peaks, and reactions are determined to provide performance parameters for aircraft and spacecraft.

DAMPING. As a vehicle moves in its orbit, it may have undesired, attitude-changing motions in pitch, roll, yaw, or along a combination of these axes. A "damping maneuver" takes place when the pilot or the automatic pilot system fires small reaction jets or rockets to counteract these movements and to "damp them out" to reach stable attitude position.

DARK ADAPTATION. Moving suddenly from bright light into darkness—as in the orbital path of a manned spacecraft from the daylight to the nightside of the earth—produces a sudden and usually severe loss of sight. At first, almost nothing can be seen. After several minutes, dim forms and large outlines become visible, and slowly more details of the environment become perceptible. Dark adaptation is thus the increase in sensitivity of the eyes at low levels of illumination. During the first 30 minutes of dark adaptation, the sensitivity of the eye increases roughly 10,000-fold, with little further increase after that time. Under ideal atmospheric conditions, the completely dark-adapted eye can detect the flare of a match at a distance of 25 miles.

DARKSIDE. That side of the earth in which the direct light of the sun is blocked out by the earth's shadow, as seen by the observer in an orbiting space vehicle. Also known as **nightside.**

DARK–SPACE SKY. The intensity of light encountered in space when the sun is *not* directly visible, as on the darkside of earth during orbit. The total light encountered in the dark-space sky includes direct starlight, zodiacal light, and galactic light, of which the dominant light source is the stars. Under vacuum conditions in space the stars appear 30% brighter than from the earth's surface—30% is the amount of attenuation of light while traveling vertically through the atmosphere. The sun-illuminated portion of the moon as seen from an orbiting vehicle is also approximately 30% brighter than when seen from the earth's surface, because of the lack of atmospheric interference.

DASHBOARD. That place in the cockpit of an aircraft or control cabin of a spacecraft, usually a panel directly in front of the pilot, upon which most of the gauges and instruments required for the operation of the vehicle are located.

DATA (in Project Mercury). Specifically, in the Mercury Orbital Mission: three kinds of data pour into the Mercury computing system as soon as the Atlas booster vehicle lifts one-half inch from its launch stand. *Radar data* trigger the Cape Canaveral IBM 7090 computer which monitors the spacecraft flight path and predicts its impact point if mission must at any time be aborted. *Guidance data* are radioed from the spacecraft to a special-purpose computer at Canaveral. *Telemetry data* report mission checkpoints, e.g., liftoff, booster separation, escape tower ejection. *Complete data* feed to Goddard Space Flight Center in Maryland, where twin-bank 7090 computers compare the flight mission against a predetermined flight path—and flash back results and ·comparisons to Mercury Control at Cape Canaveral.

DATA CAPSULE. A sealed capsule in which data are recorded on tape during the flight of a vehicle, sometimes as part of the system of the vehicle itself; usually a data capsule is ejected from the primary carrier and recovered for detailed analysis and study.

DATA LINK EQUIPMENT. Electronic equipment that co-ordinates, from flight or ground tests, data collection, reduction, and analysis.

DATA REDUCTION. Process wherein raw data on vehicle's flight, gathered by optical, radar, and other devices, are fed through automatic reduction machines to produce usable information on the vehicle's performance.

DAWN ROCKET. A rocket booster launched within a brief, specified time period at dawn, in the direction of the orbital motion of the earth—from west to east. In terms of interplanetary flights outbound from the earth, as toward Mars, the cutoff velocity of the booster vehicle is thereby added to the earth's orbital velocity of 18.5 miles per second. See **dusk rocket.**

DEADSTICK LANDING. To land an aircraft or aerospace craft without any engine power: involuntarily, as in an aircraft with engine failure; deliberately, in terms of a high-speed glider such as X-15 and X-20; and, specifically, in the case of the Gemini spacecraft, when descending beneath the flexwing. See **flexwing.**

DEBUG. To isolate and then effectively to remove or remedy one or more malfunctions from a device or system. See **bug.**

DECELERATION. The process of moving, or causing to move, with decreasing speed; i.e., from a higher to a lower velocity. Example: the Mercury capsule during atmospheric re-entry undergoes a deceleration force in suborbital re-entry of 12 g, or 12 times the force of gravity as measured at rest on the surface of the earth.

DECELERATION. Colonel J. P. Stapp, USAF, undergoes a deceleration force on a rocket sled of 46.2 times normal gravity—46.2 g's

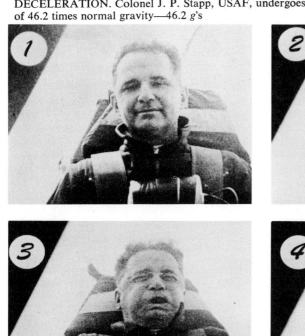
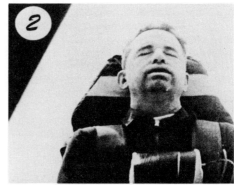

DECIBEL. A unit for measuring the relative loudness of sounds, being the smallest degree of difference ordinarily detectable by the human ear. Example: the decibel is used to measure the sounds of a booster vehicle as it ascends. These vary as they are absorbed or are reflected from clouds, as in the roar of an ascending booster that seems to steadily rise and fall.

DECOMPRESSION CHAMBER. See **altitude chamber.**

DECOMPRESSION SICKNESS. A syndrome including bends, creeps, chokes, neurological disturbances, and collapse, resulting from exposure to reduced ambient pressure and caused by gas bubbles in the tissues, fluids, and blood vessels. Bends are pain in the joints or muscles. Creeps are hot or cold sensations or itching of the skin, annoying but not dangerous. Chokes are a burning sensation or stabbing pain in the chest, coughing, and difficulty in breathing, and may result in collapse. See **aeroembolism; bends; dysbarism.**

DEEP SPACE NET. A combination of three radar and communications stations in the United States, Australia, and South Africa, so located as to keep a spacecraft in deep space under observation at all times.

DEEP SPACE PROBES. Spacecraft designed for exploring space to the vicinity of the moon and beyond. Deep space probes with specific missions may be referred to as "lunar probes," "Mars probes," "solar probes," etc.

DEIMOS. The outer of the two moons of Mars, orbiting approximately 12,500 miles from the planetary surface. Diameter is about 5 miles, orbital period 30 hours 18 minutes. Deimos and Mars' other moon, Phobos, are considered as landing sites for initial manned space expeditions to Mars. See **Phobos.**

DELUGE COLLECTION POND. Also: *skimmer basin.* The water-collection basin at a launch site that is used to collect the water sprayed for cooling into the flame bucket during static firing or ascent of a rocket booster vehicle. See **flame bucket.**

DENITROGENATION. The process whereby an aircraft or spacecraft pilot for at least one hour before reaching an ambient barometric pressure altitude or cabin altitude of 25,000 feet breathes only 100% pure oxygen. The denitrogenation process restricts the pilot's breathing only to oxygen and eliminates nitrogen from the bloodstream. During the interval much of the nitrogen in the tissues moves into the bloodstream and is exhaled from the body, avoiding nitrogen bubbles later in the joints or muscles, and thus preventing the bends and other effects of high-altitude and low-pressure flight. See **bends; dysbarism.**

DEPRESSURIZE. To release the pressure from the pressurized compartment of a spacecraft; generally, to adjust the pressure of the compartment to ambient air pressure.

DEPTH PERCEPTION. The judgment of distance; this is accomplished subconsciously in a combination of ways by the individual. *Close up,* the individual depends on binocular vision, each eye seeing an object from a different angle. At distances beyond binocular range, which is usually the case in flight (and in space rendezvous and docking maneuvers, except for terminal maneuvers), the airman judges depth perception on a one-eye basis:

(1) From the known size of an object and how much of the visual field it fills.

(2) From knowledge of perspective and the convergence of parallel lines at a great distance.

(3) From overlapping—an object overlapped by another is known to be farther away.

(4) From light and shadow—an object casts a shadow away from the observer if the light is nearer.

(5) From aerial perspective (clarity)—large objects seen indistinctly apparently have haze, fog, or smoke between them and the observer and therefore can usually be recognized as being at a great distance.

(6) From terrestrial association—objects ordinarily associated are judged to be at approximately the same distance.

(7) From motion parallax—when the observer fixes his sight on one object while his head or body moves, other objects apparently moving in the same direction as the observer are judged to be more distant while those apparently moving in the opposite direction are judged to be nearer.

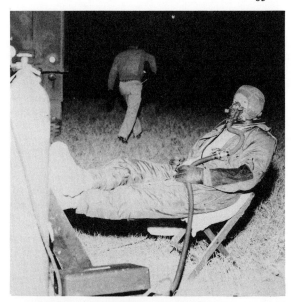

DENITROGENATION. Captain Joseph W. Kittinger, Jr., USAF, breathing 100% oxygen prior to balloon ascent for stratospheric parachute jump of Project Excelsior

DELUGE COLLECTION POND

DESCENT RANGE. The ground distance as measured on the surface of the earth by a manned spacecraft (or satellite) from the point of firing the retrorockets to "break orbit" to the point of impact on the earth's surface. See **re-entry profile.**

DESERT SURVIVAL TECHNIQUES. Survival techniques practiced by pilots, astronauts, etc., to be used in the event of remote landing in an area where desert or near-desert conditions obtain. The basic training course in these techniques consists of indoctrination and training in classrooms and on the airbase under field conditions. Then the men are sent out into the desert for three days under the "worst possible" conditions. There they practice protecting themselves from the sun; utilizing a limited water supply; fashioning clothing and shelter from parachutes; signaling, etc. The course is held at Stead Air Force Base, Nevada.

DESICCATOR. A unit containing a chemical which absorbs moisture from the air, as in a life-support system.

DESTRUCT. Missile-age term which signifies the act of destroying a rocket in flight by remote-control detonation of explosives within the missile or rocket booster.

DESERT SURVIVAL TECHNIQUES being practiced by Astronaut Alan Shepard

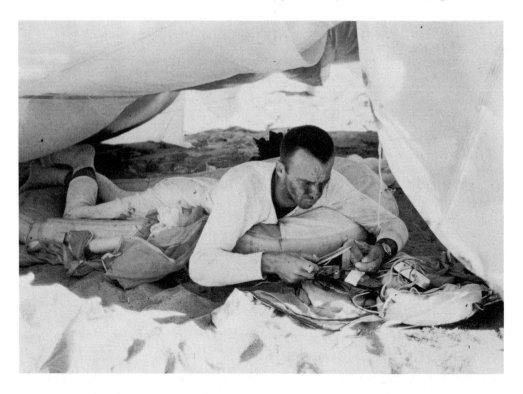

DESTRUCT BUTTON

Atlas ICBM seconds after DESTRUCT signal is received

DESTRUCT BUTTON. Control switch activated to send a radio command signal to detonate explosives inside a rocket booster in flight; element of a safety system that destroys a rocket deviating from an assigned flight path or corridor in the atmosphere.

DESTRUCT LINE. A boundary line on either side of a flight corridor assigned to the flight profile of a booster rocket vehicle. If the booster reaches or crosses this line it will be destroyed by the Range Safety Officer. See **destruct; Range Safety Officer.**

DIFFUSION RESPIRATION. The maintenance of oxygen passage through the respiratory system to the blood in the absence of respiratory movements.

DIGITAL COMPUTER. A computer which operates on the principle of counting as opposed to measuring. See **analogue computer.**

DINGHY. A collapsible pneumatic liferaft for emergency survival use in water landings. In its common sense in aviation and astronautics, the term refers to a one-man liferaft.

DINGHY, with Astronaut Wally Schirra

DIOXIDE CAPSULE. A small pressurized container for carbon dioxide, which when punctured by jerking on a short lanyard permits the dioxide gas rapidly to inflate a life vest, dinghy, or the like. Also known as a CO_2 cartridge.

DIPLEXER. A device permitting an antenna system to be used simultaneously or separately by two transmitters. Compare with **duplexer.**

DISCOVERER. A spectacularly successful Air Force satellite program using the Thor-Agena A and Thor-Agena B booster combination to launch satellites into polar orbit. It was established with its first launch in February 1959 as the most active satellite program in the world, to test designs and techniques for several areas—future military applications, man-in-space programs, recoverable satellites, and open-end scientific investigations. Discover 36, as an example, orbits in the form of the Agena stage including a recoverable capsule. The Discoverer satellite weighs approximately 2,100 lbs. including 300 lbs. for the capsule, retro-rocket, and all recovery systems and aids. Discoverer satellites are polar-orbiters, launched from Vandenberg Air Force Base in California. In the first 38 launch attempts, 26 satellites went into orbit. There were attempted recoveries from orbit of the recovery capsule; 12 of these were successful.

DISH. A parabolic type of radio or radar antenna, roughly the shape of a soup bowl.

DISINTEGRATION BARRIER. A condition postulated as a limiting factor for space flight with the velocity in the higher fractions of the speed of light; in this condition the velocity would become a limiting factor by its effect upon the environment of a space vehicle and its occupants. The collision energy of meteorites, dust particles, and the atoms of interstellar gas would become so high as to create problems of structural disintegration.

DISORIENTATION SIMULATOR. See **human disorientation device; iron maiden.**

DISCOVERER, Air Force satellite program using Thor-Agena booster combination. Orbiting Discoverer consists of Agena booster plus integral payload. Discoverer satellites are sent into polar orbit

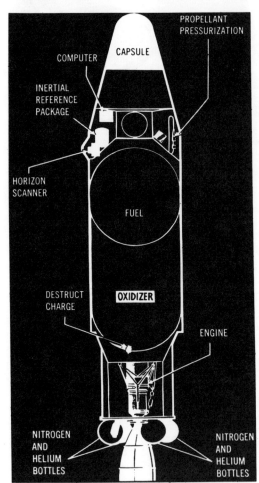

Cutaway view reveals basic components of DISCOVERER booster vehicle and payload section. Nose capsule is ejected and can be recovered

DISPERSION. The deviation of a rocket booster vehicle or any rocket booster stage from the predicted flight path.

DISPLAY. The graphic presentation of the output data of a device or system as, for example, a radarscope.

DOCKING. The process of bringing two spacecraft together while in space; accomplished after rendezvous of the spacecraft is assured. Docking usually means to secure the spacecraft to prevent their inadvertent drifting or separation. Distinguished from mating, which means to secure for the purposes of single propulsion operation. See **hard docking; soft docking.**

DOG DIP. Jargon for deep tank of warm water used for sensory deprivation tests, in which the test individual is submerged in the water kept at body temperature and isolated from all normal sensory stimuli. See **sensory isolation experiment.**

DOGHOUSE. A rounded blister or protuberance on the normally smooth skin of a booster rocket or spacecraft vehicle, used to house instruments or special test devices.

DOG–LEG–TO–ORBIT. An ascent and orbital-insertion maneuver. A vehicle placed into equatorial orbit from Cape Canaveral, for example, cannot be launched in a due easterly heading. The booster rocket must first bend toward the equator as it climbs, and during the climb must program when it is over the equator into a true easterly heading. This process of changing ascent direction to achieve a specific orbital direction other than that at launch is the dog-leg-to-orbit maneuver.

DOPPLER EFFECT. The apparent change in frequency of a sound or radio wave reaching a receiver, caused by a change in distance or range between the source and the receiver during the interval of reception.

DOSAGE. The total amount of radiation absorbed by an individual; the total radiation dosage that might be absorbed by an individual passing through the radiation belts beyond the earth.

DOSE RATE. The rate at which ionizing radiation strikes a particular object measured in terms of roentgens per hour.

DOVAP. Doppler Velocity and Position. A tracking and receiving system that obtains information on the position and velocity of a missile and/or booster. The **doppler effect** is employed.

DOWNRANGE. Any point along the range of a missile or space booster tracking corridor, away from the launching site.

DRAG. The aerodynamic force in a direction opposite to that of flight and due to the resistance to movement brought to bear on an aerospace vehicle by the atmosphere through which it passes.

DRAIN RATE. In terms of a manned spacecraft (but applicable to any rocket or space vehicle), the specific rate at which electrical power in the system or subsystems is consumed, permitting extrapolation of the time when energy sources will be exhausted.

D–RING. The handle which a pilot grasps to pull in opening a parachute.

DROGUE PARACHUTE. A small parachute used to reduce the speed of a falling object, or an aircraft moving rapidly along the ground. In Project Mercury: a 6-foot-diameter parachute used to stabilize the capsule during the atmospheric descent from approximately 21,000 feet to 10,000 feet. The drogue chute is a conical ribbon parachute, ejected by an explosive mortar from the neck of the capsule. It stabilizes the capsule and decelerates the vehicle to a descent speed of 185 mph. At 10,000 feet the drogue chute is jettisoned and the main 63-foot canopy deploys.

DRY RUN. A simulated mission; a rehearsal; a practice exercise of a launching, flight program, or other involved activity of numerous sequences, usually repeated several times.

DRY WEIGHT. The weight of a liquid-propellant booster without its fuel; i.e., empty weight. Pertains also to any airborne or space vehicle that employs liquid fuels for propulsion and/or stabilization.

DUCK. Common term for amphibious vehicle used for beach or offshore emergency recovery operations in event of launch-pad or liftoff mission abort.

DUPLEXER. A device which permits a single antenna system to be used for both transmitting and receiving. Duplexer should not be confused with **diplexer,** a device permitting an antenna system to be used simultaneously or separately by two transmitters.

DUSK ROCKET. A rocket booster launched within a brief, specified time period at dusk, opposite to the direction of the orbital motion of the earth. In terms of interplanetary flights outbound from the earth but inbound toward the sun, as toward Venus, the velocity of the booster vehicle is thereby subtracted from the earth's orbital velocity of 18.5 miles per second. See **dawn rocket.**

DUTCH ROLL. A combined yawing and rolling motion in any airborne vehicle, especially pronounced in the forward or cockpit area.

DYNAMIC FORCES. Forces imposed upon the human occupant of a space vehicle in the process of achieving orbital velocity, during re-entry, through the flight profile, and in landing and recovery.

DYNAMIC PRESSURE. (Symbol q) (1) The pressure exerted by a fluid, such as air, by virtue of its motion. (2) The pressure exerted on a body by virtue of its motion through a fluid; for example, the pressure exerted on a rocket moving through the atmosphere. See **max q.**

DYNAMICS. The field of mechanics that involves the motion of bodies and of the forces acting upon bodies in motion or in the process of changing motion.

DYNA–MOWS. Dyna-Soar III, an advanced study project of the Dyna-Soar system. MOWS stands for Manned Orbital Weapon System.

DYNA–SOAR X-20 orbital research vehicle shown in artist's concept at launch with Titan III booster

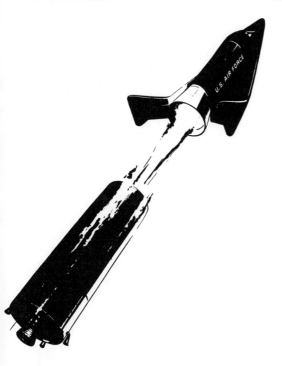

DYNA–SOAR fires transstage rocket to separate from Titan III final-stage booster

DYNA–SOAR. Winged, manned, hypersonic aerospace vehicle under joint development by USAF and NASA. To be boosted into orbit by Titan III rocket. Single-crew Dyna-Soar vehicle weighs 15,000 lbs., is designed to re-enter atmosphere in long, flat trajectory, and to gain aerodynamic lift from sharply sweptwing delta configuration. Dyna-Soar is to descend through atmosphere under full pilot control as high-speed, powerless glider. Official USAF designation is X-20.

DYSBARISM. A general term which includes a complex group of a wide variety of symptoms within the body caused by changes in ambient barometric pressure, exclusive of hypoxia. Characteristic symptoms caused by decreased barometric pressure (other than hypoxia) are the bends and abdominal gas pains at altitudes above 25,000 to 30,000 feet. Increased barometric pressure, as in descent from high altitude, is characterized by painful distention of the eardrums and sinuses. See **aerosinusitis; anoxia; bends; decompression sickness; evolved gases; hypoxia; Valsalva maneuver.**

E

EARLY SPRING. A Navy program for a vertical interceptor satellite. It would carry an advanced optical scanning system and, possibly, destructive systems. See **Saint.**

EARTH. Third planet from the sun; the planet we inhabit, including its atmosphere. Without its atmosphere, this planet's diameter is 7,900 miles at the poles and 7,927 miles at the equator, and its mean radius 3,959 miles. Orbital speed averages 18.5 miles per second. One satellite, the moon. Escape velocity approximately 7 miles per second.

EARTH FIXED REFERENCE. An oriented system using some earth phenomena for positioning.

EARTH–GRAZERS. The asteroids (minor planets, planetoids) whose orbits bring them "close to the earth" by passing well within the orbit of Mars. Earth-grazers include Hermes (closest approach to earth, 400,000 miles), Adonis (1,500,000 miles), Albert (20,000,000 miles), Amor (10,000,000 miles), Apollo (7,000,000 miles), Icarus (4,000,000 miles), etc.

EARTHLIGHT. The sunlight reflected by the earth's surface; generally referred to as "earthlight across the lunar surface." Approximately 6 times brighter on the lunar surface than brightest moonlight on the earth surface.

EARTH–MOON ORBIT. An orbit of an earth satellite that describes an ellipse about both the moon and the earth; i.e., the orbit of Lunik III.

EARTH–MOON SATELLITE. A satellite vehicle that orbits in an ellipse about both the moon and earth, as Lunik III.

EARTH SATELLITE. Generally, an artificial body placed into orbit about the earth. Also termed *earth orbiter.*

EARTHSIZE, LUNAR VIEW. As seen by an observer standing on the surface of the moon, the "full earth" will appear in the lunar sky with a size 13 times greater than the moon appears to a terrestrial observer in the earth sky.

EARTH WEIGHT. The static weight of a given object as measured at the surface of the earth; equal to weight of an object under acceleration of 1 *g*. See **g.**

EBULLISM. The formation of bubbles, with particular reference to water vapor bubbles in biological fluids, caused by reduced ambient pressure. See **aeroembolism; bends; blood, boiling of; decompression sickness; dysbarism.**

ECCENTRIC. Of an orbit: deviating from the line of a circle to form an ellipse. (The state or degree of being eccentric, expressed by the difference of the greatest and least distances between the two centers of mass, divided by the sum of the greatest and least distances. The eccentricity of earth orbit is 0.016751.)

ECCENTRICITY. The degree of deviation from a circular orbit. See **eccentric.**

ECHO. An aluminized-surface mylar-plastic inflatable sphere 100 feet in diameter (Echo I) placed in orbit at approximately 1,000 miles, for use as a passive reflector communications satellite and to investigate space conditions at 1,000 miles altitude. The function of the spherical satellite is tested by monitoring its reflectivity to radio waves, by "measuring the satellite radar cross-section."

ECLIPTIC. The apparent annual path of the sun among the stars; the intersection of the plane of the earth's orbit with the celestial sphere. This is a great circle of the celestial sphere inclined at an angle of about 23°27′ to the celestial equator. See **ecosphere (2).**

ECG. See **EKG.**

ECOLOGICAL SYSTEM. A habitable environment, either created artificially, such as in a manned space vehicle, or occurring naturally, such as the environment on the surface of the earth, in which man, animals, or other organisms can live in mutual relationship with each other. Ideally, the natural ecological system furnishes the sustenance for life, and the resulting waste products revert or cycle back into the environment to be used again for the continuous support of life. See **closed ecological system.**

ECOSPHERE (1). A spherical extent which is inhabited by living organisms or is suitable for the life of such organisms. Also, generally, the biosphere of the earth. See **atmosphere.**

ECOSPHERE (2). The great circle on the celestial sphere which describes the apparent path of the sun in the course of the year. The plane of the ecliptic is the plane in which the center of mass of the earth and moon revolves about the sun. It is inclined to the plane of the equator at an angle of about 23°27′.

ECU. Environmental Control Unit. A sealed system designed in the form of a backpack for an astronaut to wear when leaving the pressurized protection of his orbiting spacecraft, and providing necessary power, heat, cooling, pressure, oxygen, venting, and other physiological requirements while also permitting mobility of the astronaut outside his vehicle.

EDWARDS AIR FORCE BASE. Air Force base near Muroc, California. Site of the Air Force Flight Test Center (AFFTC); Rocket Engine Test Laboratory (RETL); and the NASA High Speed Flight Station. Operations center for X-15 flights; landing area site for Gemini and Apollo spacecraft and for Dyna-Soar aerospace vehicles.

EFFECTIVE ATMOSPHERE. That part of the atmosphere which influences effectively a particular process of motion, the outer limits of which vary according to the terms of the process or motion considered. Also: **sensible atmosphere.** See **aerothermodynamic border; atmosphere.**

EGADS. Electronic Ground Automatic Destruct Sequencer. An electronic timing device which automatically selects and provides control for a number of command destruct (ground) transmitters so that, as a missile or booster vehicle progresses in flight, it is under control of the transmitter which can most effectively "illuminate" it. The sequencing is manually set into the device, based upon time computations of the missile/booster flight.

EGOCENTRIC THRESHOLD OF WEIGHTLESSNESS. As determined by USAF zero-*g* experiments: the subjective differentiation between weight and weightlessness made under extreme concentration of one's attention upon oneself.

EGRESS TRAINER. In Project Mercury, the Mercury spacecraft vehicle is placed in a large hydrodynamics tank and floats on the surface in different attitudes and at different angles. Egress capability is practiced by the astronauts first with the capsule in smooth water and then in artificially generated waves. Training also is conducted with the capsule sinking and completely beneath the water surface. After hydrodynamics tank training, the capsule egress trainer is taken out to sea, placed in the water, and training continues under realistic conditions.

EJECTION. Explosive separation of pilot seat or pilot capsule from an aircraft or spacecraft while in the atmosphere. Ejection is accomplished by explosive shell or a rocket charge and can be directed upward or downward from the vehicle.

EGRESS TRAINER being used by Astronaut Wally Schirra

EJECTION CAPSULE

EJECTION CAPSULE. (1) In an aircraft or manned spacecraft, a detachable compartment serving as a cockpit or cabin, which may be ejected as a unit and parachuted to the ground. (2) In an artificial satellite, probe, or unmanned spacecraft, a boxlike unit usually containing recording instruments or records of observed data, which may be ejected and returned to earth by a parachute or other deceleration device.

EJECTION SEAT. The pilot seat of an aircraft or spacecraft which is explosively ejected with its pilot from the vehicle. The seat is mounted on rails, and often is equipped with lock-guards for the arms and legs, fins or other devices for aerodynamic stabilization, a facial windscreen, and automatic devices to separate the pilot from the seat while in free fall. The acceleration ranges from 14 to $22g$ (rate of onset is at 150 to $200g$ per second, depending on the type of catapult); this is not excessive in terms of human tolerance, inasmuch as slow-burning powder is used, which delivers a smooth stroke with cumulative force rather than a severe or painful jolt. The speed of ejection is 60 to 80 feet per second; the

g force is not sustained for more than a part of a second. Ejection has been successful from subsonic to supersonic speeds and in nearly every conceivable aircraft attitude.

EJECTION VELOCITY. The specific velocity that is needed to decelerate a spacecraft in orbit, so that it will enter a new trajectory that intersects the earth's surface before another full orbit is completed. See **re-entry profile; retro-rockets.**

EKG. Also as **ECG.** Abbreviation for electrocardiogram, a graphic record of the heart's action traced by an electrocardiograph. Considered the single most vital continuing medical status report of an astronaut in orbit.

ELECTRICAL ENGINE. Specifically, an ion or plasma propulsion system, so described because of the separation of charged particles as part of the propulsive operation. Its chief characteristic is low thrust sustained over a long duration to permit constant low-g acceleration or deceleration for specialized earth-orbit or deep-space missions.

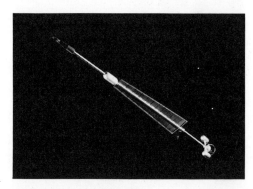

ELECTRICAL ENGINE. NASA design for nuclear-reactor electrical propulsion vehicle for manned deep-space missions

ELECTRO–ENCEPHALOGRAPHIC EXAMINATION. The graphic recording of the electrical currents continuously produced by the brain. Traced as brain waves by an electro-encephalograph, the currents form patterns by which the normal or abnormal condition of the brain can be evaluated.

ELECTROJET. Charged sheet or stream moving in an ionized layer in the upper atmosphere of a planet and, with respect to earth, generally caused by solar activity.

ELECTROMAGNETIC RADIATION. Comprising the complete "electromagnetic spectrum." Includes radio waves, infrared, visible light, ultraviolet rays, X-rays, and gamma rays. Radio waves are longest in wavelength; gamma rays are shortest.

ELECTRON. The subatomic particle that possesses the smallest possible electric charge. The term *electron* is usually employed in reference to the orbital particle whereas the term *beta particle* refers to a particle of the same electric charge inside the nucleus of the atom.

ELECTRONIC DATA PROCESSING. The use of electronic devices and systems in the processing of data so as to interpret the data and put it into usable form. See **data; data reduction; FLAC.**

ELECTRONIC INTERFERENCE. Any electrical or electromagnetic disturbance that causes undesirable response in electronic equipment. Electrical interference refers specifically to interference caused by the operation of electrical apparatus that is not designed to radiate electromagnetic energy.

ELECTRONICS. A branch of physics concerned with the emission, transmission, behavior, and effect of electrons. Electronics receives its practical application through the use of devices such as the vacuum tube, cathode-ray tube, photoelectric cells, and other such instruments.

ELECTROPHYSIOLOGICAL STUDIES. Measurements of the electric current and voltage produced by living tissue such as the heart and brain, to evaluate physiological condition.

ELEPHANT EAR. Launch-crew term for a thick plate on a rocket booster skin to reinforce a hatch or hole.

ELLIPSE. A curve described about two fixed points (the *foci*) so that the sum of the distances between any point on the curve and the two foci is equal to the sum of the distances between any other point on the curve and the foci. An ellipse appears as an elongated circle; the orbits of planets, satellites, planetoids, and comets are ellipses, in which the center of attraction is at one focus. See **conic section.**

EMISSIVITY. The relative power of a surface, a material, or the area comprising a surface to emit heat by radiation.

EMPTY–SPACE MYOPIA. A problem encountered often by jet pilots flying long missions at high altitudes, and a potentially serious difficulty for orbital flight. The eyes at rest tend to accommodate for a distance of approximately 6 feet. Objects that lie beyond this distance are perceived at first only with difficulty, because they are out of focus. In ordinary flight, this presents no difficulty; the eyes accommodate rapidly and effectively because a series of objects is presented in progressive fashion to them. Traveling in space (or at the upper atmospheric regimes) the pilot lacks this procession of objects before him. Thus his eyes remain at the resting accommodation of only 6 feet or even less. The eyes lack a yardstick comparison by which a man can assure that he is focusing at 6 feet, 60 feet, or infinity. Under such conditions jet pilots have failed completely to see other aircraft several hundred yards away. In space, an object no more than a 100 feet off may visually be missed entirely. Special conditions enhance eye accommodation—contrast, color, relative brightness, movement, etc. At high flight altitudes, the pilot is often in a world of harsh glare and blank space, and empty-space myopia remains a serious problem.

ENCAPSULATED SEAT. A seat in a spacecraft or aircraft that is placed inside a sealed, protective capsule so as to obtain a desired immediate-area environment for the seat occupant. The entire seat may be designed for ejection as a separate unit, with the pilot inside the capsule.

END VELOCITY. The velocity of a booster or payload at the exact moment of cessation of thrust.

ENGINE SPRAY. That part of a launch-site water-deluge fire system that is directed specifically at cooling the booster combustion chambers during launch.

ENVIRONMENT. The aggregate of conditions and influences that surround and affect a thing or being, either natural or artificially created and sustained.

ENVIRONMENTAL CHAMBER. An enclosed and sealed chamber in which temperature, pressure, humidity, fluid contents, light, noise, movement, and other factors may be controlled so as to simulate different and specifically desired environmental conditions.

EORBS. Earth Orbiting Recoverable Biological Satellite. A Mercury capsule modified to carry animals on orbital missions extending to 14 days in space. The animals to be used include a chimpanzee on a restrained couch; a rhesus monkey unrestrained in a cubicle; and a colony of mice. Deep brain probes in the primates will permit assessment of unconsciousness in the weightless state; extensive radiation and other experiments will be conducted.

EPI. Earth Path Indicator. A dead-reckoning computer containing a mechanically operated revolving globe that continually reveals to an astronaut his position in space in relation to the earth, and where he will descend when ejected from orbit.

EPOCH. A particular instant, or time hack, for which certain data are valid. See **Master Central Timing System.**

EQUATORIAL ORBIT. An orbit that is within the plane of the earth's equator, in which the spacecraft is traveling either due east or due west. Theoretically, such an orbit means the spacecraft would at all times be directly over the earth's equator.

EQUILIBRANT FORCE. See **force.**

EQUILIBRIUM AND ORIENTATION. *Balance:* the individual maintains a sense of balance (often referred to as the "sixth sense") in three ways:

(1) The eyes provide a visual reference to whatever is around the individual and are of the greatest importance in keeping balance. They make corrections on the other two factors in balance.

(2) The "body sense" comes from changes in pressure and tension on the tendons, ligaments, muscles, and joints. The individual "feels" what position he is in; this is the significance of the old expression, "Flying by the seat of your pants." Body sense, however, provides information only of the vertical and angular movements of the body, but does not tell anything of circular movements.

(3) The inner ear (vestibular apparatus) contains an organ which is shaped roughly like a pretzel; it consists of three semicircular canals, each in a different plane and containing a fluid. The slightest movement of the head causes this fluid to press in the opposite direction and stimulate the tiny hairs of the cells lining the inside of the canal. The stimulation causes nerve impulses to be sent to the brain telling the individual "which end is up." Taken alone, however, this message may be misleading. A correct sense of balance invariably demands full co-ordination of the three senses—eyes, body sense, and inner ear.

EQUILIBRIUM AND ORIENTATION. The inner ear

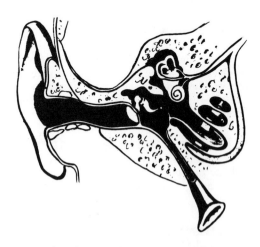

Maintaining orientation and equilibrium requires interpretation of the sensations of the eyes, the vestibular apparatus in the inner ear, and the body sense of pressure or tension sensations from skin, muscles, and joints. In flight (and under certain conditions in space under zero *g*), the combined picture received from these sensory organs may be completely unreliable—like getting a TV picture from one channel and sound from another. Flying blind without instruments—under zero visibility conditions—is similar to walking blindfolded. The tendency is to go in a circle when the eyes lack fixed points of reference; in flight, the circle tightens and quickly becomes a spin (the aircraft is in a rapidly descending rotary stall). Sensations in flight are also misleading to the brain because the vestibular apparatus cannot distinguish between gravity and centrifugal force.

These factors also apply to pilot control of spacecraft in terms of maintaining proper control co-ordination in order to "hold exact attitudes" of a spacecraft in relation to the horizontal line of the earth's horizon. Before a pilot of an aircraft can develop both confidence and skill in reading and interpreting his flight instruments, the brain must learn to *suppress* sensory illusions. The first step in successful instrument flight, therefore, is for the pilot to learn to ignore the sensations which, on the ground, an individual depends upon instinctively to maintain a sense of balance. The pilot must disregard all sensations of going up or down, slipping, sliding, turning, or tumbling, and *must* allow himself to be guided by the accurate and ungarbled information displayed to him by his instruments. It is this training and experience of the test pilot which is considered so essential a requirement for the astronaut, who in space lacks all the familiar sensory information for sustaining orientation and equilibrium. The space pilot must be absolutely competent in "instrument flight."

EQUILIBRIUM AND VIBRATION TEST.
A physiological stress test in which the subject is seated on a chair which rotates simultaneously on two axes. He is required to maintain the chair on an even keel by means of a control stick, with and without vibration, normally and while blindfolded.

ERECTABLE SPACE STATION. A type of manned space station which could be sent into orbit in collapsible form. Crews would use pressure systems and other devices to erect the station in final and usable configuration under orbit conditions.

ERECTION. The process of raising, or erecting, a rocket booster vehicle from the horizontal transport position to the vertical position on its launch ring.

ERECTOR SERVICE TOWER. A large steel tower assembly which can pivot about its base during transition from the horizontal to the vertical position. A major modification of the gantry system, it is used to erect such boosters as the Titan II. The booster vehicle is secured in horizontal position to the service tower, and the entire tower then pivots to the vertical; the gantry uses a system of cranes and hoists to position the rocket booster in place on the launch ring.

EQUILIBRIUM AND VIBRATION TEST. Blindfolded subject on equilibrium chair during test run

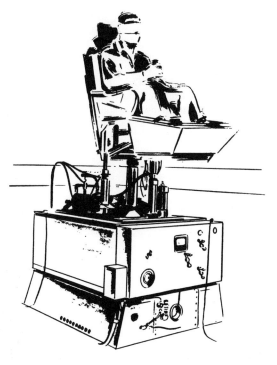

ESCAPE ROCKET for Mercury capsule

ERGOMETER. A device similar to a bicycle used for a test of physical competence. Test subject pedals an increasing amount of weight while wearing an oxygen mask. Heartbeat and oxygen consumption are measured during this process, and evaluation is made by considering the amount of weight pedaled by the time subject's heart reaches 180 beats per minute.

EROSION GAUGE. An instrument or device that is used to measure the eroding effect of micrometeors and dust on the outer surface of any earth-orbiting vehicle.

ESCAPE ORBIT. One of various orbital paths flown by a vehicle from a central force field in order to escape the direct influence of that force field. See **escape velocity.**

ESCAPE ROCKET. A rocket used in a system to ensure the escape of an astronaut from a booster in the event of malfunctioning. In Project Mercury, a 6-foot rocket mounted on and partially within a 17-foot pylon structure attached to a Mercury capsule during the early flight stages. Escape rocket fires in event of abort, produces 50,-000 lbs. thrust for .7 second, through 3 canted nozzles to direct flames away from capsule. Escape rocket system designed with .999 reliability factor. In firing, this rocket pulls the capsule off the Atlas and in one second carries it upward 250 feet. From ground liftoff, at 2,600 feet the main parachute opens for descent. If abort occurs during ascent, separation distance in one second may be only 125 feet.

ESCAPE ROCKET for X-20 Dyna-Soar

Mercury capsule with ESCAPE TOWER and rocket atop Atlas booster. Swinging platform is for emergency egress

ESCAPE TOWER. Metal tower or pylon weighing 900 lbs. and 17 feet in length. In Mercury program, attaches to capsule and at tower top contains a 6-foot escape rocket (see **escape rocket**). After escape rocket firing or, if flight is normal, the escape pylon superstructure is jettisoned. A single rocket weighs 18 lbs. It fires for 1.5 seconds with 860 lbs. thrust. In normal flight both escape rocket and jettison rocket fire simultaneously to separate the escape tower from the capsule during jettison process.

ESCAPE VELOCITY. The minimum velocity required to escape permanently from a particular point in a gravitational field. To escape from the earth's surface, without additional propulsion and disregarding the effects of air drag, a velocity of 7 miles per second is required.

ESCAPE VELOCITY, DIMINISHING. As a vehicle traveling at escape velocity along an escape orbit moves outward from the central force field (i.e., gravitational pull of earth or moon) its velocity diminishes because of gravity. At the same time, however, the pull of gravity also diminishes with distance. Escape velocity, therefore, is that initial velocity which, though diminished at each continually successive point on the orbit, will provide enough remaining velocity at each successive point to overcome gravity pull at that point.

ESCAPE VELOCITY, SOLAR SYSTEM.

Planet	Gravity Ratio	Escape Velocity in Feet per Second
Mercury	0.27	11,600
Venus	0.85	33,200
Earth	1.0	36,900
Moon	0.16	7,750
Mars	0.38	16,360
Jupiter	2.64	195,000
Saturn	1.17	116,000
Uranus	0.92	68,600
Neptune	1.12	73,800
Pluto	0.05?	17,300?

ESV. Earth Satellite Vehicle.

EVOLVED GASES. Air expanding within the intestinal tract of a pilot or astronaut during ascent to high altitude and lowered ambient air pressure is a major source of pain and physical difficulty often encountered in aerospace flight. The gastrointestinal tract normally contains about one quart of gas, mostly swallowed air but partly gases— such as methane and hydrogen sulfide— produced by the ferment and decay of food being digested. At an air density altitude of 16,500 feet this gas doubles in volume. At 25,000 feet the increase is up to 3 quarts. At 39,000 feet the one quart has become 7, and at 50,000 feet density altitude the one quart expands to 17 quarts. Normally the individual begins valving off this gas (belching or passing) at around 20,000 feet. Unless this body-gas valving occurs at a satisfactory rate, gastrointestinal pains may become severe; in some instances pilots have fainted from the intensity of the pain.

EXACT ORBIT. An orbit programmed into a satellite mission that the satellite, manned or unmanned, must reach and follow if the data sought from the flight are to be obtained.

EXCELSIOR. Project Excelsior was the exhaustive Air Force high-altitude survival program to develop special equipment and techniques for airmen to abandon their aerospace craft in space-equivalent conditions and maintain a stabilized but rapid free fall to denser and "safer" atmospheres. Jumps were made by Captain Joseph W. Kittinger, Jr., USAF, from 76,400 feet, 75,000 feet, and 102,800 feet. During this latter jump from an open balloon gondola, Captain Kittinger at 90,000 feet achieved a free-fall speed of 702 mph. See **flat spin; free fall; gondola.**

EXERCISER. A machine that grasps securely an unmanned satellite vehicle or manned spacecraft and then subjects that vehicle to the stresses which the vehicle is expected to encounter in actual flight, in order to determine the vehicle's structural and functional integrity under these stresses.

EXHAUST STREAM. A stream of gaseous, radiant, or nuclear particles emitted from the orifice of a rocket or any other type of reaction engine. Often referred to as a "jet stream" or "exhaust gases."

EXOBIOLOGY. The study of living organisms existing on celestial bodies other than the earth.

EXOLIFE. See **exoterrestrial life.**

EXOSPHERE. The outermost or topmost portion of the atmosphere; the region where molecular escape from the earth's atmosphere is significant. The base of the exosphere is thought to be at an altitude above 200 miles and possibly as high as 625 miles.

EXOTERRESTRIAL LIFE. Living organisms that might exist on an extraterrestrial planetary body. Such organisms might contaminate an earth-launched space vehicle that landed on the extraterrestrial planetary body, and the vehicle might return with these organisms or microorganisms to the surface of the earth. Also termed **exolife.**

EXCELSIOR. Captain Joseph W. Kittinger, Jr., USAF, beginning free fall from 102,800 feet—above 99% of the earth's atmosphere

EXOTIC FUEL. Any fuel that is considered to be unusual in makeup, such as liquid hydrogen with a fluorine oxidizer, and that generates greater thrust than the "standard" rocket booster fuel-oxidizer combination of kerosene and liquid oxygen.

EXPLORER. The Explorer series of earth satellites cover a wide gamut of experiments, satellite shapes and sizes, and booster rockets. A Jupiter-C booster on January 31, 1958, sent Explorer I into orbit as the first American satellite. The satellite package included the fourth rocket stage; the payload was 30.8 lbs., of which 18.13 lbs. was instrumentation. Explorer II, generally similar, failed to orbit on its attempt of March 5, 1958. Explorer III went into orbit on March 26, 1958, as did Explorer IV on July 26, 1958. Explorer V was launched on August 24, 1958, failing to orbit. This ended the Explorer series with the Jupiter-C booster.

Explorer VI (also known as Project Able III and the Paddlewheel Satellite) was the next major phase of the Explorer series. It was an irregular spheroid with a slightly flattened area at the bottom. Four solar cells extended from the spacecraft on hinging arms. It weighed 142 lbs. The spheroid diameter was 26 inches, the over-all diameter with paddles extended was 86 inches. A Thor-Able vehicle fired Explorer VI into orbit on August 7, 1959. On October 13, 1959, a Juno-II booster rocketed Explorer VII into orbit. This satellite weighed 91.5 lbs. and was formed of two truncated cones

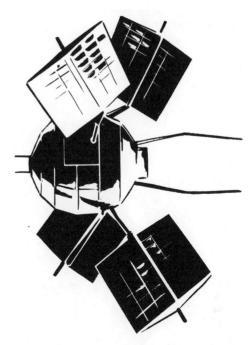

EXPLORER VI, high-orbiting satellite, used large paddles of solar cells for power source

joined at the base. Other satellites in the series included the 91.5-lb. Explorer Project, which failed to orbit with a Juno-II launch attempt on July 16, 1959; the Explorer Radiation Satellite, which failed in a launch attempt on March 23, 1960; Explorer VIII, which orbited with a Juno-II booster on November 3, 1960; a Scout-boosted Explorer, with a launch failure on December

EXPLORER I, first United States satellite, in orbital configuration

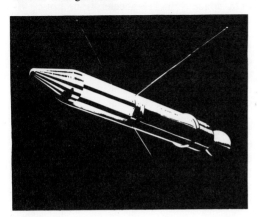

EXPLORER VII, scientific probe satellite, in orbit

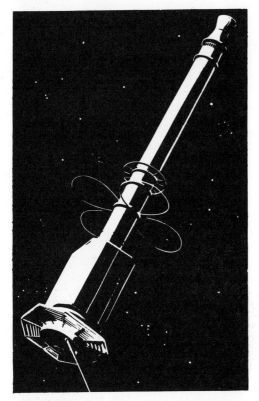

EXPLORER XI satellite, launched April 27, 1961, carrying a gamma-ray astronomy telescope to detect and chart cosmic gamma radiation

4, 1960; Explorer IX, orbited by a Scout booster on February 16, 1961. Since then, all earth-satellite orbiters with scientific payloads, unless otherwise specifically identified, are considered as part of the Explorer series, such as Explorer S-45 I (failed to orbit February 24, 1961); Explorer X (successfully orbited on March 25, 1961); Explorer XI (successfully orbited on April 27, 1961); Explorer S-45 II (failed to orbit May 24, 1961); Explorer S-55 (failed to orbit June 30, 1961); Explorer XII (successfully orbited on August 15, 1961); Explorer XIII (successfully orbited on August 25, 1961).

EXPLOSIVE BOLT. A bolt incorporating an explosive which can be detonated on command, thus destroying the bolt. Explosive bolts are used, for example, in separating a satellite from a booster, a retrorocket package from a manned vehicle, etc.

EXPLOSIVE DECOMPRESSION. The loss of air pressure explosively from a sealed cabin caused by a rupture of the cabin wall, exposing the personnel within to a dangerously sudden loss of air and pressure and resulting in rapid decompression of the lungs. At extreme altitude or under space-environment conditions, explosive decompression results in unconsciousness within 10 to 15 seconds, and death almost immediately afterward.

EXPLOSIVE HATCH. The hatch of a spacecraft secured by bolts to the spacecraft proper, but equipped with a means of explosively actuated ejection. Either **explosive bolts** (q.v.) are used for the separation, or an explosive lanyard (primer cord) is inserted in the space seal between the hatch and the spacecraft. The ignition and explosion of the cord split the bolts, and the rapid expansion of gases from the explosive process forcibly ejects the hatch away from the spacecraft.

EXPULSION BAG. A propellant container system developed especially for transfer of propellants and oxidizers under the sustained zero-g condition of orbital rendezvous and fueling. The expulsion bag acts like a giant balloon in that it is expanded to full size by its propellant; when the expulsion bag throat is vented, the fuel is forced out by the action of the collapsing (constricting) bag, and in this manner is pressure-fed through lines to another tanker or stage.

EXTERNAL IRRITANTS. To the occupant of a space vehicle—acceleration, noise, vibration, etc.

EXTINCTOSPECTROPOLARISCOPE-OCCULOGYROGRAVOADOPTOM-ETER. A device used for 16 astronomical and physiological tests during a manned orbital flight. See **V-meter.**

EXTRANEOUS SENSORY EVENTS. General, normal activity around a person, producing a more or less steady flow of "background" impressions such as noise (radio static and noise produced by pressure regulators and other devices) and movement.

EXTRATERRESTRIAL. Anything or any being beyond the earth, or from some place other than the earth.

EXTRA–VEHICULAR SUIT. Official NASA designation for spacesuit to be worn by Gemini and Apollo astronauts for the purpose of leaving the pressurized environment of their spacecraft and carrying out activities and maneuvers beyond the spacecraft while exposed to the space environment.

EXTRA-VEHICULAR SUIT. Propulsion backpack, experimental unit under test for orbital operations by astronauts outside spacecraft. Has power, oxygen, and pressure systems, as well as small propulsion units for zero-*g* maneuverability

"EYEBALLS IN." The direction of the pressure caused by *g* forces during the *acceleration* of a rocket booster ascent.

"EYEBALLS OUT." The direction of the pressure caused by *g* forces during the *deceleration* of a space vehicle, such as during the re-entry period.

F

FACEPIECE. A transparent, curving plastic sheet that fits securely into a pressure-suit helmet in order to seal the helmet for safe physiological operations under conditions of dangerously reduced ambient pressure. Distinctive from a helmet faceplate which is attached permanently to the helmet but which moves upward on guide slots or rails.

FACEPIECE

FAI. Federal Aeronautique Internationale. The international organization that establishes criteria for, and confirms, official world records for atmospheric and space flight. The United States and USSR are member nations. The criterion internationally agreed upon for an official space flight is an ascent by a manned vehicle to at least 100 kilometers, or approximately 62 miles.

FALL. Relating to any space vehicle or spatial body: to drop toward another spatial body under the influence of the latter's gravity. The moon, as an example, falls toward the earth, but its tangential velocity compensates for this motion and keeps it in orbit. An earth-launched vehicle could be directed to fall toward the sun; once outside the gravitational influence of the earth, propulsion maneuvers would cancel out a part of its velocity.

FALLAWAY SECTION. Any section, part, member, or other piece of equipment of a booster vehicle that is jettisoned and falls away from the vehicle in flight, under the influence of gravity at less than orbital velocity. A protective nose shield, side fairings, or empty booster stages are examples of fallaway sections.

FALLBACK AREA. At a launch site, an area to which technicians, photographers, and observers fall back once a missile or booster vehicle is ready for firing.

FALSE–POSITIVE RATE. This rate expresses the proportion of personnel denied selection for training for a program (as in the astronaut program for Mercury, Gemini, Apollo, X-15, X-20, etc.) because their expected performance was incorrectly predicted to be unsatisfactory.

FALSE TUMBLING SENSATION. A psychological reaction of an individual that occurs during the transition from a high-level positive-g acceleration abruptly to a low or $1g$ level, such as takes place during the sequence of propulsion cutoff of an orbital booster vehicle. The individual experiences the conviction that he is suddenly tumbling end-over-end; the reaction is one of abrupt g-force transition rather than of actuality.

FATIGUE. A weakening or deterioration of metal or other material, or of a structural member, occurring under load, especially under repeated, cyclic, or continued loading. An aircraft wing may suffer from metal fatigue, for example; such a structural member is considered unsafe for continued flight operations.

FBW. Fly By Wire. The hand-control (manual) system of the Mercury spacecraft which operates through the linkage of the automatic control and fuel-supply and thruster system by operating the automatic system's

solenoid control valves directly, and bypassing the ASCS (Automatic Stabilization and Control System, or automatic pilot) of the spacecraft. See **Mercury Capsule Control System.**

FEMALE COPILOT. An aural emergency-situation crew warning system. See **VIPS.**

FENCE. A line of redoubt or tracking stations for pickup of signals from an orbiting or deep-space-probe vehicle; or, a network or line of radar stations for tracking such a vehicle. See **NSSS; SPADATS.**

FIBER–OPTICS. A camera system in which a camera "takes pictures around corners." A flexible hose loaded with tiny glass fibers is connected to a camera and the end of the hose directed at the subject. The hose may be bent, wound, crooked, and turned without interfering with the picture. Fiber-optics cameras loaded with 16mm. film are used in rocket vehicle flight tests to obtain valuable study data of liquid oxygen sloshing in tanks, engine chilldown, ignition and separation of upper stages. The cameras are ejected and recovered.

FIDO. In Mercury Control Center at Cape Canaveral, Fido refers to a flight-dynamics officer concerned with the dynamics of the mission such as velocity, elevation, angular direction, speed of change, attitude, etc.

FIELD. A region of space at each point of which a given physical quantity has some definite value, thus a "gravitational field," an "electric field," a "magnetic field," etc.

FINAL COUNT. The second half of a split countdown. It is separated by a built-in hold from the first half, or precount, of the countdown. See **split countdown.**

FINAL TRIM. That action in the flight of a ballistic-type rocket booster (i.e., Atlas or Titan) that adjusts the booster to the exact direction programmed for its flight. Final trim of a rocket vehicle is normally accomplished by use of vernier engines. See **verniers.**

FIN STABILIZATION. The addition of fixed fins to the body of a booster vehicle, usually in the afterbody section (as with Saturn C-1B, Mercury-Redstone) of the booster, to provide an additional level of aerodynamic stability during the initial ascent.

FIREBALL. An extremely bright meteor consumed by friction in the earth's atmosphere; seen as a blazing sphere of fire with a long fiery trail.

FIRE–DELUGE SYSTEM. Assembly of pipes, hoses, automatic spray outlets throughout launch stand and launch area, remotely controlled, to deluge launch area in event of fire or explosion.

FIRING CHAMBER. That part of a rocket engine consisting of a chamber in which the fuel and oxidizer are ignited and in which pressure of gases is built up to provide an exhaust velocity sufficient for thrust for flight. See **combustion chamber.**

FIRST LIGHT. The beginning of morning nautical twilight, i.e., when the center of the morning sun is 12° below the horizon.

FIRST MOTION. The first indication of motion of any missile or space booster vehicle from its launch stand or pad. Synonymous with **takeoff** and **liftoff.**

FIX. Determination of a position by means of terrestrial, electronic, or astronomical data; used in navigation and astrogation.

FIXATION/BLOCK-CONFUSION PHENOMENON. A three-phase, sequential occurrence in which the operator (astronaut, pilot, crewman, ground controller, etc.) suddenly realizes that he is monitoring only one particular indicator (such as yaw rate and attitude only, out of yaw, pitch, roll rates and attitudes). He then freezes or blocks and is powerless to act. This is followed by momentary confusion which can be so extreme that the operator does not know which control is associated with which indicator (a common occurrence when an inexperienced pilot attempts to fly under lack of visual conditions and fails to operate his flight controls properly in relationship to their control of the attitude and movement of the aircraft). With the termination of block and confusion, which occurs after one or more seconds, the operator resumes his instrument scanning and attains his immediately previous level of proficiency.

FIXED SATELLITES. A satellite of the earth that orbits the planet from west to east at such a velocity as to remain fixed over a given place on the earth's equator. See **synchronous satellite.**

FLAC. FLorida Automatic Computer. Computer in Technical Laboratory at Patrick Air Force Base, headquarters for Atlantic Missile Range, into which is fed "raw data" telemetered from a vehicle in flight, to be reduced and processed for readout display of missile or space-vehicle performance.

FLAME BUCKET. A powerful curving steel tube mounted beneath a rocket booster on a launch stand, through which the flame is deflected and sprayed with water during time of ignition and liftoff.

FLAME DEFLECTOR. A sharply pointed, conical steel assembly placed beneath a rocket booster for a "dry launch" (one in which protective liquid cooling is not used). The rocket stands on a low steel ring above concrete; the deflector curves the flame to push away from the rocket in a circular horizontal pattern.

FLARE. See **solar flares.**

FLASHBACK. A reversal of flame propagation in a system, counter to the usual flow of the combustible mixture.

FLASH POINT. The temperature at which the vapor of a propellant or lubricating fluid will flash or ignite momentarily.

FLAT SPIN. The unstabilized human body in a free fall from high altitude has a tendency to go into a very rapid flat spin, with the airman either face up or face down. In this spin he can reach peak speeds of 240 rotations per minute. At about 60 rpm a man reaches his "psychological limit" and will panic. At 80 to 90 rpm he reaches his physiological threshold and blacks out. Unconscious, he may suffer serious injury from severe *g* forces and will spin down into the ground.

Inflatable FLEXWING, intended for use with Gemini spacecraft, undergoing manned flight tests atop special research vehicle

FLEXWING. A flexible-winged, kitelike vehicle designed for use in a recovery system for launch vehicles or as a re-entry vehicle; assigned to Project Gemini for lower atmospheric descent under limited directional control. Unlike the conventional wing composed of a rigid skin covering a forming structure, the flexwing is composed of a membrane of flexible material attached to three supporting members. The center keel and the two side members or leading edges are joined at the foremost point to define a triangular shape. The edges of the flexible membrane are attached to the side membrane and the membrane is joined to the keel throughout its length at the centerline. The flexwing supports the vehicle by means of either cables or rigid structural members. The flight trajectory of flexwing vehicles is controlled by a simple shift of the center of gravity of the vehicle, with respect to the center of pressure of the wing. The wing may be compactly stored and released in flight much in the manner of a parachute.

FLICKER FUSION FREQUENCY TEST. A test to demonstrate or determine the effects of hypoxia on the central nervous system; the test is based on a subject's ability to discriminate between a flickering light and a steady light. See **hypoxia.**

FLICKER VERTIGO. See **photic stimulation.**

FLIGHT BIRD. Any vehicle that is awaiting flight test. See **bird.**

FLIGHT CONTROL SYSTEM. System of a booster vehicle consisting of actuating devices or mechanisms that control the propulsion units; also the system that imparts movement to jet stream vanes (i.e., Redstone), swiveling engines (i.e., Atlas, Thor, Titan, Saturn), or to aerodynamic surfaces, when applicable, so as to provide vehicle stability and desired guidance notwithstanding all unstabilizing influences. An integral part of the guidance system.

FLIGHT ENVELOPE. The entire spectrum of the flight of any airborne or spaceborne vehicle from a position of rest at launch to a position of rest at completion of the mission.

FLIGHT PATH. The line, route, or direction, inclusively, that connects the continuous positions occupied, or to be occupied, by any atmospheric or space vehicle, exclusive of reference to the vertical or horizontal planes.

FLIGHT PROFILE. A graphic portrayal of the line of flight of any atmospheric or

Exaggerated profile sequence of flareout and landing of FLEXWING-borne Gemini spacecraft

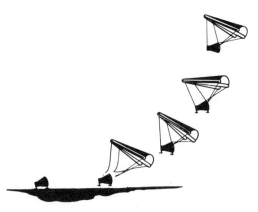

space vehicle as seen from a side view, indicating continuously the various altitudes along the route. See **flight envelope; flight path.**

FLIGHT TEST. The "acid test" by means of actual flight to study and interpret the performance and capabilities of any vehicle intended to fly in the atmosphere or in space.

"FLIP THE LID." Pilot expression meaning to actuate the control that explosively or otherwise releases the plexiglas canopy of an aircraft cockpit.

FLOTATION COLLAR. An inflatable double-walled "raft" that is wrapped around a spacecraft capsule floating in water, and is then inflated to provide both flotation and water stability to the spacecraft, especially to maintain the spacecraft in an upright position.

FLOTATION COLLAR

FLUID SHIFT. The movement to and pooling of blood in the lower extremities of the body caused by a positive-g force, in a head-to-foot direction, in a seated individual. See **g-suit; positive-g tolerance.**

FLUORESCEIN. Also: *fluorescine.* A fluorescent dye in powder form; it is put in emergency survival kits for personnel down at sea to spread on the water in order to form a brilliant yellow-green, daylight marker, visible for many miles.

FLUTTER. One of the so-called **barrier reefs** of high-supersonic and hypersonic flight in the upper atmosphere; a problem especially encountered in rocket aircraft and winged re-entry vehicles. Metal airfoils and structures enjoy a certain "flex ability" in that they can bend and twist slightly, but essentially they are stable platforms with a minimal "give" for safety load factors. At high speeds airflow sometimes bends suddenly or twists sharply to impose heavy, unexpected loads on a wing or tail surface. Simultaneously with these loads the vehicle undergoes the vibration of "ramming" its way through the resisting air. Under certain conditions the combination of sharp airflow loads and vibration becomes excessive. A new vibration sweeps throughout the metal parts. In moments the metal is unable to withstand the combination of airflow and vibration forces. The airfoil begins to "ripple" through its length, and it is no longer a stable platform. It becomes dangerously flexible, and it begins to flutter wildly. The net result is swift and conclusive—violent flutter, metal failure, disintegration of parts, and separation of the airfoil from the vehicle.

FLUX. The rate of flow of some quantity, often used in reference to the flow of some form of energy.

FOLLOW–ON. Also: *second generation.* Any development, unit, equipment, procedure, group of objects, or techniques which is considered to be a second or subsequent generation in the development of the subject concerned. Example: the two-man Gemini craft is a follow-on project of the one-man Mercury capsule.

FORCE. Something that changes the shape or motion of a body. **Equilibrant force** is a single force producing equilibrium with several forces. **Resultant force**—if two forces at a point are represented in magnitude and direction by line segments, the diagonal of the parallelogram with the line segments as sides represents the resultant of the two forces. **Moment of force** about a point equals the product of the perpendicular force and the distance from the line of action to the point (i.e., a fulcrum).

FREEDOM 7

FPM. Feet Per Minute.

FPS. Feet Per Second.

FREEDOM 7. Name assigned to Mercury capsule flown in suborbital flight on May 5, 1961, by Astronaut Alan B. Shepard, Jr.

FREE FALL. The motion of any unpowered body traveling in a gravitational field. Free fall in orbit beyond the earth's atmosphere produces a condition of zero g or weightlessness. Free fall as applied to the falling body of a parachute jumper within the earth's atmosphere—because of atmospheric drag—does not produce a similar effect.

FREE GYRO. Sometimes referred to as a space reference gyro in that the free gyro will maintain its orientation with respect to the stars rather than with respect to the earth. Its inability to maintain this space reference is a measure of its inherent inaccuracy. See **gyroscope.**

FREQUENCY SPECTRUM. Range of frequencies from a low to a high in terms of the number of vibrations or cycles in a unit of time.

FREE RADICAL. An atom or group of atoms broken away from a stable compound by application of external energy and, although containing unpaired electrons, remaining free for transitory or longer periods. Of special interest for use as high-energy fuels for manned space flight. Interest centers on three radicals—atomic hydrogen (H), atomic nitrogen (N), and the imine radical (NH). Their use in propulsive systems depends upon their being isolated and available in bulk, either in pure form or dissolved in a desired concentration in another fuel. See **aeroduct; ASP.**

FREE SPACE. Space unoccupied by any orbiting body; more specifically, space unoccupied by any body or vehicle except by occasional meteoroids.

FREEZE–OUT METHOD. A method for controlling humidity within a sealed and pressurized cabin by passing the moist cabin air over a cold surface, condensing and freezing out water vapor and possibly carbon dioxide.

FRIENDSHIP 7. Name assigned to Mercury capsule flown in 3-orbit mission of February 20, 1962, by Astronaut John H. Glenn, Jr.

FRUSTRATION THRESHOLD. The point at which an individual feels or manifests frustration over inability to achieve an objective; also, that point where the manifested frustration begins to interfere with operational efficiency.

FTV. Flight Test Vehicle. See **flight test.**

FUBAR. Fouled Up Beyond All Recognition. Expression that denotes confusion or complete lack of order during any incident; a chaotic situation.

FUEL. Any substance used to provide reaction or any other means of thrust for atmospheric or space flight. See **chemical fuel.**

FREE FALL. Captain Joseph W. Kittinger, Jr., USAF, in a free fall from 76,400 feet during Project Excelsior (photo taken by automatic camera)

FUEL CELL BATTERY. A battery with an ion-exchange membrane fuel cell which produces electricity through the chemical reaction of oxygen and hydrogen. It produces, also, one pint of pure drinkable water as a by-product of each kilowatt-hour of operation. As used in the Gemini spacecraft the fuel cell battery will deliver a peak load of almost 2 kw of DC electricity as the primary electric power for all spacecraft equipment. A fuel cell battery is made up of many individual sandwichlike ion-exchange membrane cells, connected in series to form building blocks that can be connected in series or parallel to meet specific power requirements. The ion-exchange membrane is a sheet of tough plastic that separates each cell into two sections. Hydrogen gas is fed to one side of the membrane and oxygen to the other. Electrons from the hydrogen atoms are picked up by a thin metallic electrode in contact with the surface of the membrane while the remaining hydrogen ions travel through the membrane. The electrons feed into the electrical circuit to do work, and after flowing through the circuit return to the other side of the membrane where they recombine with the ions in the presence of oxygen to form water. In a typical spacecraft application, the hydrogen and oxygen gas for the fuel cell battery would be stored in a cryogenic or supercooling liquid condition to conserve space.

FULL FLOW. The flow of liquid propellants at a maximum or near-maximum rate into a booster's combustion chamber.

FUMING NITRIC ACID. Highly concentrated solution of nitric pentoxide in water, red or brown in color and more active than the clear nitric acid. Used as an oxidizer for a rocket booster or missile.

G

g. The symbol used to express the acceleration due to gravity at the surface of the earth, which is approximately 32 feet per second per second. A man standing on the earth's surface is constantly being pulled downward by surface gravity. The surface of the earth constantly resists this downward pull. Thus the man is constantly subjected to 1*g*. This translates into a force equal to his own weight in pounds. Thus a man accelerated by a rocket at a force of 10*g* weighs 10 times his "normal" weight (at rest on the earth's surface). Under 10*g* a 200-lb. man weighs 2,000 lbs. See **acceleration; acceleration profile; acceleration tolerance; g-forces.**

g-FORCES (MERCURY). In the Mercury capsule, at the moment of injection into orbit—just before sustainer engine cutoff—the astronaut experiences a *g* force of 7.7*g* (MA-6); *g*-force loads during normal re-entry are approximately 8*g; g* forces sustained in re-entry of the suborbital flight capsule (MR-4) reached to 12*g* because of steeper, higher deceleration flight profile. See also *g*.

g-SUIT. A protective personnel garment with air bladders by the legs, thighs, and over the stomach. During flight maneuvers that create high *g* forces, the bladders are automatically inflated, constricting the immediate body area and restricting the blood from moving downward to the legs. The garment's purpose is to prevent blackout and unconsciousness because of the "fluid shift"—the movement of blood to the lower extremities, caused by sharply increased *g* force.

g TOLERANCE. The tolerance of a pilot, astronaut, aircraft, booster, spacecraft, animal, etc., to *g* force of a specific value.

GALAXY. (1) When capitalized, Galaxy refers to the group of several billion stars, planets, nebulae, etc., to which the earth's sun belongs. Also referred to popularly as the Milky Way. (2) Any of the similar groups of stars forming isolated units in the universe.

GAMMA RAY. An electromagnetic radiation of wave form emitted by a radioactive nucleus and similar to an X-ray but of higher energy and shorter wavelength.

GANTRY. A service tower that surrounds the rocket on its launch stand. Used to erect the Atlas and to mate upper stages, such as upper-stage rockets or the Mercury capsule. The Atlas ICBM gantry is 12 stories high, weighs several hundred tons, rolls on steel rails away from the Atlas prior to launch, to a safe lock-and-hold position. The Atlas gantry has electrical and pneumatic systems for machine, automatic tools, and a demineralized water system for washing down Atlas, plus sliding waterproof curtains. It has two separate fire protection systems and an emer-

GANTRY during launch preparations for Atlas 9B

gency escape cable system. The 112-foot gantry also has large elevators for workmen, astronauts, service technicians. The maximum transfer speed to lock-and-hold position is 125 feet per minute (1.4 mph), over a distance of 500 feet from the launch stand proper.

GARBAGE. A profusion of antenna, electronic, and other equipment mounts and structures jutting out from the otherwise smooth skin of an aircraft or spacecraft; an airplane or aerospace vehicle on its landing approach with "all garbage down"—i.e., landing gear, flaps, and other equipment. Also: the many miscellaneous objects orbiting the earth, such as payload fairings, boost-

Mercury-Atlas pre-launch condition: GANTRY removed, emergency egress platform and catwalk in place

ers, disintegrated satellite parts, protective nose cones, etc.

GARBLE. An error in transmission, reception, encryption, or decryption which renders a message or a portion thereof incorrect or undecryptable.

GAS CAP. The gas immediately in front of a re-entry vehicle or a meteoroid as it travels through the atmosphere; the leading portion of a meteor. This gas is compressed and adiabatically heated to incandescence. See **shock wave.**

GEGENSCHEIN. Faint light area of the sky always opposite the position of the sun on the celestial sphere. *Believed* to be the reflection of sunlight from particles moving beyond the earth's orbit.

GEMINI. Two-man space capsule, follow-on project to Mercury, and considered a "bridge" between Mercury and three-man Apollo. One foot wider and one foot higher than Mercury spacecraft, Gemini is of same external configuration, has 50% greater internal volume. Booster is Titan II; normal orbital weight, 6,000 lbs. For two-week orbiting mission, orbital weight 7,700 lbs.; recovery by flexwing. Capability of "vehicle exits" for crew, and rendezvous and docking with Agena-B spacecraft.

GEMINI HEAT SHIELD. Modified from Mercury spacecraft heat shield, the Gemini

GEMINI two-man spacecraft approaches Agena-B satellite for docking maneuver in orbit

unit is a combination of glass fibers and phenolic resin, non-uniform in thickness to compensate for special hot spots and corners, plus additional ablative materials protecting particular heat-buildup areas of the spacecraft.

GEMINI REACTION CONTROL. Bi-propellant hypergolic fuel is used in the two-man Gemini spacecraft. In orbit, an adapter section at the base of the spacecraft houses 8 maneuver control thrust chambers plus 6 of the spacecraft's 24 attitude control jets. The 8 maneuver control units each have a thrust of 100 lbs., 2 fire forward, 2 aft or down, 4 in the direction of displacement. The 24 attitude control jets each fire with a thrust of 25 lbs.

GEOCENTRIC. Relative to the earth as a center; measured from the *center* of the earth.

GEODETIC. Pertaining to geodesy, the science which deals with the size and shape of the earth; as with *geodetic* satellite.

GEOMAGNETISM. The magnetic phenomena, collectively considered, exhibited by the earth and its atmosphere; by extension, the magnetic phenomena in interplanetary space.

GEOPHYSICAL CONSTANT. A quantity that expresses a fixed value for a law or magnitude that applies to the physics of the earth, e.g., the constant of gravitation.

GEOPHYSICS. The physics of the planet earth, and in respect to its modification by motion, radiation, and other forces and agents.

GEOPROBE. A rocket vehicle designed to explore space near the earth at a distance of more than 4,000 miles from the surface of the earth. Rocket vehicles operating at less than 4,000 miles height are termed "sounding rockets."

GHOST. A pip on a radar screen, unidentified as to source or identity.

GIBSON GIRL. A portable, hand-operated radio transmitter. By operating a crank, a downed airman or astronaut in a remote area can provide radio transmission power for the broadcast of emergency distress signals.

GIGA–. A prefix meaning multiplied by one billion, as *gigaton*.

GIMBAL. A device with two mutually perpendicular and intersecting axes of rotation on which a mounted booster rocket engine may be inclined freely in one direction or another. A gimbal is employed to move a rocket engine (or any reaction device) about for guidance programming and/or corrections in pitching and yawing correction moments.

GIMBALED MOTOR. A rocket motor mounted on a gimbal for movement to obtain inflight pitch and yaw corrections resulting from any deviation from the programmed flight path.

GLENN EFFECT. Title given by NASA to luminous particles encountered in orbit by Astronaut John Glenn. See **luminous particles.**

GLIDESAIL PARACHUTE. A flexible wing used for the controlled gliding descent of space vehicles within the atmosphere, as with Gemini, the two-man space capsule. See **cable reels; flexwing; Gemini.**

GLITCH. A change in voltage on a line which is minute, but enough to trigger a hairspring-sensitive system feeding off the same line. A glitch is no joke to engineers; almost impossible to locate quickly, it is extraordinarily troublesome in countdowns.

GNOTOBIOTICS. The study of germ-free animals for medical and other research in space probes and satellite vehicles.

GO. Aerospace term in wide usage among launch, blockhouse, tracking, communications, flight, and other crews to indicate that a system is operating normally, that all systems are "in the green," and that operations are fully prepared to proceed.

GODDARD SPACE FLIGHT CENTER. NASA electronics and research and development facility at Greenbelt, Maryland, for activities in tracking, communications, data reduction, data transmission and display; and for the development of satellite, probe, and other payload vehicles.

GO JUICE. Rocket fuel.

GONDOLA. An open circular, rectangular, or square-shaped vehicle, with low sides, usually made of lightweight metal and suspended by shroud lines beneath a large plastic balloon to carry men and/or animal subjects to altitudes which may exceed 100,000 feet, for aerospace medicine research and experiments. See **Excelsior.**

GONDOLA of Project Excelsior, lifting off

"GO—NO GO." A point where instant decision is required to (1) continue with a mission, or (2) abort the mission. In terms of aircraft, the "Go—no Go" point is reached where an aircraft has takeoff speed but may still be stopped on the runway. "Go—no Go" for a manned space flight is reached several minutes before scheduled booster ignition, when the test conductor makes his final decision as to whether to scrub the mission or to GO.

"GOOD LANDING." As proverbially applied to aircraft or spacecraft—"*any* landing from which the pilot can walk away under his own power."

GOOP. See **paste food.**

GOX. Gaseous oxygen.

GOXING. A booster is goxing when vapors from liquid oxygen are seen to vent through a valve in the side of the tank to prevent excessive pressure buildup. In Project Mercury, for example, as the Atlas stands ready and fueled during countdown, liquid oxygen in the oxidizer tank continually "boils off" vapors. These appear usually in white or bluish-white form, streaming from the side of the tank.

GRASS. Random interference on a radarscope due primarily to circuit noises, such as thermal agitation.

GRAVIPAUSE. The boundary in space at which the dominant gravity of a particular spatial body ends, and is matched by the counter-gravity of another spatial body. Also: **neutral point.** For example, the neutral point of gravity between the earth and the moon lies approximately nine-tenths of the distance from the earth to the lunar surface, or about 23,760 miles from the lunar surface.

GRAVIRECEPTORS. Highly specialized nerve endings and receptor organs located in the skin, connective tissue, skeletal muscle, and the inner ear. Gravireceptors furnish information to the brain with respect to body position, equilibrium, and the direction of gravitational forces. See **equilibrium and orientation.**

GRAVISPHERE. The spherical extent in which the force of a given spatial (or celestial) body's gravity is predominant.

GRAVITATION. (1) The universal phenomenon of every particle of matter being attracted by other particles, the force of attraction between particles varying inversely as the square of their distance from one another and directly as the product of their masses. (2) The attraction that inheres in this phenomenon.

GRAVITY. The force imparted by the earth to a mass on or close to the earth. Since the earth is rotating, the force observed as gravity is the resultant of the force of gravitation and the centrifugal force arising from this rotation.

GRAVITY ANOMALIES. Deviations between theoretical gravity and actual gravity due to local topographic and geologic conditions, such as the existence of mountains, valleys, oceans, or abnormally high or low density of the materials near the place of measurement.

GRAVITY SIMULATION. Use of centripetal force to simulate weight reaction in a condition of free fall; sometimes achieved by spinning the vehicle to use the centripetal force of the outer periphery so that bodies within the vehicle will have a substitute for the normal weight reaction experienced at the earth's surface. Also known as *artificial gravity* or *simulated gravity*.

GRAVITY WELL. Analogy in which the gravitational field is considered as a deep pit out of which a space vehicle has to climb to escape from a planetary body.

GREB. Galactic Radiation Experiment Background. A scientific satellite in the form of a 20-inch aluminum sphere, weighing 58 lbs., for in-space measurement of X-ray radiation and a study of ultraviolet radiation in the earth's night sky.

GREEN APPLE. A small, spherical green handgrip that is pulled outward by a pilot from a bailout oxygen bottle in order to activate the oxygen pressure-feed system preparatory to bailing out or ejecting from a disabled aircraft at extreme altitude, necessitating an extended free fall to lower and denser atmosphere. See **free fall.**

GREENHOUSE. Pilot and space-crew terminology for the glass and/or plexiglas canopies of their aircraft/spacecraft; the transparent sections of a cockpit, cabin, or other visual observation area of an aircraft or spacecraft.

GREEN ROOM. The "nerve center" or main control room that serves as the command center of Cape Canaveral and the Atlantic Missile Range, located in the Central Control Building. See **Central Control Building.**

Composite satellite payload. Three satellites— Transit IV-A, Injun, and GREB—in positions they occupy atop booster. In orbit, the three satellites are separated by springs

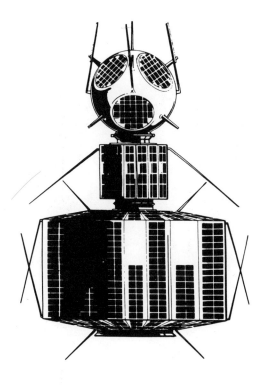

GROUND CLUTTER. The reflection of ground objects on a radarscope when the radar is tracking a missile close to the ground. In tests at Cape Canaveral, good radar tracking coverage is considered generally impracticable or impossible below 2,000 feet because of ground clutter—dozens of meaningless pips appearing on the scope.

GROUND HANDLING EQUIPMENT. Equipment, stationary or mobile, that remains on the ground and is used to move, lift, transport, service, or otherwise meet any special requirements of a booster, space vehicle, or any other equipment related to a launch activity. See **GSE.**

GROUND TRACE. For purposes of communications and especially for tracking, the theoretical line traced upon the earth's surface by any atmospheric or space object in flight as it moves over the surface, the line being drawn vertically from the object in flight.

GSE. Ground Support Equipment. All equipment and power sources of ground-based equipment necessary to check out, prepare for flight, and support the operation of a vehicle or an entire system.

GT. Gemini-Titan. Code identification for any launching in Project Gemini—as GT-3, GT-4, etc.—in which a Gemini spacecraft is boosted in flight by the Titan II rocket booster vehicle.

GUIDANCE. The effect upon a booster, missile, aircraft, spacecraft, or any other vehicle of any device that moves that vehicle in the direction desired; guidance may occur as a response to commands from a preset or self-reacting device contained either within the vehicle, or outside, in which case guidance is exercised by remote control. In *manned guidance,* the vehicle occupant exercises command of the devices that assure guidance.

GUIDANCE SYSTEM. The system contained within or outside any vehicle to produce desired results in guidance. See **Atlas-D guidance system; guidance.**

GUIDANCE, TERRESTRIAL REFERENCE. A technique of rocket control wherein the predetermined path set into the control system of a booster vehicle or a missile can be followed by a device in the vehicle which reacts to some property of the earth, such as magnetic or gravitational effects.

GYRATING. An unsatisfactory attitude situation in which a vehicle continues on its flight, but turns end-over-end about its center of gravity, while simultaneously moving through yaw and roll movements.

GYROSCOPE. A device which utilizes the angular momentum of a spinning rotor to sense angular motion of its base about one or two axes at right angles to the spin axis. Also called *gyro*.

H

HACK. See **Time Hack.**

HACK WATCH. A particular kind of wrist watch so constructed that the works stop operating when the winding knob is disengaged, allowing for an accurate time-hack setting. The hack watch can be synchronized to within a second. See **time hack.**

"HAIRY." A mission or part of a mission where danger is extreme or where constant attention without any interruption is vital to overcome an emergency or where the outcome of an issue is in doubt. Pilots and astronauts often use the phrase **"cliff hanger"** to denote the same situation.

HALF STAGE. A particular booster-propulsion unit in a one-and-a-half stage booster rocket. See **Atlas-D propulsion system.**

HANGAR S. NASA hangar located in Cape's industrial area. An immense, instrument-packed building where capsules and related equipment are checked out. Room S-205, one of a row of rooms used by astronauts, is also called the Ready Room. Here the astronauts live preparatory to a mission.

HANGAR TEST. At a launching base hangar, an inspection and test of a booster or other flight/orbital vehicle that consists of inspecting vehicle for possible damage incurred during transport to base, hooking up all mechanical, electrical, and hydraulic connections followed by a test of their operation, and testing of all subsystems with applicable checkout equipment. See **checkout.**

HARD DOCKING. In the process of orbital rendezvous and docking, the mechanical coupling of two spacecraft for a secure mating of the two vehicles. This may be accomplished in a side-to-side coupling or nose-to-nose coupling in order to achieve an airtight seal of airlocks for the purposes of crew or material transfer. See **docking; soft docking.**

HARD DOCKING. In top drawing, a cylindrical striped space laboratory, attached to a Gemini space capsule, orbits the earth as an astronaut exits Gemini and prepares to enter the laboratory. Below, in another proposed configuration, the spaceman passes through the larger modified Gemini fore section directly into the laboratory. Gemini and the space laboratory would rendezvous and dock during an earth orbit

HARDWARE. The physical object, as distinguished from its capability or function. The actual engines, case, pumps, guidance system, or other components of a vehicle. Often used in regard to the stage of development, as in the passage of a device or component from the design or planning stage into the hardware stage as the finished object.

HARVARD-TYPE TEST with Astronaut Donald Slayton as the subject

HARVARD–TYPE TEST. An exercise test for physical fitness and the efficiency of the heart. The subject steps up onto a platform 20 inches high and down again repeatedly until exhausted, usually within less than 5 minutes. The pulse rate is recorded before the test and at intervals afterward, and a physical fitness index is calculated.

HASH. A type of clutter appearing in the form of unsynchronized signals on a radar screen.

HEADING DRIFT. A determination of yaw movement in an orbiting spacecraft. As conducted by Astronaut John Glenn during the MA-6 mission:

"To determine yaw in the spacecraft, advantage must be taken of the speed of the spacecraft over the ground which produces an apparent drift of the ground below

the spacecraft. When the spacecraft is properly oriented, facing along the plane of the orbit, the ground appears to move parallel to the spacecraft longitudinal axis. During the flight I developed a procedure which seemed to help me use this terrain drift as a yaw reference. I would pitch the small end of the spacecraft down to about −60° from the normal attitude where a fairly good vertical view was available. In this attitude, clouds and land moving out from under me had more apparent motion than when the spacecraft was in its normal orbit attitude and I looked off toward the horizon. At night with the full moon illuminating the clouds below, I could still determine yaw through the window but not as rapidly as in the daytime. At night I could also use the drift of the stars to determine heading but this took longer and was less accurate."

HEAT. *Temperature* is the intensity of heat in a body. *Conduction* is transfer of heat by molecular impact. *Convection* is transfer of heat by currents in a fluid produced by unequal heating and expansion. Convection occurs only in liquids and gases.

HEAT CHAMBER. A sealed chamber in which equipment or men are exposed for specifically desired time periods to various

HEAT CHAMBER

high temperature levels in order to test the capacity of the equipment and the test subjects to function under extended high heat conditions.

HEAT EXCHANGER. A device for transferring heat from one substance to another, as by regenerative cooling. A vital element of a life support system in a sealed cabin, in which the heat is transferred from one fluid to another without intermixing the fluids.

HEAT SHIELD. In Project Mercury, an ablation device used at the blunt or forward end of the Mercury spacecraft to protect capsule and occupant against the tremendous heat of air friction during re-entry into atmosphere from orbit. During great heating from friction the surface of shield is transformed into vapor by a process of ablation. Ablative material is laminated glass resin, which reaches temperatures up to 3,000°F. during peak of heat pulse in re-entry.

HEAT SINK. A device for protection against heat, to absorb or transfer heat away from a critical part or assembly of parts, as in a heat shield or nose cone where intense friction-induced heat is conducted to a special metal for absorption. The suborbital Mercury manned flights used heat sink shields rather than an ablating system (see **ablation shields**). The General Electric nose cone for the Atlas ICBM is a heat sink shield; it is manufactured of extremely smooth copper, plated with a thin film of nickel, and especially fabricated to provide for laminar flow and for heat diffusion. The **stagnation temperatures** (q.v.) at the front of the cone are diffused before the melting point is reached.

HEAT TEST. A physiological stress test in which the subject spends two hours in a heat chamber with the temperature sustained at 130°F., to measure reaction of heart and body functions while under this stress.

HEAVISIDE–KENNELLY LAYER. The ionospheric region that reflects certain radio waves back to earth; the E layer of the ionosphere.

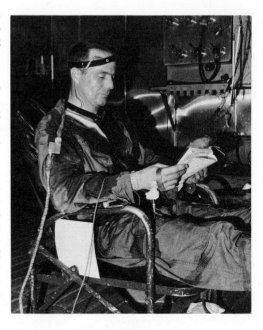

HEAT TEST with Astronaut Scott Carpenter

HEAVY COSMIC RAY PRIMARY. A cosmic ray considered to consist of a particle, the nucleus of an element heavier than the nucleus of helium, but less heavy than the nucleus of iron. See **cosmic radiation.**

HEF. High Energy Fuel.

HERMES. A small asteroid with a diameter of 1 mile, whose orbit brought the asteroid to within 400,000 miles of the earth (1937), the closest approach known of any spatial body to our planet.

HETEROSPHERE. That part of the upper atmosphere wherein the relative proportions of oxygen, nitrogen, and other gases are unfixed, and wherein radiation particles and micrometeoroids are mixed with air particles. See **atmosphere; homosphere.**

HIGH ALTITUDE. Conventionally, an altitude above 10,000 meters (33,000 feet).

HISTOXIC HYPOXIA. See **hypoxia.**

"HIT THE DIRT!" A loud, sometimes frantic, always urgent vocal command which, when heard during a booster launch, always results in the instant transformation of observers and launch participants into creatures with a frenzied desire to burrow as deeply into the earth as is possible—their actions hastened by the sight of an exploding rocket or an errant vehicle overhead.

HOICK. To abruptly jerk or yank any flightborne vehicle about in sharp maneuvers.

HOLD. Period of interruption to countdown lasting from seconds to days. A hold may result from technical difficulties with booster or capsule, also from problems with radio systems, communications, tracking, recovery forces, or weather, sometimes entirely unrelated to the launch vehicle. Some holds are deliberate and planned into the countdown to best meet an exact firing time.

HOLDDOWN CLAMPS. Powerful steel shackles that clamp a missile or booster to the launch stand during ignition and early motor operation. After thrust builds up to desired level, clamps fly back to allow booster to lift from launch stand. During ignition and thrust buildup, a malfunction causes automatic engine cutoff.

HOLDDOWN TEST. A propulsion system test in which thrust or other reaction is generated, but the propulsion vehicle is restrained by clamps, shackles, or other devices to prevent any movement.

HOLD–FIRE CAPABILITY. During an Atlas countdown, the Range Safety Officer, Pad Safety Supervisor, and Supervisor of Range Operations each have for safety purposes a Hold-Fire Capability. Any of these persons can prevent the Atlas launch from a point of T minus 300 seconds until that moment in the countdown when the Atlas is actually committed to the liftoff.

HOMOSPHERE. That part of the atmosphere which for the most part consists of atoms and molecules found near the earth's surface, and which retains throughout its entire extent the same relative proportions of oxygen, nitrogen, and other gases. See **atmosphere; heterosphere.**

HORSECOLLAR. Astronaut Alan B. Shepard, Jr., is lifted by helicopter sling horsecollar from capsule

HORSECOLLAR. A curving ring shaped in the form of a horsecollar designed to be placed about the body beneath the arms for the purpose of lifting an individual from the surface into a hovering helicopter, the lifting motion accomplished by a winch-operated cable in the helicopter. The horsecollar is the apparatus placed over the body of an astronaut, for example, for helicopter recovery from his spacecraft or raft after splashdown.

HOT PAPA

HOT PAPA. An asbestos-clothed member of an emergency squad whose duty is the rescue of personnel in event of fire, explosion, or other disaster in the launch-pad area.

HOT ROCK. A hot, flashy type of pilot or astronaut; one who leans toward public attention. See **space cadet.**

HOT RUN. Static testing of booster rocket motors or engines. See **static test.**

HOUR CIRCLE. See **spatial references.**

HOWLER. An audio device for warning a pilot or operator of an aerospace craft that abnormal signals are appearing on the radar screen.

HUMAN CALORIMETER. A laboratory facility at the Naval Medical Research Institute, New London, Connecticut, which is considered the world's leading laboratory device for basic studies of human heat-ex-

change problems. The man-in-space programs of the various military services and NASA have developed their thermal and refrigeration equipment, and established full parameters of thermal stress and endurance, through this facility.

HUMAN DISORIENTATION DEVICE. A training device at the U.S. Navy School of Aviation Medicine at Pensacola, Florida, that permits simulation (except for zero g) of tumbling, gyrating, and other out-of-control maneuvers through the axes of pitch, yaw, and roll, individually, in combination, or all three simultaneously. The Human Disorientation Device is about the size of a large concrete mixer, with the appearance of a drum that can be sealed, with a human occupant inside, and spun around either its vertical or horizontal axis or both, with any form or combinations of rotations desired, and with rates of rotation running from a tenth of a degree of arc per second to 300° of arc per second.

HUMAN ENGINEERING. The art or science of designing, building, developing, and flight-testing in the atmosphere and/or space any vehicle capable of flight in such regimes which is tailored especially in equipment and internal devices to meet the anthropometric, physiological, or psychological requirements of the man or crew who will use them.

HUNT. In an aircraft or spacecraft: to make weaving motions about its medium flight path, as in longitudinal or phugoid oscillation, or to vary in forward speed, as if seeking a changed angle of attack. Generally, to yaw repeatedly; a swinging or oscillating motion not induced by the pilot.

HUNTING. The erratic or intermittent fluctuation of an instrument needle. Sometimes reflects unsatisfactory operation of a device, but also used deliberately in a homing needle that is hunting for a transmitting source.

HYDRAZINE. A rocket fuel. May be used as a mono-propellant, or more commonly as a fuel that combines with an oxidizer, such as liquid oxygen, fluorine, or nitrogen tetroxide.

HYDROGEN. An element that is flammable and lighter than any other chemical element; in its uncombined state, colorless, tasteless, and odorless. As a liquid, it is used as a high-energy rocket fuel in combination with liquid oxygen. See **liquid hydrogen.**

HYDROGEN PEROXIDE. Highly corrosive chemical used in Mercury capsule to generate high-pressure steam, vented through reaction jets for purposes of attitude control.

HYDROSPHERE. That part of the earth—or of any other planet or spatial body—that consists of its oceans, seas, lakes, and rivers.

HYDROSTATIC EFFECT. The pressures exerted by a column of liquid under normal gravitational conditions on the surface of the earth or in a gravitational field during an acceleration.

HYPERBARISM. A disturbed condition in the body arising when ambient gas pressure or atmospheric pressure is higher than the pressure within the body tissues, fluids, and cavities, such as may occur in a sudden descent from a high altitude (low ambient pressure) to a low altitude (high ambient pressure). See **decompression sickness; dysbarism.**

HYPERENVIRONMENT. An environment, natural or induced, encountered at altitudes in excess of approximately 15 miles.

HYPERGOL. Rocket propellant that ignites spontaneously upon contact with an oxidizer. See **hypergolic; hypergolic fuel.**

HYPERGOLIC. Self-igniting; said of a fuel, propellant, or propulsion system. Of ignition: occurring spontaneously upon contact with an oxidizer. See **hypergolic fuel.**

HYPERGOLIC FUEL. A liquid rocket fuel that can be stored within the tanks of the rocket booster, as can the oxidizer. For example, the Titan II and Titan III booster vehicle uses a storable hypergolic mixture of 50% hydrazine and 50% unsymmetrical dimethylhydrazine. The oxidizer is nitrogen tetroxide. No ignition system is required, as with Atlas, since the fuels ignite spontaneously upon contact. The advantages of the storable fuel are many, including elimination of the complicated process of loading liquid oxygen and, above all, the ability to keep the booster on an "immediate firing capability" status in order to launch the rocket on an exacting time schedule.

HYPEROXEMIA. A condition in which the oxygen content of the blood exceeds that normally existing at sea level; excessive acidity of the blood. See **blood, saturation of.**

HYPEROXIDATION. Any pathological or non-pathological elevation of oxidation within a cell or cells above the usual metabolic rate.

HYPERSONIC. (1) Pertaining to speeds of Mach 5 or better. See **mach number; sonic.** (2) Pertaining to hypersonic flow. See **hypersonic flow.**

HYPERSONIC FLOW. In aerodynamics, flow of a fluid over a body at speeds much greater than the speed of sound and in which the shock waves start at a finite distance from the surface of the body.

HYPERTHERMIA. Excessive temperature of the body. Human tolerance of such temperatures depends upon individual resistance capacity, and other factors—much higher temperatures can be tolerated, for example, if the humidity is low. Important factors affecting hyperthermia tolerance include body activity, wind velocity, thermal radiation sources, acclimatization, etc. Hyperthermia symptoms (depending upon the many factors) include loss of efficiency, lassitude, headaches, physical weakness, inability to concentrate, nausea, increase in cardiac work, visual disturbances, increased body temperature, increased oxygen intake, heat stroke, and finally convulsions.

HYPERVENTILATION. An excessive loss of carbon dioxide from the blood, resulting in rapid breathing rates accompanied by dizziness, tingling of the extremities, and if continued sufficiently in duration, tetanic spasms of the limbs and then unconsciousness. See **breathing, control of.**

HYPOACOUSTIC ZONE. A zone from approximately 60 to 75 miles above the earth in which air particles are so reduced in number and density that sound is transmitted with appreciably less volume than at lower levels.

HYPOBARISM. A condition in which the gas pressure within the body tissues, fluids, or cavities is greater than the surrounding gas or atmospheric pressure.

HYPOCAPNIA. A deficiency of carbon dioxide in the blood. See **altitude alkalosis; hyperventilation.**

HYPOHISTODIABATISM. A condition characterized by an inadequate gas diffusion between the bloodstream and a cell, caused by a qualitative or quantitative alteration in the blood-cell barrier. See **alveolar air; respiration.**

HYPOPNEA. A condition of hypoventilation resulting from abnormal shallowness and rapidity of breathing.

HYPOPNEUMONISM. A lack of proper diffusion of gas between the blood and lungs, caused by a qualitative or quantitative alteration of the blood-gas barrier. See **alveolar air; blood, saturation level; respiration.**

HYPOTHERMIA. Subnormal temperature of the body.

HYPOTROPHY. A condition of progressive degeneration and loss of function of certain cells and tissues, brought on by an insufficiency of oxygen. See **breathing, process of; blood, saturation level; hypoxia; respiration.**

HYPOVENTILATION. Diminished ventilation. See **respiration.**

HYPOXEMIA. Oxygen deficiency in the blood, cells, or tissues. See **blood, saturation level; hypoxia.**

HYPOXIA. An oxygen deficiency in the blood, cells, or body tissues, or in all of these, in such degree as to cause psychological and physiological disturbances, varying in degree from mild headache to unconsciousness and death. Hypoxia may result from several varying and interrelated causes, such as a scarcity of oxygen in the air being breathed, or from an inability of the body tissues to absorb oxygen under conditions of low barometric pressure, even when 100% oxygen is being supplied to the airman. In the latter instance, water vapors from body fluids increase in the alveolar sacs of the lungs, crowding out the oxygen. This condition becomes total at a pressure altitude of about 50,000 feet. **Hypoxic hypoxia** is a condition in which the cells suffer some degree of oxygen deficiency as a result of decreased oxygen tension (partial pressure is referred to as tension) in the inspired air. **Anemic hypoxia** is a deficiency in the oxygen-carrying capacity of the blood. **Stagnant hypoxia** results from decreased circulation of the blood. **Histoxic hypoxia** is the inability of the body tissues to utilize the available oxygen in the blood. See **anoxia; alveolar air; alveoli.**

HYPOXIC HYPOXIA. See **hypoxia.**

HYPOXIDOSIS. A condition in which the oxidation within the cells is too low for the cells to accomplish their functions. See **hypoxia.**

HYPOXYPATHY. A disorder of the body characterized by pathological changes of tissues, brought on by hypoxia. See **hypoxia.**

HYPOXYPHOREMIA. A condition in which the blood and circulatory system do not function properly in the transportation and distribution of oxygen. See **hypoxia.**

I

ICBM. Intercontinental Ballistic Missile. ICBMs include Atlas, Titan, and Minuteman. Atlas-D and Titan II are ICBMs modified for space booster missions.

ICE CRYSTAL SHOWERS. A rare meteorological phenomenon encountered along the lower base of the stratosphere, at an altitude of approximately 40,000 feet. First encountered and conclusively established by open-gondola U.S. Navy balloonists. At the stratosphere base, thin cirrus clouds on rare occasions produce showers of dazzling ice crystals. The direct scientists' observations report the showers as "dancing, sparkling motes of light. They are pure crystals of ice, reflecting brilliantly the sun in a rarefied atmosphere." The exact origin and composition of these clouds is still open to question.

ICE FROST. The coating of ice that accumulates on the external surface of a liquid oxygen or liquid hydrogen fuel tank when the tank is supercooled by the loading of the fuel inside. See **"shedding her skirt."**

IGNITER. A squib or pyrotechnic device that is used to ignite a rocket engine or rocket propulsion system.

IGNITION. (1) The initiation of combustion in the combustion chambers of the rocket booster. (2) The precise moment when such combustion begins.

ILLUMINATION. The measure of the amount of light falling on a unit area. Illumination one foot from one candlepower lamp = 1 foot-candle.

IMMERSION SUIT. A protective outer garment worn over normal flight clothing, including partial pressure and pressure suits, which is worn by personnel operating over water. The suit is waterproof and prevents water-soaking of flight clothing and provides some protection against cold water.

ICE FROST

IMP (1). Inflatable Micrometeoroid Paraglider. A lightweight, loose-skinned delta-wing of plastic and fabric stiffened by inflation of tubes along its leading edges—a combination parachute and glider in flexwing form. IMP is a device to measure the count of micrometeoroids in the upper atmosphere to heights of 700,000 feet, and to test the paraglider concept as an atmospheric research re-entry vehicle for the recovery of space payloads. See **flexwing.**

IMP (Inflatable Micrometeoroid Paraglider) re-enters atmosphere, is landed automatically by inflatable flexwing

IMP (2). Interplanetary Monitoring Probe. A solar-powered satellite intended to provide detailed information for the Apollo program by carrying out scientific investigations of the space environment in cislunar space, with IMP placed in an orbit of 150,000 miles apogee.

IMPACT. The exact point, or moment of time, of landing of a spacecraft. Also: the uncontrolled crash—impact—of any booster vehicle or other vehicle. See **impact area; impact predictor; impact velocity.**

IMPACT AREA. Area or zone where capsule, warhead, or missile will strike the surface. In the Mercury program, the area of the ocean where the Mercury capsule is expected to land after descent from orbit.

IMPACT BAG. An inflatable bag attached to a spacecraft or re-entry capsule to absorb part of the shock of landing. See **landing bag system.**

IMPACT MICROPHONE. A microphone device that picks up and transmits, or records, the vibration of an object impinging or impacting upon another; equipment used especially in space vehicles to record the frequency and intensity of meteoroid particle impacts. See **erosion gauge.**

IMPACT PREDICTOR SYSTEM. An electronic system that follows the powered flight of a rocket booster predicting, at regular fractions of a second, where the booster would impact if its thrust failed at that instant. The system consists of a transponder carried in the booster that receives signals from ground antennas, then sends signals to the impact predictor station; there they are analyzed for the computer which, in turn, plots the course on a board. As used in Project Mercury, for example, the Canaveral Impact Predictor System includes (1) the **Azusa** tracking system, (2) an IBM 704 high-speed digital computer, and (3) a plotting board in the main control room of Central Control. See **instantaneous impact predictor; Range Safety Officer.**

IMPACT VELOCITY. Velocity of any object as it impacts with the surface.

IMPULSE. The product of a force's average value and the duration in which it acts, equal to the change in momentum produced by the force.

INCLINATION. The angle between one line and another or one plane and another, as the angle between the plane of an earth satellite orbit and the plane of the earth's equator. Sputnik I, for example, had an orbital inclination of 65°.

INDUSTRIAL AREA. At Cape Canaveral: the collection of buildings, hangars, and other installations of government agencies and contractors where rocket boosters, missiles, and other parts and assemblies are checkout-processed and prepared for launch.

INERT GASES. All stable gases not participating in body metabolism and not reacting chemically at room temperature (nitrogen) or at any temperature (e.g., helium and argon).

INERTIAL FORCE. The force produced by the reaction of a body to an accelerating force, equal in magnitude and opposite in direction to the accelerating force. An inertial force endures only so long as the acceleration force continues.

INERTIAL GUIDANCE. Guidance by means of acceleration measured and integrated within the craft. See **Atlas-D guidance system.**

INERTIAL ORBIT. The type of orbit described by all celestial bodies, according to Kepler's laws of celestial motion. This applies to all satellites and spacecraft provided they are not under any type of propulsive force, their driving force being imparted by the momentum at the instant propulsive power ceases. See **Keplerian trajectory.**

INERTIAL SPACE. Any segment of space considered to have fixed co-ordinates in respect to a particular object moving within it.

INFLIGHT START. Also: *inflight ignition, inflight restart.* The ignition sequence of a booster propulsion system that occurs during flight, or that occurs after the engine is shut down and then re-ignited.

INFRAHUMAN. A live animal other than a man that is used instead of a man in life-science experiments, such as the chimpanzee Enos orbited about the earth in the Mercury capsule for Mercury-Atlas 5 in late 1961; or an animal used for rocket-sled experiments or ejection-seat tests.

INFRARED LIGHT. Light in which the rays lie just below the red end of the visible spectrum. Often shortened in common usage to *infrared*. Infrared light is emitted by a hot non-incandescent source, such as an operating aircraft engine. Infrared equipment is used for tracking and detection purposes in unmanned and manned spacecraft.

INFRASONIC FREQUENCY. A sound frequency below the audible range of the unaided human ear.

INITIAL MASS. The takeoff mass of any booster, rocket, or complete booster-spacecraft system.

INITIAL ORBITAL PERIOD. The orbiting period of an earth satellite or manned spacecraft during the first orbit or first several orbits, during which time radar and other tracking devices supply data to computers to determine exact orbital parameters, in order to extrapolate future orbital altitudes and periods. A satellite that "brushes" the upper atmosphere at perigee in its initial orbital period will have a rather rapidly changing orbit.

INJECTION. The process of putting an artificial satellite or spacecraft into orbit. Also the time of such action. Also known as **insertion.**

INJECTOR. A device that injects propellants under forced flow into the combustion chamber of a rocket engine.

INJUN. A 16-inch, 59-lb. satellite in the shape of a cube with a magnetometer extending on a boom. A satellite for the measurement of magnetic forces and radiation intensities.

INSERTION. See **injection.**

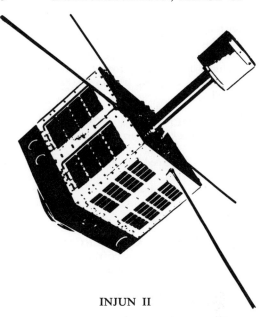

INJUN II

INSTANTANEOUS IMPACT PREDICTOR. Guideline system for a Range Safety Officer. At Cape Canaveral, an electronic recording, computing, and display system that computes for each instant of flight the point where a booster will impact if at that given instant thrust were terminated. This information is plotted automatically on a range chart at the rate of 10 times a second or 12,000 times for a 20-minute test. See also **impact predictor system.**

INSTANTANEOUS READOUT. Readout by a radio transmitter or visual display panel for ground or spacecraft-contained systems that is instantaneous with the computation of data to be transmitted.

INSTRUMENTATION. (1) Electronic, gyroscopic, photographic, and other instruments used for the purpose of detecting, measuring, recording, telemetering, processing, and/or analyzing different values or quantities in the mission performance of a booster system, unmanned satellite, manned spacecraft, or any other airborne vehicle. (2) The installation of such instruments.

INSTRUMENTATION, RANGE AND ACCURACY OF. One segment of range safety equipment at Cape Canaveral includes a radar so accurate that from a distance of

88 miles it can call "fair" or "foul" a baseball hit out of Yankee Stadium. Another example is a ballistic plate camera that takes pictures of ascending rockets with a margin of error of only one part in 50,000. See also **ROTI.**

INSTRUMENTED VEHICLE. Also: *instrumented package, instrumented capsule.* A test unit—sphere, box, or any packaged system—contained within or part of a vehicle, with instrumentation to detect and report on conditions encountered as the vehicle carries out its mission. See **instrumentation.**

INTEGRATING ACCELEROMETER. An electromechanical device that measures the forces of acceleration along its sensitive axis and produces an output signal proportional to velocity. See **accelerometer.**

INTERFACE. That part of a rocket booster structure that is a common boundary between one component and another, or is involved as a structural linkage between two stages, or adapter.

INTERFERENCE. (1) In radio communications, the disturbance of reception owing to stray or undesired signals. (2) In radar, confusing signals accidentally produced on the indicator by the effect of electrical apparatus, machinery, or by atmospheric phenomena.

INTERFERENCE CONTROL. The monitoring of radio frequencies assigned to a missile range or booster range for detection of interfering signals that could result in malfunctioning of booster-borne equipment, and the concerted effort to locate and terminate the source of interfering radiations.

INTERGALACTIC SPACE. The space between galaxies; e.g., the space between the Milky Way Galaxy and the Spiral Nebulae of Andromeda. It is characterized by an extremely small number of particles per cubic mile of space. See **Galaxy.**

INTERLOCK. A device in electrical circuitry that prevents any inadvertent electrical signal error to activate when there is no need for the system to be activated. See **glitch.**

INTERPLANETARY SPACE. That part of space that is dominated by the influence of the sun, and ranges from the sun to a distance outward in all directions of perhaps 5,000,000,000 miles. Interplanetary space is a function of distance from the earth, and not of planetary influence. In this space the sun is the dominant source of attraction except in the proximity of a planetary body or the natural satellite of a planetary body.

INTERSTAGE SECTION. The adapter and structural section of a booster that lies between two stages.

INTERSTELLAR FLIGHT. Flight between stars; more strictly, between orbits around the stars. The shortest interstellar flight from the solar system would be to Proxima Centauri; traveling at the velocity of light, an interstellar vehicle would require (without consideration of acceleration and deceleration) approximately 4½ years to accomplish this journey.

INTERSTELLAR SPACE. That part of space conceived, from the standpoint of the earth, to have its lower limit at the upper limit of interplanetary space, and extending to the lower limits of intergalactic space. From the standpoint of a detached observer, it is that part of space within the Galaxy. See **Galaxy; interplanetary space.**

"IN THE GREEN." Phrase signifying that everything is proceeding as planned—green lights signify successful completion of part of a mission or readiness to initiate a new control sequence. In terms of the latter, the statement also may be given as "My condition is GO."

INTRAPLEURAL SPACE. The potential "space" between the lungs and the chest wall. See **breathing, process of.**

INVERTER. Electrical equipment that converts direct current (DC) to alternating current (AC). Specifically, the inverter of a rocket booster vehicle converts the vehicle's battery power to a higher voltage at the frequency appropriate to power electrical components.

ION. An atom that has lost or acquired one or more electrons. (A positively charged ion is an atom or group of atoms with a deficiency of electrons; a negatively charged ion is an atom or group of atoms with an added electron.)

ION ENGINE. An advanced research type of reaction engine in which the thrust is obtained from a stream of ionized particles, accelerated by electrical power, which can, in turn, be derived from solar or nuclear energy. See **aeroduct; electrical engine; photon engine.**

IONIC PROPULSION. Propulsion of any manned or unmanned space vehicle in reaction to a stream of ionized atomic particles. See **aeroduct; electrical engine; photon engine.**

IONIZATION. Formation of electrically charged particles; can be produced by high-energy radiation, such as light or ultraviolet rays, or by collision of particles in thermal agitation (as during the heat pulse period of re-entry by a spacecraft).

IONIZE. To make an atom or molecule give off an electron, as by X-ray bombardment, and thus be converted into a positive ion, the freed electron then attaching itself to another molecule to form a negative ion. See **ionized layer; ionosphere.**

IONIZED LAYER (1). In Project Mercury, re-entry of the capsule produces a boundary layer of air surrounding the heated capsule surface where temperatures reach 2,200°F. This boundary layer is ionized. It acts as an electrical shield surrounding the capsule, and for several minutes completely blanks out all radio communications.

IONIZED LAYER (2). Any of the regions, or layers, of increased ionization within the atmosphere, and identified as the D, E, and F layers. Responsible for absorption and reflection of radio waves for communications.

IONOSPHERE. Region of earth's atmosphere made up of several layers of ionized gases (see **ion**). Ionosphere extends from approximately 30 miles altitude to undefined maximum altitude believed to be about 300 miles. Ionosphere, however, does not have "fixed" upper or lower limits, but fluctuates greatly.

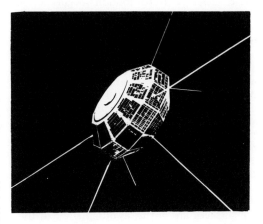

Alouette satellite (S-27) produced by Canada, launched by United States, to examine structure of the IONOSPHERE up to 600 miles height

IOT. Initial Orbit Time.

I.P. Impact Point: exact point of impact of a missile, warhead, or space vehicle.

IRON MAIDEN. An advanced human disorientation device in any one or combination of the three axes of motion employed extensively in the cosmonaut training program of the USSR. The individual cosmonaut is fitted with biosensors, and then dons his complete pressure suit. He climbs into a metal box, well padded inside and just large enough to contain the cosmonaut in a replica of his spaceship cabin seat. The cosmonaut is strapped down, seat adjustments are made to his individual body sizes, and all electrical connections made. The outer shell of the metal container is then closed and sealed. The cosmonaut is then in total darkness, unable to move, and pressed down upon by the soft contoured padding of the box's interior. The box (called a *coffin* by the cosmonauts) begins to revolve on a large spindle, turning over and over. Then a second movement begins. Two large metal arms gripping the spindle begin to move in a huge circle. The cosmonaut now is spinning over and over about his own body axis, and simultaneously being carried around and around in a vertically inclined circle. Then a third motion begins in a horizontally inclined circle. The end result is movement about all three axes to simulate uncontrolled tumbling and gyrating. Cosmonaut reactions were "feelings of nausea and body sickness that persisted for several hours afterward, then abated." Gradually the men became accustomed to the sensation of the three-axis motion, and became more adept at carrying out specific commands by manual motions within their seats. See **human disorientation device.**

IRREVERSIBLE CONTROL. A system of control for aerodynamic control surfaces so designed that aerodynamic forces acting on the surfaces are not transmitted back to the pilot's controls; especially important in re-entry of manned and controlled vehicles through the stratosphere and troposphere.

ISCHEMIA. A local and temporary deficiency in the supply of blood, chiefly due to the contraction of a blood vessel.

ISOTHERMAL REGION. The stratosphere considered as a region of uniform temperature. See **atmosphere; stratosphere.**

J

JERK. A vector that specifies the time rate of change of an acceleration; the third derivative of displacement with respect to time.

JET. Any gaseous or liquid stream ejected under pressure or flowing rapidly from a nozzle; more specifically, the stream of gases expelled from a liquid or solid rocket, a jet engine, an electrical engine, or any reactive device.

JETAVATOR. A control surface that is inserted in the jet exhaust stream or against the jet exhaust stream of any reaction engine, and used through its movements to change the direction of the jet flow in order to control the thrust vector. As in the Redstone booster, jetavators (also *jetvanes*) deflect the jet exhaust stream for guidance and trajectory control during powered flight.

JET STREAM. A stream of gas or fluid expelled by any reaction device. See **jet.**

JETSTREAM. A narrow band of high-velocity winds especially near the base of the stratosphere. These winds reach speeds exceeding 200 mph and flow in definite patterns and rivers. They present a serious danger at times to vertically ascending booster rockets or balloons because of the sudden "shear effect" of their force against the vehicle.

JITTER. The jittering or unstable motion of a signal on a radar screen.

JODRELL BANK. The site of a huge radio telescope located near Manchester, England. The telescope has a paraboloidal receiver 250 feet in diameter and 60 feet deep. It has demonstrated outstanding accuracy and performance and has been called upon for aid in space-vehicle tracking by both the United States and the Soviet Union.

JOVIAN PROBE. Any space vehicle, unmanned or manned, which would approach close enough to the planet Jupiter for its instruments or crew to discover and report back to earth new data on the planet.

"JUMPING THE COUNT." Also: "Advancing the count." During a countdown, the test conductor of the mission, for purposes of facilitating the launch, may "jump" or advance the time of scheduled launch; e.g., he may move the count from T minus 2 hours up to T minus 45 minutes, providing all systems in the countdown schedule are in their proper sequence to enable this to be done.

JURISDICTIONAL SPACE. That area of limited space above the sensible atmosphere that may become subject to use in accordance with international agreements or conventions. Since space by international agreement is considered to begin at 100 kilometers (62 miles), jurisdictional space would lie from above 100 kilometers, as a minimum height, to some undetermined distance beyond.

K

KEPLERIAN TRAJECTORY. Elliptical orbits described by celestial bodies and artificial satellites, according to Kepler's first law of celestial motion. See **Kepler's Laws.**

KEPLER'S LAWS. The three empirical laws describing the motions of planets in their orbits. These are:

(1) The orbits of the planets are ellipses, with the sun at a common focus.
(2) As a planet moves in its orbit, the line joining the planet and the sun sweeps over equal areas in equal intervals of time. Also called "law of equal areas."
(3) The squares of the periods of revolution of any two planets are proportional to the cubes of their mean distance from the sun.

KEROSENE. A liquid rocket fuel; in this form it is highly refined. Kerosene is a mixture of hydrocarbons produced by distillation from petroleum or oil shale. In Atlas, kerosene is the hydrocarbon fuel and liquid oxygen the oxidizer.

KICK ROCKET. A small rocket engine, solid or liquid-propellant, attached to the base of an airborne or spaceborne vehicle, especially an orbiting satellite vehicle, which when fired increases the velocity by 50 to 100 mph. The kick rocket in the Explorer VI satellite, for example, may be fired by ground-control command signal when the satellite approaches to 100 miles of the earth's surface; the kick rocket thrust is sufficient to change the orbit perigee sufficiently to increase the satellite's lifetime. See **apogee rocket.**

KILL. To reduce, retard, or cut back the velocity of any spaceborne vehicle as it approaches another vehicle for rendezvous and docking maneuvers; or to kill the downward-falling speed of a lunar probe as it nears the moon surface in order to accomplish a soft landing, i.e., a landing of a payload without appreciably damaging that payload, allowing its instruments to function perfectly after impact.

KINESTHETIC PERCEPTION. Ability of the body and mind to perceive, evaluate, and attain a sense of equilibrium and orientation through the stimulation by gravity and acceleration forces of the kinesthetic apparatus, i.e., kinesthetic receptors of the muscles, skin, viscera, etc., with their nervous connections. See **equilibrium and orientation; orientation in space.**

KINETIC ENERGY. Energy due to motion.

KIWI. Code name for a nuclear rocket engine test device, but which is strictly earthbound and will never achieve flight; kiwi (the bird that never flies) is used for studying, testing, and proving nuclear-reaction engine concepts and designs.

KNOT. Measurement of speed employed widely by civilian and military research, flight, and space-flight organizations. One knot equals one nautical mile per hour, i.e., 1.1516 statute miles per hour.

KRASNEY KOOT. Landing area in the USSR used for recoveries of spacecraft from manned and unmanned orbital flight. Krasney Koot lies in the Saratov region, and the exact landing area is at 50° 51 minutes north latitude, 47° 01.5 minutes east longitude.

L

LABORATORY TEST. In special reference to booster vehicles, spacecraft, etc.: a quantitative test of a subsystem or of checkout equipment carried out in a laboratory to evaluate or confirm functional and operational design.

LACE. Liquid Air Cycle Engine. Employs liquid oxygen and liquid hydrogen in a nuclear mono-propellant system, in which the aerospace craft "scoops up" its fuel in gaseous form in high-altitude flight, and converts the gases into liquid-fuel form for rocket flight beyond the atmosphere. See **aeroduct.**

LAIKA. First animal ever to be placed into orbit; launched in special compartment of Sputnik II on November 3, 1957. The female dog was approximately 45 lbs. in weight, about 20 inches high, survived all space environment conditions until November 11, when poison in the dog's automatic food system put her to sleep and caused subsequent death.

LAMINAR FLOW. A non-turbulent airflow over and about a vehicle surface or part of its surface, made up of a series of thin parallel layers. A laminar airflow wing is aerodynamically superior to conventional airfoils, resulting in less resistance, drag, and higher speeds.

LANDING BAG SYSTEM. In Project Mercury, a landing air cushion consisting of a 4-foot skirt of rubberized fiberglas is attached on one end to the spacecraft and on the other end to the heat shield. During main parachute descent, the heat shield drops down. Skirt extends and fills with air. Upon impact, the air trapped between spacecraft and the shield vents through a series of holes in upper and lower ends of the skirt. The explosive venting of the air absorbs much of the impact load. The landing bag then fills with water and serves as ballast to keep the capsule floating upright.

LANDING BAG SYSTEM. Landing bag fully extended (*left*); bag explosively vents air during impact (*right*) to cushion force of striking water

LANDING PARACHUTE. During descent of Mercury capsule the drogue chute jettisons at 10,000 feet. Thereupon, a Radioplane Ringsail parachute 63 feet in diameter deploys in two steps. Parachute is released in reefed condition. The lower edge (skirt) of the chute is restrained from opening beyond a diameter of 10 feet. Four seconds later, after capsule decelerates, reefing line is cut automatically and chute deploys to full diameter. Parachute descent is at 30 feet per second (approximately 20 mph).

LANYARD. A cord, thong, wire, or cable for firing pyrotechnic devices, activating pressure systems; a cord, wire, or cable for immediate or emergency activation of an emergency device, such as a bailout bottle. See **bailout bottle; dioxide capsule.**

LASER. Light Amplification by Stimulated Emission of Radiation. A device which emits an intense and exceptionally coherent beam of light when "pumped" (exposed to a light source under controlled conditions). Dispersion is extremely slight and laser energy remains concentrated or focused over great distances. Laser energy may be instantaneously multiplied as much as one thousand times by powerful magnetic fields that surround the laser and force it to store energy. When the field is removed, the laser releases energy in a concentrated pulse. Laser light beams have been used to weld hard metals, drill holes in diamonds and other hard substances, and are under accelerated development as "heat beam weapons" and as a means of long-distance space communications.

LATERAL ATTITUDE. The attitude of a flightborne vehicle with respect to its position about the longitudinal axis; the lateral attitude of the vehicle changes when it rolls. See **attitude; attitude control movements.**

LATERAL AXIS. The side-to-side axis of an aircraft or spacecraft, about which the vehicle revolves in pitching movements. See **attitude; attitude control movements.**

LAUNCH. The entire action or series of actions taken to bring a booster vehicle from static repose to dynamic flight. See **first motion; liftoff.**

LAUNCH BASE AREA. A geographical area encompassing numerous command posts, launch stations and associated guidance stations, a control facility, and a support base.

LAUNCH COMPLEX. Also: *complex*. The entire complex of launch site, stands, supporting equipment, control facilities, and other items necessary to launch a rocket vehicle. Often the launch crew is considered as an integral part of the launch complex.

LAUNCH COUNT. The final countdown phase prior to launch. The count for the Mercury-Atlas launchings initiates with a split countdown, which begins with a precount, then a 15-hour built-in hold, and initiation of the final count. Launch count commences at T–390 minutes, with the installing and connecting of the escape-rocket igniter. The service tower is then cleared and the spacecraft powered to verify that no inadvertent pyrotechnic ignition will occur. Personnel return to the service structure to prepare for static firing of the spacecraft reaction control system at T–250. At T–120 the astronaut boards the spacecraft. At T–90 the capsule hatch is installed and sealed. From T–90 to T–55 final mechanical work and spacecraft checks are made. The gantry is evacuated and rolled away from the launch vehicle. At T–35 loxing begins, as well as final spacecraft and launch-vehicle systems checks. At T–10 the spacecraft goes to internal power. At T–3 the launch vehicle goes to internal power. At T–35 seconds the spacecraft umbilical is ejected. At T–0 the launch-vehicle main propulsion system ignites. At T+4 seconds liftoff occurs. See **split countdown.**

LAUNCH ENABLE SYSTEM. A mechanical, electrical, or electromechanical restraint imposed upon the normal launch procedure to preclude inadvertent launch. See **holddown clamps.**

LAUNCHER. Any one or multiple of several devices employed to hold, support, and sometimes direct any rocket, booster, or other vehicle from the surface.

LAUNCH RING. Heavy metal ring, part of launch stand, which supports weight of booster rocket.

LAUNCH STAND. Raised platform for launch operations, containing electrical, power, other booster-support systems. Includes launch ring.

LAUNCH VEHICLE. Any rocket booster used as the vehicle to lift, fly, and carry into orbit an upper-stage payload.

LAUNCH WINDOW. An interval of time during which a rocket vehicle can be launched to accomplish a particular purpose, as "liftoff occurred 5 minutes after the beginning of the 82-minute launch window."

"LAUNDRY BAG." A parachute.

LAWS OF MOTION. The three laws of Galileo and of Sir Isaac Newton found to be basic to the science of astronautics. These are: (1) A material body, if left to itself, will maintain its condition of rest or motion unchanged. (2) A change in the motion indicates the presence of a force, and is proportional to the force. (3) Action and reaction are equal, and in opposite directions.

LAYER–CAKE DESIGN. A spacecraft design in which systems, components, power supplies, environmental support systems, and other similar devices are contained within the pressure area of the spacecraft by being piled one atop the other in successive layers. This is the Mercury design concept, but it is being replaced in Gemini and other spacecraft by the **shelf design,** in which equipment is kept in bays along shelves for ready access, servicing, and replacement.

LEAN BODY MASS TEST. An anthropomorphic test series by which a correlation of various tests determines an individual's lean body mass. The tests include a *total body radiation count* to determine the amount of potassium in the body; a *determination of specific gravity,* by weighing the subject while he is standing in normal air and while he is totally immersed in water; *blood volume test,* measured by inhaling a small amount of carbon monoxide and observing the amount absorbed by the blood after a specified time; and a *water volume test,* determined by swallowing a small amount of tritium and observing its rate of dilution.

LEIBNITZ MOUNTAINS. See **lunar mountains.**

LEM. Lunar Excursion Module. See **Apollo.**

LEVELED THRUST. A rocket power plant equipped with a programmer or engine control unit that maintains the output at a relatively constant thrust against variations in tank pressures, head-on pump inlets, turbo-pump output, and thrust-chamber performance.

LIBERTY BELL 7. Name assigned to Mercury capsule flown on suborbital mission of July 21, 1961, by Astronaut Virgil I. Grissom. After successful water landing, capsule sank below surface and was lost.

LIBRATION. The real or apparent oscillatory motion, particularly the apparent oscillation of the moon. Because of libration, more than half of the moon's surface is revealed to an observer on the earth, even though the same side of the moon is always toward the earth because the moon's periods of rotation and revolution are the same.

LIFE SCIENCES. The study of the physical, chemical, biological, and psychological stresses of flight through space. Also known as aerospace medical sciences, aerospace sciences, aerospace life sciences, bioastronautics, aviation and space medicine, aerospace medicine, space biology, human factors, etc.

LIFE–SUPPORT SYSTEM. The system providing the astronaut with an artificial life environment controlling oxygen, pressure, temperature, odor, carbon dioxide and humidity content. In Project Mercury, the life-support system is fully automatic, with manual override. The main system is self-contained beneath the astronaut's contour couch.

LIFETIME. Of a satellite or spacecraft: the time duration between achieving orbit and return to earth, or return to the atmosphere when, in an uncontrolled re-entry, disintegration occurs within the atmosphere.

LIFTOFF. The exact instant of first motion when a booster lifts from its launch ring. The term "liftoff" is applicable only to vertical ascent; "takeoff" is applicable to ascent at any angle. *A liftoff is action performed by a rocket; a launch is action performed upon a rocket or upon a satellite or spaceship carried by a rocket.*

LIGHT. Radiant energy that stimulates the organs of sight to perform their function, consisting (according to modern theory) of quanta transmitted at about 186,000 miles a second; by extension, a related radiant energy, such as infrared, that does not affect the retina, but otherwise acts like the same energy. See **light year.**

LIGHT YEAR. Unit of measurement used for great distances. The distance which light travels in a year. Since the speed of light is 186,271 miles per second, light travels approximately 5.88 trillion miles per year.

LIMB OF THE EARTH. The edge of the earth at the horizon.

LINEAR ACCELERATION. Acceleration in a straight line; acceleration along the longitudinal axis of an aircraft or spacecraft.

LINE OF POSITION. In navigation or astrogation, a line representing all possible locations of a craft at a given instant. In astrogation specifically, this concept is extended to "sphere of position," "plane of position," etc.

LIQUEFIED GASES. Gases which have been converted to liquids under certain pressure and temperature conditions. When pressure is released from such liquids, they will revert to gases either quickly or slowly, depending upon the type of gas, the initial temperature, and the rate of warming.

LIQUID HYDROGEN. Supercold liquid fuel. When used with liquid-oxygen as high-energy fuel, the liquid-hydrogen/lox combination produces, pound for pound, 40% more thrust than the combination of kerosene/lox. Liquid hydrogen (a cryogenic fuel) boils at minus 423° F.

LIQUID OXYGEN. Also known as lox. Oxidizer in a booster vehicle to permit combustion under vacuum conditions. It is used most often with kerosene fuel. Lox is so cold that it boils at 297° below zero, and is extremely explosive. Lox tanks during fueling are usually coated with layers of ice.

LIQUID PROPELLANT. Rocket propellant in liquid form, such as kerosene, alcohol, acid, gasoline, etc. RP-1 is a superfine kerosene used as a liquid rocket fuel.

LITHIUM CHLORIDE. A chemical compound under test and study for water absorption qualities within a spacecraft cabin.

LITHOSPHERE. The solid part of the earth or of any spatial body, as distinguished from the atmosphere and hydrosphere.

LITTLE JOE 1. Powerful solid-propellant rocket booster with 250,000 lbs. thrust, used to boost test models of Mercury capsule. The 44.5-foot rocket boosts a 4-ton capsule to about 4,000 mph.

LITTLE JOE 2. Solid-propellant rocket booster for unmanned test launches in suborbital flights of Apollo Command and Service modules. Aerojet Senior rockets in

clusters comprise the booster; in maximum-thrust configuration, six 110,000-lb. thrust motors will be clustered for a launch thrust of 660,000 lbs. Firings will be made at the Army's White Sands Proving Ground in New Mexico.

LITTLE JOE 1 solid-propellant booster for unmanned tests of Mercury spacecraft and systems

LIVE TESTING. The testing of a propulsion system, aerospace vehicle, or other device by actually launching it and subjecting it to loads and pressures of the flight and/or space environments.

"LOADING FOR BEAR." Flight mission term signifying that a rocket booster is being loaded with its propellants with the full intention of continuing the countdown to the actual launch; as opposed to fueling or servicing during a checkout or dry run.

LOCAL VERTICAL. At a particular point, the direction in which the force of gravity acts.

"LOCKED ON." Phrase to signify that a tracking radar, camera, or other device is in good, continuous tracking contact with an object in flight.

LOFTI. Low Frequency Trans-Ionospheric. A 20-inch spherical satellite of 58-lb. weight, intended to conduct measurements of solar-source radiations on the ionosphere.

LONGITUDINAL AXIS. The fore-and-aft line through the center of gravity of a craft; nose-to-tail in an aircraft.

LORAN. A long-range electronic navigation system which uses the time divergence of pulse-type transmission from two or more fixed stations. (The term is derived from the words "LOng-RANge electronic Navigation.")

LOW POINT. Synonymous with perigee.

LOX. See **liquid oxygen.**

LPR. Liquid Propellant Rocket.

LUMINOUS BANDS. Faint luminous bands that appear in the night afterglow, believed to be caused by the passage of micrometeorites through the upper atmosphere. Details regarding origin, height, duration of the phenomenon remain open to question.

LUMINOUS PARTICLES. Small particles discovered in same orbital configuration as manned spacecraft, witnessed by orbiting astronauts. Astronaut John Glenn described the "luminous particles" as of a "light yellowish green color. It was as if the spacecraft were moving through a field of fireflies. They were about the brightness of a first-magnitude star and appeared to vary in size from a pinhead up to possibly ⅜ inch. They were about 8 to 10 feet apart and evenly distributed through the space around the spacecraft." Glenn's sighting of the luminous particles was confirmed on the MA-7 mission of Astronaut Scott Carpenter, who stated that rather than fireflies or luminous particles, they looked more like "snowflakes . . . whitish in color." Carpenter reported their size from ¹⁄₁₆ to ½ inch in diameter. Carpenter and Schirra reported that when they "thumped" or "rapped" the spacecraft wall, a "whole cloud of particles" pushed away from the spacecraft. The conclusion was that the particles are actually ice or frost clinging to the capsule, and dislodged by motion or vibration.

LUNAR ATMOSPHERE. For all practical purposes the moon is barren and a dead world. But in the strictest sense of the word there does appear to be change on the lunar surface, and even the possibility of the most tenuous sort of atmosphere and a primitive plant life. Telescopic studies reveal unexplained radial bands appearing in a dozen or more craters which hint at a very primitive order of vegetation. The subject, however, is one only of speculation and demands on-the-spot investigation. In terms of atmosphere, several factors govern the ability of a planetary body to retain an atmosphere of mixed gases. On the earth there are natural and artificial factors that not only favor the retention, but sustain the natural production of such gases as oxygen. These factors do not apply to the moon. It is characteristic of gas molecules to exist in a constant state of agitation, with the lighter elements achieving velocities exceeding 6 miles per second. The gravitational mass of the earth, establishing an escape velocity of 7 miles per second, retains these gases as a permanent atmosphere. The lunar escape velocity is but 1.5 miles per second; thus the moon must have lost most of its gaseous constituents millions of years past. The lighter gases, with

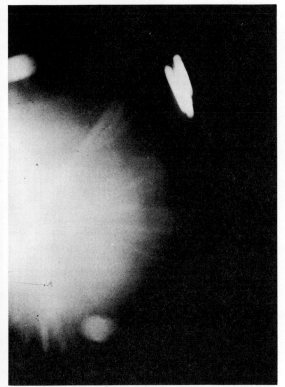
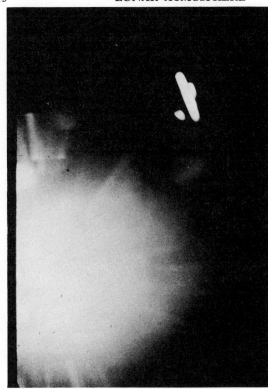

LUMINOUS PARTICLES. Two photographs taken during MA-7 flight of Scott Carpenter

a faster rate of speed, "leaked off" into space first and were followed by the heavier, slower gases. Theoretically, then, the moon should be totally airless. If there were any atmosphere on the moon, we might determine its existence not through direct observation but by watching the passage of the moon in its orbit directly before a star. If an atmosphere existed, the star would momentarily flicker before disappearing beyond the lunar curve. Instead, it snaps out of sight instantly, indicating an airless world. The "test" is, however, not a final one. A lunar atmosphere might be detected telescopically from a twilight witnessed near the cusps of the crescent moon; some astronomers lay claim to sighting such a twilight. The difficulty is that this evidence is tenuous; the supposed lunar twilight and the light reflected from the earth may be one and the same. Earthlight on the moon is many times greater than is moonlight on the earth, and this may mask any possible lunar twilight. Meteor passage through a lunar "atmosphere" and surface mists may offer greater clarification of the

mystery prior to future tests on the lunar surface personally directed by man. Astronomers theorize that the tremendous number of meteor strikes on the moon's surface should create a minimum of 100 visible annual impacts on the dark parts of the earth-turned hemisphere bright enough to be visible from the earth. No such visible spots have been reported. There are cases of reported brilliant flashes above the lunar surface, giving rise to serious consideration as to the possible existence of a lunar atmosphere. Only some two dozen of these reported incidents appear to be meteor flare-ups, yet not meteors flaring in the earth's upper atmosphere and projected against the lunar background. Their particular characteristics differ sufficiently from the familiar meteor tracks to constitute a definite distinction. If such evidence of meteor trails can be supported, then it would appear that an extremely tenuous atmosphere did exist on the moon. The term "atmosphere" is here employed loosely, since the density of such gases could be no more than one ten-thousandth that of the terrestrial atmosphere. In support of claims for a lunar atmospheric mist, there are definite and confirmed observations of lunar mists filling certain craters. On occasion, when seeing conditions were perfect and adjacent details were sharply defined, astronomers have sighted mists completely filling the boundaries and floors of walled plains and craters. The observations strongly indicate the existence of some form of atmosphere on the moon, a substantial part of which would originate from gases leaking to the surface from ruptures and passages beneath the surface.

LUNAR BASE. Any projected installation on or beneath the surface of the moon for use as a base in scientific and/or military operations.

LUNAR COLORS. Although lack of color characterizes the lunar surface, and it appears predominantly gray and black with dull browns and reds appearing in the rock formations, there are several areas which promise some variety of color. Inside the great crater of Grimaldi and in the Mare Crisium, there seem to be greenish hues. The brilliant east crater wall of Aristarchus has been telescopically observed to possess a distinct bluish glare. At least one crater with a distinct red color has been sighted.

LUNAR CRATERS. More than 30,000 craters have been photographed, charted, and classified; the U.S. Army and Air Force recently have prepared in exhaustive detail topographic feature charts of the moon. Full details as to crater bed heights, crater wall slopes, peaks, and ridges, etc., are provided. The craters exist in various sizes, from the tremendous Bailly Crater, which is 170 miles across (see **Bailly**), to innumerable pits less than 100 feet in diameter from rim wall to wall. Some of the larger crater rims extend more than 10,000 feet above the surface; in others, large mountain peaks stand in the crater centers. Near the moon's center is one of the larger, circular-walled formations, the crater Ptolemaeus, with a diameter of 90 miles. Its rim walls average 3,000 feet in height; one rim peak juts 8,000 feet above the crater surface. Within the great crater's center a craterlet, 4 miles across, rises from

the surface. Deeper than Ptolemaeus, the Arzachel crater has rim walls extending more than 2 miles above the depressed interior. In the center of this 56-mile formation is a large central mountain; this central peak is common to numerous craters, both large and small. Extending from many craters are the enigmatic lunar features—the bright rays which stretch more than 1,000 miles from their source. Most famous of these ray centers are the craters Copernicus and Tycho. The origin of the rays is unknown, although the majority opinion contends that the bright ray formations resulted when basalt was powdered white by massive, hypervelocity meteor impact, spraying the shattered remnants of the crash radially across the lunar surface. Although the lunar circular-walled formations are customarily described as "craters," many of these deep and immense features are actually shaped in the form of a shallow dish. An observer at the center of many of these areas could not see the distant "crater" walls rising above the surface and would believe he was actually standing on a flat plain.

LUNAR CRATERS

LUNAR EXCURSION MODULE (LEM).
See **Apollo.**

LUNAR GREAT WALL. One of the most
outstanding surface features of the moon,
the Great Wall extends for more than 60
miles across the surface. Distinct and clear
on photographs, the wall stretches from east
to west and has a sheer face of more than
300 feet. The Great Wall would appear to
be a sheer precipice; to an observer along its
base it would appear as a towering cliff extending beyond the horizon.

LUNAR HORIZON. Because of the great
difference in size between the moon and
the earth, an observer standing on the lunar
surface would see the visible surface extend
for only approximately 2 miles to the horizon before it curved out of sight. On the
earth the distance to the horizon when as-
suming an essentially level viewing angle
may extend to as much as 20 miles.

LUNAR IMPACT. A "hard" landing on the
surface of the moon, made without any
attempt to decelerate the vehicle before its
impact with the surface. For example, when
Lunik II impacted the lunar surface at
7,200 mph, most of the vehicle was demol-
ished.

LUNAR LANDING. In contrast to "lunar
impact," this term is used to denote (1) any
soft landing on the surface of the moon
so made that the instrumented payload will
survive the landing and remain functional,
and (2) a landing made under complete control without any damage whatsoever to the
vehicle, contents, or occupants.

LUNAR LOGISTIC VEHICLE. A lunar-
landing vehicle to be launched by the Saturn
C-5 booster, directed to the moon and
through a landing on the lunar surface by
combinations of on-board memory computer
and earth-commanded control systems. The
vehicle will be used to carry matériel to the
lunar surface in logistics support of the
Apollo Lunar Orbital Rendezvous program,
which calls for descent from lunar orbit to
the lunar surface of a two-man Bug (LEM—
Lunar Excursion Module).

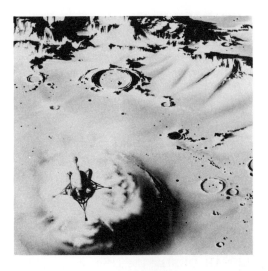

LUNAR LANDING

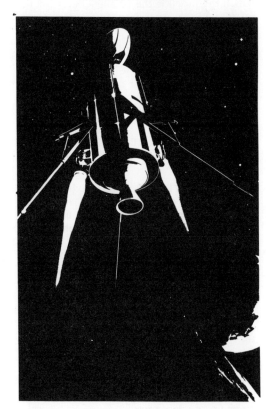

LUNAR LOGISTIC VEHICLE. Engineering
design for automatic-control vehicle descending
to lunar surface

LUNAR MOUNTAINS. The highest mountains on the moon are the Leibnitz Mountains in the southern hemisphere, with peaks reaching to more than 30,000 feet. Proportionally these mountains are much higher than any range on earth. The summit of Dörfel Mountain also rises more than 30,-000 feet from the lunar plains; to proportionally approximate this peak, Mt. Everest would have to extend to a height of 116,564 feet above the earth. Another of the more impressive ranges on the moon is the Apennine Mountain Range, which forms the southwest boundary of the Mare Imbrium. The Apennine peaks reach to more than 20,000 feet and extend over a distance of more than 200 miles.

LUNAR ORBIT. The orbit of any spacecraft placed in orbit about the moon, in which the moon is the primary body for the satellite Lunar orbit is distinct from **translunar orbit,** in which an earth-launched vehicle swings around the moon and continues back to earth without executing a complete orbital path around the moon. Lunik III carried out a translunar orbit, which is actually a high earth orbit, by reaching to an apogee of 292,000 miles from the earth.

LUNAR ORBITAL RENDEZVOUS (LOR). See **Apollo.**

LUNAR PAYLOAD. The payload of a lunar probe, consisting chiefly of instruments for detecting and reporting conditions encountered. The payload of a vehicle that lands on the moon does not include the rockets required for the return launch unless data are to be obtained from such a return launch.

LUNAR PROBE. Any vehicle sent into space to pass close by the moon, to orbit the moon, impact upon or land on the lunar surface, with the specific mission of detecting and reporting conditions encountered.

LUNAR SATELLITE. Any space vehicle placed in an orbit about the moon. Also referred to as a **selenoid.**

LUNAR SPACE. The space near the moon, in which the gravitational attraction of the moon is predominant. See **gravipause.**

LUNAR TRANSPONDER. A device designed especially to determine with precision, at any time, the distance of the moon from the earth. The lunar transponder is a solid-state electronic device which is subminiaturized to an operating unit weight of less than 10 lbs., with the built-in strength to withstand a force of 3,000g on hard impact with the lunar surface. Once on the surface of the moon, the transponder will respond to earth-broadcast signals by retransmitting them continuously at a different frequency. The lunar transponder will be used to determine lunar gravity, distance, and other characteristics.

LUNIK. Soviet lunar probe. In 1959 the Russians fired Lunik I (passed the moon surface at 3,200 miles); Lunik II (impacted the lunar surface at 7,200 mph); Lunik III (went into high earth—translunar—orbit to apogee of 292,000 miles, and photographed far side of the moon).

M

MA. Mercury-Atlas. Said of any launching in Project Mercury that involves use of the Atlas-D as the booster vehicle.

MACH NUMBER. The speed of an aircraft or rocket vehicle at any given altitude or under any atmospheric conditions as expressed in multiples and fractions of the speed of sound. Mach 1 is the speed of sound. If the Mach number is less than 1, the flow is subsonic and local disturbances can propagate ahead of the flow. If the Mach number is greater than 1, the flow is supersonic and disturbances cannot propagate ahead of the flow, with the result that shock waves form. See **hypersonic; sonic.**

MACROMETEORITE. Any meteor (meteoroid) particle larger than a pea.

MAE WEST. An inflatable life jacket (vest) for emergency flotation in water.

MAGNETIC FIELD. The magnetic lines or zones of force that surround the earth and move about the planet in space from north to south. They vary greatly in intensity, area, and effect.

MAGNETIC STORM. A world-wide disturbance of the earth's magnetic field. Magnetic storms are frequently characterized by a sudden onset, in which the magnetic field undergoes marked changes in the course of an hour or less, followed by a very gradual return to normality, which may take several days. Magnetic storms are caused by solar disturbances, though the exact nature of the link between the solar and terrestrial disturbances is not understood. Sometimes a magnetic storm can be linked to a particular solar disturbance. In these cases, the time between solar flare and onset of the magnetic storm is about one or two days, suggesting that the disturbance is carried to the earth by a cloud of particles thrown out by the sun.

MAGNETOHYDRODYNAMICS (MHD). A field of scientific and engineering study concerned with the action of a superheated gas (such as superheated deuterium) when subjected to electromagnetic forces. Tests indicate that a plasma (ionized hot gas) may be held in "magnetic bottles" and employed to yield a high order of sustained thrust with a reaction engine. The thrust could be employed in a spacecraft, especially for interplanetary missions. Extensive engine flight tests are now in advanced stages. Also called magnetoplasmadynamics, magnetogasdynamics, hydromagnetics.

MAGNETOMETER. An instrument, often carried in earth satellites and lunar probes, for measuring a magnetic field or the intensity and direction of trapped charged particles. Obtaining maximum possible data on the magnetic field of the moon—if the moon indeed has a magnetic field—is considered a prime requisite for major manned lunar exploration programs.

MAGNITUDE. Relative brightness of a celestial body. The smaller the magnitude number, the brighter the body. (Decrease of light by a factor of 100 increases the stellar magnitude by 5.00. Hence the brightest objects have negative magnitudes: e.g., Sun: -26.8; mean full moon: -12.5; Venus at brightest: -4.3; Jupiter at opposition: -2.3; Sirius: -1.6; Vega: $+0.2$; Polaris: $+2.1$.) The faintest stars visible to the naked eye on a clear dark night are of about the sixth magnitude. *First magnitude is the brightness of a candle flame seen at night at a distance of 1,300 feet; a first-magnitude star is 100 times brighter than the sixth.*

MAIN BANG. The specific transmitted pulse of a radar antenna or a radar system.

MAIN STAGE. (1) In a multi-stage rocket, the stage that develops the greatest amount of thrust, with or without booster engines; usually the first stage. (2) In a single-stage rocket vehicle powered by one or more engines, the period when full thrust (at or above 90%) is attained. (3) A sustainer engine, considered as a stage after booster engines have fallen away, as in "the main stage of the Atlas." (4) The oral signal in a blockhouse to signify that the main engines of a rocket have ignited, in a sequence of ignition; i.e., in the Atlas booster, first the two verniers ignite, and then the two booster engines and one sustainer engine ignite. The ignition of these three engines is announced by the call, "Main Stage." See **Atlas-D propulsion system.**

MALFUNCTION DETECTION SYSTEM. Designed specifically for the Titan II two-stage booster of Project Gemini. The MDS will monitor vehicle flight performance and the operation of subsystems, much like the ASIS abort system of the Atlas-D for Project Mercury. In event of an emergency or malfunction, the MDS will alert the astronauts to ignite the ejection-seat rocket-boost charges of the Gemini capsule. For details of the Atlas-D abort system, see **ASIS.**

MALHYPOXIA. A moderate oxygen lack. See **hypoxia.**

MAN–HIGH. Former Air Force manned-balloon program for sustained high-altitude flight. One pilot, Major David G. Simons, was sealed into a pressurized capsule and carried to approximately 20 miles altitude. Major Simons remained at heights varying from 70,000 to 102,800 feet for more than

MAN-HIGH II balloon-gondola system flown by Major D. Simons, USAF, to height of 102,-800 feet

24 hours in a "space environment survival experiment."

MAN–IN–SPACE PROGRAM. Any one of several coexisting or second-generation programs each intended specifically to develop a usable space vehicle provided with the necessary environmental control to allow it to carry one or more persons into space and to return them safely to earth. Each includes personnel training, test flights, and all supporting and subsidiary activity. Man-in-space programs include Mercury, X-15, ASP, Gemini, Dyna-Soar, Apollo, Manned Saint, etc.

MANNED FLIGHT TRACKING NETWORK. An extensive world-wide tracking and communications network based upon the present Mercury net as the nucleus for major expansion and updating of equipment and procedures. Steady growth through the development period of Gemini and Apollo will provide full facilities and experience by the time Apollo lunar missions occur.

MANNED LUNAR LANDING PROGRAM. The official NASA program to place American astronauts safely on the moon, conduct exploration and experiments, effect safe departure from the lunar surface back to the earth, and effect safe re-entry, landing, and recovery on the earth. A series of subprograms is under way to accomplish this over-all goal, the most essential of which are the Saturn C-5 booster vehicle and Apollo Modular Spacecraft, which involves a series of possible combinations and systems for earth orbit and rendezvous; lunar orbit, landing, and lunar rendezvous; circumlunar flight; and other lunar missions. See **Apollo.**

MANNED SURVEILLANCE ORBIT. A two-hour-period orbit which will permit every 24 hours direct surveillance of the entire inhabited surface of the earth from a manned space station. The station is placed into a circular polar orbit at 1,075 miles above the planet. There are twelve complete orbits during the 24-hour rotation period of the earth, during which time the combined movement of the station's orbit and the earth's rotation brings the entire planetary surface into visual range during every period of 24 hours.

MANOMETER. An instrument for measuring pressure of gases and vapors both above and below atmospheric pressure.

MAN–RATED. Said of a rocket booster vehicle or booster stage that has met the most rigid requirements of reliability and performance in order for the vehicle to be rated as acceptable in launching manned spacecraft.

MANUAL STANDBY. A manually operated emergency control or device that is kept poised for immediate use in the event that an automatic system malfunctions at its prescribed instant of operation. See **override.**

MARIA (singular *Mare*). The "seas" or "oceans" of the moon; large and level areas of the lunar surface.

MARINER. An advanced-system interplantary probe to study the planets Venus and Mars. Failure of the Centaur booster development program to be completed in scheduled time forced reduction of the probe from over 800 lbs. payload to approximately 450 lbs. payload, with the Atlas-Agena B booster. Intended to approach within 10,000 miles of the planets in early shots; later, in the 7-shot series, intended to dispatch small instrumented capsules by parachute to the surface of Mars and Venus.
Mariner II on December 14, 1962 passed within 21,454 miles of Venus in a "flyby surveillance mission" of that planet. The first Mars missions are scheduled for 1964.

MARS I. A heavy (1,965 lbs. payload) probe launched in late 1962 by the USSR for a flyby surveillance of the planet Mars.

MARSARIUM. A sealed chamber in which ambient air pressure, humidity, air circulation, temperatures, and other environmental factors are maintained at what are believed to be surface conditions of the planet Mars, permitting the examination of terrestrial microorganisms under simulated Martian conditions.

MARTIAN PROBE. A space vehicle, unmanned or manned, with the capability of journeying to and exploring and reporting on conditions about the planet Mars and/or its natural satellites, Deimos or Phobos.

MASER. An amplifier utilizing the principle of Microwave Amplification by Stimulated Emission of Radiation. Emission of energy stored in a molecular or atomic system by a microwave power supply is stimulated by the input signal.

MASS. A measure of the quantity of matter in a body, determined by comparing the resultant changes in velocities when the body impinges upon a standard body. Mass differs from weight in that the weight of a body on the earth's surface is the attraction of the earth's force of gravity upon it. A body at rest on the surface of the earth has equivalent values of mass and weight. At other points the mass remains the same, but the *weight* varies according to gravitational forces and other influences. A body in orbit is weightless, but it retains its mass.

MASS RATIO. The ratio of a booster vehicle system's mass (or that of any rocket) at the time of launch, as compared to its mass after fuel consumption is completed. For example, suppose the launch mass of a rocket is 12 tons—the rocket casing and assembly weigh 3 tons, the payload one ton, and the fuel 8 tons. At burnout of the fuel the remaining mass (vehicle and payload) is 4 tons. The mass ratio of this rocket is 3 to 1.

MARINER interplanetary vehicle for studies of Mars and Venus. Mariner I failed in launch; Mariner II launched on successful flight to Venus, passed within 21,454 miles in late 1962.

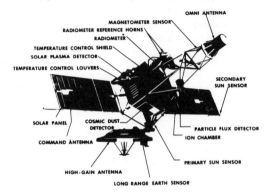

MASTER CENTRAL TIMING SYSTEM (MCTS). Located in Central Control at Cape Canaveral. In order to co-ordinate all activities of launch and tracking of a space shot or missile test so that all data is synchronized to a thousandth of one second, MCTS flashes through entire Atlantic Missile Range and to Goddard Space Flight Center a time signal accurate to one ten-millionth of a second. MCTS can transmit time signals to various instruments in a variety of desired pulsations.

MASTER CONSOLE. A console from which over-all monitoring and control may be exercised, as in the "Go—no Go" launch of a rocket vehicle.

MASTIF. Multiple Axes Space Test Inertia Facility. A training simulator device to provide Mercury (and Gemini) astronauts familiarization with physiological and psychological effects of tumbling, and procedures for recovering from tumbling when it occurs. The training programs include a slow buildup of axes and rates to a maximum of 30 rpm rotating about all three axes, with corrective control exercised through the Mercury spacecraft rate indicator and hand controller. See **iron maiden.**

MATE. To bring together and assemble with secure fitting two major components of any system, such as a booster vehicle and its payload.

MATTER. Whatever occupies space and has mass. Does not include energy.

MAX–q. Point in ascending flight of booster vehicle when vehicle reaches maximum dynamic pressure—i.e., the point in the exit trajectory at which the launch vehicle and spacecraft are subjected to the severest aerodynamic load. Atlas D of Project Mercury encounters Max-q between 35,000 and 40,000 feet altitude.

MP. Manual Proportional attitude control system of Mercury spacecraft, not requiring any electrical power sources of the vehicle. See **Mercury capsule control system.**

MCC. Mercury Control Center; Mercury orbital operations center located on Cape Canaveral, and the nerve center for worldwide activities to support orbital flights.

MDF. Mild Detonating Fuse. An explosive cord (fuse) installed in a channel between an inner and outer seal around the periphery of a spacecraft hatch. The explosive ignition and resulting gas pressure of the MDF fractures attaching bolts and forcibly hurls away the hatch. See **explosive hatch.**

MDS. Malfunction Detection System, q.v.

MEAN DISTANCE. *Average* distance. The mean distance of a satellite orbiting above the earth's surface is the average of the apogee and perigee; in this case, the mean orbital height from the surface.

MEAN FREE PATH. Of any particle, the average distance that the particle travels between successive collisions with the other particles of an ensemble—used especially in describing the upper atmosphere and the mean free path of air molecules. See **exosphere.**

MECHANICAL CREWMAN. A device that simulates essential respiratory and metabolic activities of a human being, to test a spacecraft life-support system during actual orbital flight. The "crewman simulator" consumes oxygen, expels carbon dioxide, and fills the spacecraft cabin with heat and moisture much as would a man in the course of normal breathing. Voice tapes are used to test transmission of radio voice communications.

MECHANORECEPTOR. A nerve ending of the body that reacts to mechanical stimuli, such as touch, acceleration, tension, etc.

MEDICAL MONITORING. The system of receiving medical data from a man in flight and/or orbit. Instruments (medical sensors) attached to the body provide information on vital life processes. In the form of electronic coded signals, this information is radioed to ground stations where it is reduced, translated, and displayed for medical monitoring personnel.

MASTIF

MEGA–. A prefix meaning multiplied by one million, as in "megacycles," "megatons," etc.

MEMORY. The component of a computer, control system, guidance system, instrumented satellite, or the like designed to provide ready access to data or instructions previously recorded so as to bring them to bear upon an immediate problem, such as the guidance of a physical object or the analysis and reduction of data.

MERCATOR PROJECTION. A portrayal of the curved surface of a planet (i.e., earth) as a flat surface, with marked distortions increasing toward the poles. Mercator projections are used for tracking and plotting activities, as in following the movement and position of an orbiting spacecraft.

MERCURY–ATLAS. See **Atlas; Atlas-D** headings; **Atlas vehicles.**

MERCURY CAPSULE. A bell-shaped spacecraft 9 feet high and 74 inches across at the base. Made mostly of beryllium, titanium, and nickel-base alloys. Three main sections are: heat shield, cabin, and the cylinder at capsule top which includes the recovery compartment and antenna canister. Liftoff weight is approximately 4,200 lbs., orbital weight 3,000 lbs., and recovery weight 2,400 lbs. Contains systems for life support, communications, stabilization and control, reaction control, electrical power, re-entry, earth survival, etc.

MERCURY CAPSULE CABIN SYSTEM. The cabin system of the Mercury capsule controls cabin pressure and temperature. A cabin relief valve controls the upper limit of cabin pressure. This valve permits cabin pressure to decrease with ambient pressure during ascent from the earth, until a pressure of 5.5 psi is reached. At that point the valve seals the cabin, so that the interior pressure is maintained at 5.5 psi, although the ambient pressure decreases further as ascent continues. In addition, a manual decompression feature is incorporated in the valve to permit the astronaut to dump the cabin pressure if a fire or buildup of toxic gases occurs. A cabin-pressure regulator meters oxygen into the cabin to maintain the lower limit of pressurization at 5.1 psi. A manual recompression feature is incorporated in the regulator for cabin repressurization after the cabin has been decompressed. Cabin temperature is maintained by a fan and heat exchanger. Postlanding ventilation is provided through a snorkel system. At

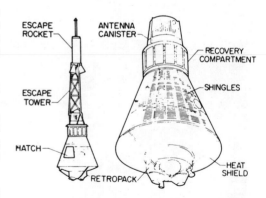

Major elements in MERCURY spacecraft system

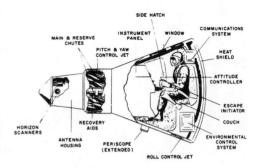

MERCURY CAPSULE

20,000 feet following re-entry, the snorkels open and ambient air is drawn by the compressor of the astronaut's suit through the inlet valve. The gas ventilates the suit and is dumped overboard through the outlet valve.

MERCURY CAPSULE CONTROL SYSTEM. Provides full attitude control of the spacecraft in orbit and re-entry through a reaction-jet system of thrusters which derive their reaction energy through the decomposition into steam of hydrogen peroxide, venting the steam through 16 fixed and movable nozzles. The Mercury system is exceptionally redundant in design so that it can perform its function in event of multiple malfunctions. There are two completely independent fuel (hydrogen peroxide) systems in the spacecraft, as well as two completely independent plumbing and thruster systems.

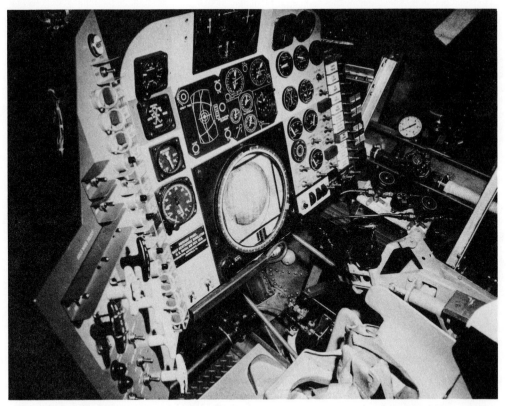

MERCURY CAPSULE instrument panel

There are two specific means of controlling the output of the thrusters. On System A the astronaut has the choice of using either the Automatic Stabilization and Control System (ASCS) or the Fly-By-Wire (FBW) system. The ASCS is automatic to the extent that it can provide the necessary attitude control throughout a complete mission without any action on the part of the astronaut. The FBW system is operated by movement of the astronaut control stick to operate the solenoid control valves electrically; it permits the astronaut while using the manual control method to use the automatic-system thrusters and to draw upon automatic-system fuel supply. On System B the astronaut has the choice of using either the Manual Proportional system (MP) or the Rate Stabilization Control System (RSCS), both of which are operated through the astronaut's control stick. Thus of the four control systems, ASCS is the only one which is completely independent

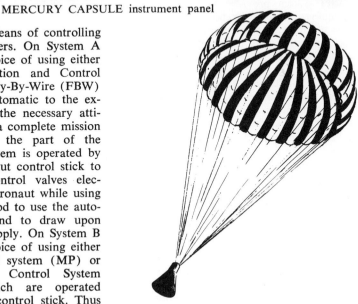

MERCURY CAPSULE descending beneath 63-foot ringsail parachute

of manual control; FBW, MP, and RSCS all require manual control of the hand control stick. In the MP system, linkages transmit the control-stick movement to proportional control valves which regulate the flow of fuel to the thrusters. The RSCS uses a combination of stick positions and the computing components of the automatic system to provide rate control. Control mode is selected easily by the astronaut's positioning of proper switches and valves mounted on the instrument panel. Certain of these control modes can be operated simultaneously, such as ASCS and MP, or FBW and MP, in order to provide "double authority," so that even with certain malfunctions in each mode, complete control can be maintained. It should be noted that for the worst possible emergency situation, the Manual Proportional control mode (MP) does not require any electrical power. Thrust ratings of the thrusters expressed in pounds thrust are 1, 4, 1 to 6, and 24. Fine attitude control as desired under orbital conditions with minimum fuel consumption is accomplished through six 1-lb. thrusters.

MERCURY CAPSULE PRESSURE–SUIT CONTROL SYSTEM. The pressure-suit control system provides breathing oxygen, maintains suit pressurization, removes metabolic products, and maintains, through positive ventilation, gas temperatures. The suit is attached to its control system by two connections: gas inlet at the waist and gas exhaust at the helmet. Oxygen is forced into the suit distribution ducts, carried to the body extremities, and permitted to flow freely back over the body to facilitate body cooling. The oxygen then passes into the helmet where the metabolic oxygen, carbon dioxide, and water vapors are exchanged. The gas mixture leaves the suit and passes through a debris trap where particles of matter are removed. Next, the gas is scrubbed of odors and carbon dioxide in a chemical canister of activated charcoal and lithium hydroxide. The gas then is cooled by a water-evaporative type of heat exchanger which utilizes the vacuum of space to cause the coolant water to boil at approximately 35°F. The heat-exchanger exit gas temperature is regulated through manual control of the coolant-water flow valve. The

resulting steam is exhausted overboard. The steam exit temperature on the overboard duct is monitored by a thermal switch which actuates a warning light when the duct temperature drops below 47°F. The oxygen supply of the capsule is from two tanks, each containing sufficient oxygen for more than 28 hours. The tanks are equipped with pressure transducers to provide data on the supply pressure. The tanks are so connected that depletion of the primary supply automatically provides for supply from the secondary bottle.

MERCURY CONTROL CENTER. Control Room in Mercury Control Building on Cape Canaveral through which flows all information from global tracking and communications network during orbital flight of Mercury capsule. In main control room, 15 NASA Flight Controllers make all vital decisions required for flight, and issue or delegate all commands.

MERCURY NETWORK. Also: *Mercury Tracking Network*. Tracking network around the world for Mercury orbital missions. Consists of 18 stations, including Cape Canaveral. Data processing and flight-path predictions are made at Goddard Space Flight Center in Maryland, with information flashed immediately to Cape Canaveral. Mercury Network communications path comprises 140,000 actual circuit miles: 100,000 miles of teletype, 35,000 miles of telephone, 5,000 miles of high-speed data circuits.

MERCURY PROCEDURES TRAINER. A complete mockup of the Mercury spacecraft with operating instruments and controls connected to an analogue computer to simulate maximum possible number of flight conditions, and to provide extensive facilities for checkout, familiarization, and training in procedures and control operations of astronauts in the Mercury spacecraft. The flexibility of the trainer permits the occupant to practice with any of the control-display modes, utilizing a variety of retrofire misalignment torques and re-entry oscillations. Entire orbital "missions" may be "flown," with capsule attitudes and rates

MERCURY CONTROL CENTER

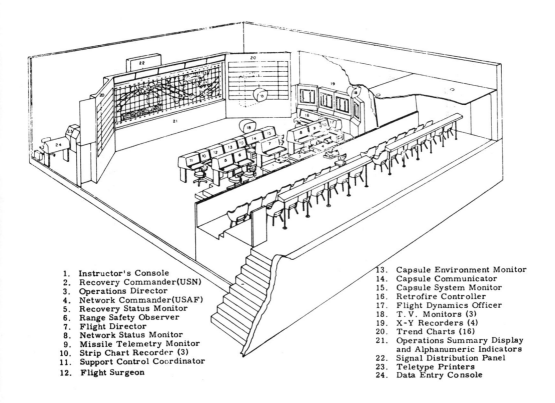

1. Instructor's Console
2. Recovery Commander(USN)
3. Operations Director
4. Network Commander(USAF)
5. Recovery Status Monitor
6. Range Safety Observer
7. Flight Director
8. Network Status Monitor
9. Missile Telemetry Monitor
10. Strip Chart Recorder (3)
11. Support Control Coordinator
12. Flight Surgeon

13. Capsule Environment Monitor
14. Capsule Communicator
15. Capsule System Monitor
16. Retrofire Controller
17. Flight Dynamics Officer
18. T.V. Monitors (3)
19. X-Y Recorders (4)
20. Trend Charts (16)
21. Operations Summary Display
    and Alphanumeric Indicators
22. Signal Distribution Panel
23. Teletype Printers
24. Data Entry Console

MERCURY PROCEDURES TRAINER

control for specific flight performance areas, and for emergency training to meet inflight systems failures.

MERCURY, PROJECT. First man-in-space program of the United States under the auspices of NASA. NASA Manned Spacecraft Center Headquarters are at Houston, Texas, formerly were at Langley Field, Virginia. Project Mercury began in October of 1958, with specific objective to determine man's capabilities in a space environment and under conditions to which he will be subjected upon going into and returning from space. Activated with seven astronauts. First suborbital flight on May 5, 1961; first orbital flight on February 20, 1962. Program has been entirely successful, will be replaced by Project **Gemini.**

MESOSPHERE. A stratum of atmosphere that lies between the stratosphere and the ionosphere; also known as **chemosphere.** The term "mesosphere" as such is not widely accepted or in general use. In its literal

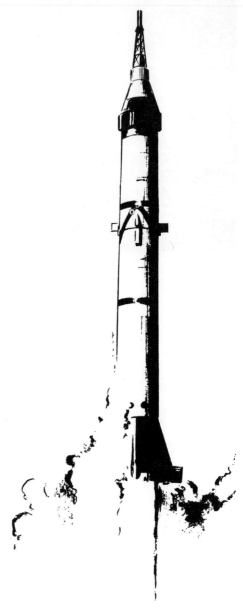

Launch of Redstone carrying MERCURY CAPSULE on first suborbital manned flight, May 5, 1961

MERCURY CAPSULE separating from Atlas booster

sense, a mesosphere is a sphere that lies between two others. See **atmosphere; chemosphere; stratosphere.**

METABOLIC CONVERSION. The variety of chemical steps and changes that occur in the body in the process of utilizing food and oxygen for the liberation of energy, the maintenance of life, and the breaking down and building up of body tissues.

METABOLIC REQUIREMENTS. See **daily metabolic turnover.**

METABOLISM. See **basic medical sciences; daily metabolic turnover.**

METEOR. A body originating in outer space (such as the asteroid belt between Mars and Jupiter) but entering the atmosphere of the earth with a velocity sufficient to become incandescent through friction, and to appear as a visible streak in the sky. A meteor when it is existent beyond the atmosphere, or is encountered beyond the atmosphere, is generally referred to as a

meteoroid, or more commonly in astronautics as a meteorite—also used to designate a metallic or stony body that penetrates the earth's atmosphere and in whole or in part strikes the surface of the earth. Most meteors that strike the earth's atmosphere are no more massive than a pinhead, but through friction become incandescent and acquire an envelope of their own vapor much larger than themselves, the air along their paths becoming ionized. The speed of meteors, relative to the earth, ranges between 10 and 40 mps as they enter the atmosphere. See **meteor bumper.**

METEOR BUMPER. An external thin shield or covering of a manned spacecraft distinctive from the spacecraft hull itself, acting as a buffer or bumper between the impact of meteorites and the spacecraft hull; the shield is comparable in thickness with the diameter of the meteor particle expected to be intercepted. The bumper is designed to dissipate thermally the energy of the meteor particles; high-impact velocity of the meteor leads to vaporization of the meteor and a part of the shield without penetration of any particles into the wall of the spacecraft. See **explosive decompression; meteor; meteoric particle.**

METEORIC EROSION. The erosion or pitting of the surface of a space vehicle from meteorite particles.

METEORIC PARTICLE. Any particle of matter from a meteor (meteorite, meteoroid). See **meteor.**

METEORITE. A meteor which has reached the surface of the earth without being completely vaporized.

METEOR SAFE WALL. Refers to the protective blanket of atmosphere through which meteors only rarely can penetrate, usually being burned up and vaporized by friction with air molecules. See **meteorite.**

MICRO–. A prefix meaning (1) divided by one million, as in "micro-ampere"—one millionth of an ampere; (2) very small, as in "micrometeorite."

MICROLOCK. (1) A "lock" by a tracking station upon a minitrack radio transmitter. (2) The system by which this "lock" is effected. See **"locked on"; minitrack.**

MICROMETEORITE. The smallest particle of a meteor or meteorite to be encountered in space operations. Also called "meteor dust." See **meteor; meteor bumper; meteoric erosion; meteoric particle.**

MICROSWITCH. A small switch in which a slight motion makes or breaks contact.

MICROWAVE REGION. Commonly that region of the radio spectrum between approximately 1,000 megacycles and 300,000 megacycles.

MIDAS. Missile Defense Alarm System. A military early-warning satellite that utilizes an infrared monitoring system to detect and warn of the launching of ballistic missiles. Launched by the Atlas-Agena B booster, the research and development models of Midas weigh 5,000 lbs. The operational system calls for 12 to 15 satellites simultaneously in orbit. Several Midas launchings have resulted in "near perfect" circular orbits.

MIDDLE EAR. The middle ear is separated from the outer ear by the eardrum. In addition to its structures for hearing the middle ear also contains air and is vented to the outer air through the Eustachian tube, which opens into the throat. It is by means of this tube, which opens when one swallows, that equal ear pressure is maintained on either side of the eardrum. The Eustachian tube operates as a one-way valve in that it opens readily when the gas in the middle ear expands, as during ascent. Thus there is usually no discomfort during a period of decreasing air pressure—not even during a sudden or even explosive decompression. During descent, however, when the pressure in the middle ear becomes less than ambient pressure the Eustachian tube tends to seal unless the individual swallows frequently. As a result, in inflammations due to head cold, sore throat, etc., the Eustachian tube becomes swollen, thus blocking the passage to the middle ear. When this happens, the air pressure in the middle ear cannot equalize the changing pressure in the outer ear and the drum is pushed inward during descent, or increasing ambient pressure. The stretching of the eardrum is painful and at times can be injurious. See **aero-otitis media; Valsalva maneuver.**

MILITARY TEST SPACE STATION. An "in-house" manned space station for testing components and manned operation procedures and techniques in the orbital-space environment. Having had study project status in 1962, in 1963 it is scheduled to reach the status of active hardware development and test-launch and test-orbit of components.

MINI–. A contraction of "miniature" used in combination, as in "minicomponent," "miniradio," "minitransistor."

MINIATURIZE. To construct a functioning miniature of a part or instrument. Said of telemetering instruments or parts used in an earth satellite or rocket vehicle, where room is at a premium, as is weight-carrying ability. Hence, "miniaturized," "miniaturization."

MINITRACK. (1) A satellite tracking system consisting of a field of separate antennas and associated receiving equipment interconnected so as to form interferometers which track a transmitting beacon in the payload itself. (2) A sub-miniature radio transmitter capable of sending data over 4,000 miles on extremely low power.

MINUS *g*. See **negative** *g*.

MISSION. The objective; the task, which, together with the purpose, clearly indicates the action to be taken and the reason therefor.

MOBY DICK. Meteorological balloon project to carry instruments in containers to altitudes exceeding 75,000 feet for flights extending from several hours to many days, for sustained high-altitude research.

MOCKUP. A full-sized replica or dummy of something, such as a spacecraft, often made of some substitute material, such as wood or plastic, and sometimes incorporating functioning pieces of equipment, such as engines.

MODIFIED CALORIC TEST. A test of an individual's balance mechanism, specifically the semicircular canals of the inner ear, carried out by running cool water into one ear and measuring the effect on eye motions (nystragmus). See **equilibrium and orientation.**

MODULAR VEHICLE. Any spacecraft that may be assembled into several different configurations and systems to perform a desired variety of space missions, such as earth orbit, lunar probe, etc. See **Apollo; module.**

MODULATION. Specifically, variation of some characteristic of a radio wave, called the "carrier wave," in accordance with instantaneous values of another wave, called the "modulating wave." Variation of amplitude is amplitude modulation; variation of frequency is frequency modulation; variation of phase is phase modulation. The formation of very short bursts of a carrier wave, separated by relatively long periods during which no carrier wave is transmitted, is pulse modulation.

MODULE. (1) A self-contained unit forming part of a space vehicle. Especially relevant to the Apollo spacecraft, which is designed on the modular concept. The module is usually designated by its primary function, as *command module, lunar landing module,* etc. (2) A one-package assembly of functionally associated electronic parts or units so arranged as to be mounted together in a space vehicle system and to function as a system or subsystem.

MOLECULAR ELECTRONICS. The science of producing a single block of matter that performs the same function as a complete circuit, by merging the function with a material, using solid-state functional blocks.

MOLECULE. An aggregate of two or more atoms of a substance that exists as a unit.

MOMENT OF FORCE. See **force.**

PROJECT MONA. Launch of third Thor-Able

MOMENTUM. The product of mass times velocity. See **motion.**

MONA, PROJECT. The first United States —and world—attempts to fire rockets with payloads directed to the vicinity of the moon. Project Mona began with the firing of a Thor-Able three-stage rocket on August 17, 1958; this booster exploded 77 seconds after flight. Various stages of failure and partial success were achieved with the firing attempts by three Thor-Able and two Juno-II boosters. Of the five shots, the fifth attempt sent a 13-lb. package past the moon at a distance of 37,000 miles, too far to activate any of its instruments. See **Pioneer.**

MONITOR. To establish and maintain track of an airborne or spaceborne vehicle and/or spacecraft, and to note, record, analyze, and sometimes to command the vehicle and/or its components; to study in complete detail all aspects of every moment of a mission.

MONOPROPELLANT. A liquid rocket propellant in which the fuel and oxidizer make up a single substance before injection into the combustion chamber. See **multipropellant.**

THE MOON

MOON. The natural celestial body that orbits as a satellite about the earth. Also applied to natural satellites of other planets. Our moon has a mean diameter of 2,160 miles, a mean distance from the earth of 238,857 miles, a mass approximately of 1/85 that of earth, a volume of about 1/49, and a surface gravity of 1/6. Mean orbital velocity is about 2,337 mph; apogee is 252,710 miles; perigee is 221,463 miles.

Scale comparison of size of MOON compared to continental United States. Lunar diameter is less than coast-to-coast distance across United States

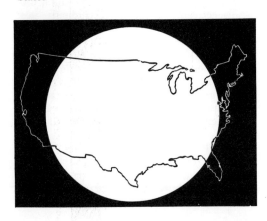

There may be some form of extremely tenuous atmosphere on the moon. See **cislunar; lunar atmosphere; lunar base; lunar impact; lunar landing, lunar orbit; lunar probe; lunar satellite; lunar space; translunar.**

MOON PHASES. The *new moon* is when the moon is most directly between the earth and the sun; at this time no illuminated surface of the moon can be seen from the earth. The *crescent moon* occurs when less than half of the moon's surface facing earth is visible. This is followed by the *quarter moon,* when we see a "hemispherical" moon —half in light, half in darkness. The *gibbous moon* occurs when the moon is more than a half but less than fully illuminated. The *full moon* appears when we see the entire lighted surface of the moon facing the earth; this occurs when the earth is between the sun and the moon.

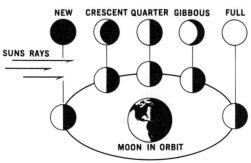

MOON PHASES

MOONPORT. The area northwest of Cape Canaveral on Merritt Island, Florida, which is the launch and support center for the Apollo spacecraft and lunar exploration projects.

MOON ROCKET. Any rocket vehicle used to carry a payload to the vicinity of the moon; or to circle the moon and return to earth; or to impact or to land upon the moon.

MOONSCOPE. Popular name for a telescope used to view an artificial satellite of the earth.

MOON SHOT. The launch of an unmanned, usually instrumented vehicle aimed at placing a lunar probe on course toward the moon, to pass by the vicinity of the moon, orbit the moon, swing around the moon and back to earth; impact on the lunar surface; or land on the moon.

MOONTRACKING. The process or action of observing and plotting the orbital progress of an earth satellite.

MOONWATCH. The surveillance by observing teams of an earth satellite passing within tracking range in its orbit.

MOTHER–OF–PEARL FORMATION. See **nacreous clouds.**

MOTION. Newton's Laws:

> **inertia.** A body continues in a state of rest or uniform motion in a straight line unless acted upon by an external force.
> **momentum.** The rate of change of momentum (mass times velocity) of a body is equal to and in the direction of the force causing the change.
> **reaction.** To every action there is an equal and opposite reaction.

MOTION SICKNESS. Motion sickness (like airsickness or seasickness) is primarily the result of the brain receiving conflicting messages from the eyes, organs of balance, and muscle receptors. Because the stomach is extremely sympathetic to nervous or mental fatigue, a feeling of dizziness and nausea often results, accompanied by vomiting. Motion sickness may be reduced or avoided if the individual keeps his eyes fixed on an unmoving reference point (in an airplane, the point should be outside the airplane, if possible). Reduction of noise and vibration also eases the effects of motion sickness, as does maximum possible ventilation to remove unpleasant odors. **Space sickness,** which may be caused by sustained disorientation of the vestibular apparatus, does not appear to be equivalent to motion sickness in terms of its source. The physical symptoms and the procedures for abating the effects, however, do appear to be equally applicable.

MOTION SIMULATOR. Any device, machine, or installation that simulates motion in roll, pitch, and yaw, or any of these axes simultaneously, for attitude-in-orbit astronaut training.

"MOTORMAN'S FRIEND." Pilot jargon for a relief tube. See **relief tube.**

MOV. Manned Orbital Vehicle. Any spacecraft capable of orbiting the earth and containing a person or crew with necessary environmental and other support facilities. See **man-in-space program; Mercury, Project.**

MPH. Miles per hour.

MPM. Miles per minute.

MPS. Miles per second.

MR. Mercury-Redstone. Any launching in Project Mercury that involved use of the Redstone as the booster vehicle. This rocket is no longer in use with Project Mercury.

MULTIPLEXER. A mechanical or electrical device for sharing of a circuit by two or more coincident signals.

MULTIPLEXING. The simultaneous transmission of two or more signals within a single channel. The three basic methods of multiplexing involve the separation of signals by time division, frequency division, and phase division.

MULTIPROPELLANT. Rocket propellant that consists of two or more liquid ingredients each separated from the others until introduced into the combustion chamber. See **monopropellant.**

MULTI–STAGE ROCKET. Any rocket or booster vehicle (*multi-stage booster*) having two or more thrust-producing units, each used for a different stage of the rocket's flight. See **half stage; Titan II.**

"MURPHY'S FIRST LAW OF PHYSICS." Phrase in common usage among ground and flight personnel of aircraft and space-vehicle flights. Murphy's First Law states: "What can go wrong *will* go wrong."

N

NACA. National Advisory Committee for Aeronautics, created in 1915 by the Congress, and in 1958 absorbed within the new National Aeronautics and Space Administration (NASA).

NACREOUS CLOUDS. Known as "mother-of-pearl formations," nacreous clouds are found at a height of 15 to 20 miles above the earth. Their composition is of ice crystals; their origin uncertain. Nacreous clouds and noctilucent clouds are the highest such formations above the earth. See **ice crystal showers; noctilucent clouds.**

NADIR. See **spatial references.**

NANO-. A prefix meaning divided by one billion, as in nanosecond—one billionth of a second.

NASA. National Aeronautics and Space Administration, established by the Congress through the National Aeronautics and Space Act of 1958. The "civilian" space agency of the United States.

NASC. National Aeronautics and Space Council. A council for NASA, made up of the President, the Secretary of State, the Secretary of Defense, the Chairman of the Atomic Energy Commission, the administrator of NASA, and four other members appointed by the President. See **NASA.**

NAUTICAL MILE. A measure of distance equal to 6,076.11549 feet, or one minute of arc on the earth's surface, or 1,852 meters (this is the International Nautical Mile). See **knot.**

NAVIGATIONAL PLANET. Navigation and astrogation term applied to Venus, Mars, Jupiter, or Saturn, the four planets commonly used in celestial navigation for obtaining lines of position.

NEAR SPACE. Phrase indicating that part of space that is relatively near the earth. "Near space" postulates an observer on the surface of the earth, and is employed as a term of distance rather than influence.

Spiral NEBULA in the constellation Colma Berenices

NEBULAE. Galactic nebulae are clouds of interstellar matter whose presence is revealed either because they are illuminated by a bright star or because they noticeably weaken the light from stars in a particular region of the sky; unborn stars.

NECK DAM. A rubber diaphragm that is fastened on the exterior of a pressure suit, usually immediately below the helmet attaching ring. The neck dam is an emergency protective device to prevent the astronaut from sinking in the event of water immersion, by providing a positive air-filled seal around the body of the suit. After the helmet is disconnected, the neck dam is rolled around the ring and up around the neck, similar to a turtle-neck sweater.

NEGATIVE g. The opposite of **positive g.** Occurs in a gravitational field, or during an acceleration, when the human body is so positioned that the force of inertia acts on it in a foot-to-head direction; i.e., the headward inertial force produced by a footward acceleration. Also known, especially in military aviation, as **minus g.** A fighter pilot, for example, encounters negative g in an outside loop or during a rapid pushover from level to diving flight, causing the blood to rush to the head instead of the feet and increasing the blood pressure in the brain. See **negative-g tolerance; positive g; transverse acceleration; transverse g.**

NEGATIVE–*g* TOLERANCE. In the negative-*g* maneuver, an airman's blood rushes to his head and increases blood pressure in the brain. The effects of negative *g* are referred to by pilots as "redout"; the pilots literally see red as contrasted to gray and black under positive *g*. This apparently is due to the lower eyelid acting as a red curtain over the eye when gravity pulls opposite to the usual direction. Under sustained, excessive negative *g* it is possible to produce hemorrhage within the eye. Other immediate effects are bloodshot eye surfaces, swollen eyelids, and double vision. The practical limit of tolerance is negative 3*g* for 10 to 15 seconds. At this point the pilot, in addition to the other symptoms, suffers a sharp headache. The heart slows down in its actions because of the high pressure in the neck arteries; the heart may even temporarily cease operating. If the negative-*g* force is sustained, hemorrhage becomes critical, unconsciousness results, and death is almost certain. (One fighter pilot became accidentally exposed to about negative 4*g* for 30 seconds during maneuvers. The pilot had extensive experience under *g* forces, but even so, this individual lost his hearing and vision temporarily, found his throat blocked, could not swallow, choked and gagged spasmodically, and said that his head felt as if it were expanding and swollen to bursting. A severe nosebleed sprayed his flight suit and the entire forward part of the cockpit with blood.) See **negative *g*; positive *g*; positive-*g* tolerance; transverse acceleration; transverse *g*.**

NERV. Nuclear Emulsion Recovery Vehicle. A system for measuring the Van Allen radiation belts surrounding the earth, in order to secure data for use in determining design factors involved in protecting man from deep-space radiation hazards. A rocket vehicle sends the NERV system to altitudes of approximately 2,000 miles. The NERV system consists primarily of a cylindrical disc containing radiation-sensitive material (nuclear emulsion). As the vehicle moves through its trajectory the disc is exposed to the radiation field and rotated past an aperture; it is then retracted for re-entry protection and subsequently subjected to laboratory analysis and data reduction to reveal the level and type of radiation with variations in altitude and latitude. See **Van Allen radiation belt.**

NERVA. Nuclear Engine for Rocket Vehicle Application. A nuclear reactor (in the NERVA engine) based on the reactor (tech-

NERVA nuclear engine; first test flight as part of Saturn upper-stage vehicle scheduled for 1967. Fuel will be liquid hydrogen

nology which has been under development since 1955 at the AEC Los Alamos Scientific Laboratory. Four reactors tested in the past at Nevada include KIWI-A in 1959; KIWI-A Prime and KIWI-A Three in 1960; and KIWI-B 1A in 1961. All four used gaseous hydrogen as the propellant material. Further tests in the KIWI-B series are expected to use liquid hydrogen. The NERVA development program covers continued engine design effort, research and development on engine components and subsystems, including work on the propellant feed system, reactor and engine control systems, nozzle, remote handling system, mechanical testing of reactor core components, bearings, and seals, and examination of systems to assure safe operation. NERVA engine development is part of the joint AEC-NASA **Rover** program to develop a nuclear rocket propulsion system. The NERVA engine will be the first of a series of nuclear rocket propulsion systems, and will be fired initially atop Saturn C-1 booster vehicles.

NEUROPHYSIOLOGY. See **basic medical sciences.**

NEUROSPORA. Bread-mold spores sent into the Van Allen radiation belts during known high-intensity radiation storms, to estimate potential damage to the human reproductive and genetic system. Rapidly reproductive lower life forms such as neurospora are subjected to high-energy protons (as in the Van Allen belts) and the radiation effects studied. An official NASA report states that a "greater incidence of deformities in succeeding generations of the exposed spores than expected from the radiations measured was observed." An intensive reproductive-and-genetic-system study program is under way.

NEUTRAL POINT. A point on a line joining the centers of gravity of two spatial bodies, such as the earth and the moon, at which the gravitational field of each cancels out the other. The neutral point between the earth and the moon is approximately 23,760 miles from the moon's surface. See **gravipause.**

NEUTRON. A subatomic particle with no electric charge, having a mass slightly more than the mass of the proton.

NIGHTSIDE. See **darkside.**

NIMBUS. An advanced or "second generation" meteorological satellite and satellite system. The 650-lb. payload will be orbited over the poles. Nimbus will carry television cameras and infrared scanners, and will be stabilized to keep camera lenses always pointing at the earth. Booster is the Thor-Agena B. Four research shots are planned, followed by four operational Weather Bureau satellites.

Cutaway view of NIMBUS advanced meteorological satellite. Nimbus will replace Tiros

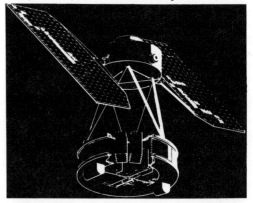

NITPICKING HOLD. Any hold built deliberately into a launch countdown in which the hold is not caused by malfunction but is created to provide a specific period of time in which launch-pad personnel may attend to any minor problems, "clean up" their assignments, and remove non-essential materials from the launch area.

NITROGEN DILUTION. The act of using nitrogen to lower the oxygen tension of inspired air and thus produce an alveolar oxygen tension equal to that at a given altitude. See **alveolar air.**

NOCTILUCENT CLOUDS. Clouds of dust (volcanic origin or interplanetary matter is suggested) that drift above the earth at a height of 50 miles. They appear only after sunset or before sunrise when contrasted against a dark sky. Their speed has been tracked at 400 mph.

NODE. Either of two points where the orbit of an orbiting body intersects the plane of the orbit of its primary. See **ecliptic.**

NOISE. Any undesired sound. By extension, noise is any unwanted disturbance within a useful frequency band, such as undesired electric waves in a transmission channel or device. When caused by natural electrical discharges in the atmosphere noise may be called *static*.

NON–CRITICAL MALFUNCTION. The failure of any equipment, system, or systems that creates an aggravating but non-critical situation, possibly interfering with the intended performance of a mission but not requiring immediate correction of the failure or the immediate cessation of the mission.

NOSE CONE. Tapered or rounded assembly at the forward end of a rocket vehicle, missile, booster, etc., from which it is separated at the end of powered flight. In a space vehicle the nose cone either shields the satellite payload against atmospheric friction and is discarded, or the nose cone itself contains the satellite and instrumentation equipment. In a missile, the nose cone contains the warhead and terminal guidance equipment. In the latter sense, the nose cone is also designed as a re-entry vehicle.

"NO SWEAT." "Absolutely no difficulty or trouble at all; everything is fine."

NOVA (1). Booster project study for direct Apollo spaceship flight to the moon. First stage has 8 F.1 engines with total 12,000,000 lbs. thrust, burning kerosene/lox. Stage II has 4 M.1 liquid-hydrogen/lox engines with total 4,800,000 lbs. thrust. Stage III has liquid-hydrogen/lox J.2 engine of 200,000 lbs. thrust. Launch weight is 5,000 tons. Nova can boast 410,000-lb. payload into low earth orbit or send 150,000-lb. payload directly to lunar surface.

NOVA N–1. First stage of Nova launch vehicle design (of 8 engines first-stage configuration). Eight F.1 engines burning kerosene/lox and each developing 1,500,000 lbs. thrust produce first-stage thrust of 12,000,000 lbs. Program is "in stretchout," with

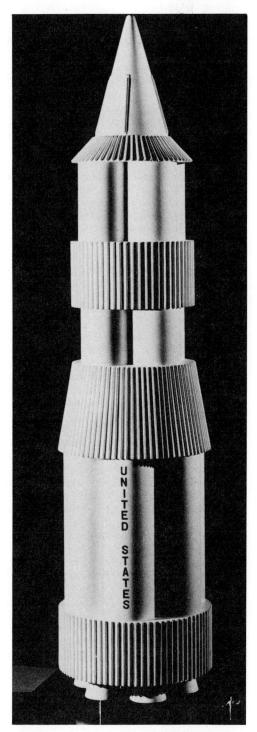

NOVA (1). Artist's conception of Nova booster

favoring trend toward 13-engine, 20,000,-000 lbs. thrust first stage, and earth-orbital capability of 300 tons payload.

NOVA N–2. Second stage of Nova launch vehicle (of 8 engines first-stage configuration), with 4 M.1 engines burning liquid oxygen/liquid hydrogen, each producing 1,200,000 lbs. thrust for second-stage thrust rating of 4,800,000 lbs.

NOVA N–3. Third stage of Nova launch vehicle (of 8 engines first-stage configuration), of one J.2 engine burning liquid oxygen/liquid hydrogen, producing 200,000 lbs. thrust. Identical to Saturn S–IV stage.

NOVA (2). A star which undergoes a sudden and enormous increase in brightness; about 25 appear every year in our Galaxy. A **supernova** is a star which explodes with a liberation of most of its energy into space.

NOZZLE. A duct through which a fluid may be directed into a jet stream, the velocity and shape of the stream being subject to control by the design of the nozzle. Generally, the exhaust duct of a rocket or jet thrust chamber in which gases are accelerated to high velocities.

NSSS. Naval Space Surveillance System. U.S. Navy's radar tracking stations for satellite sighting, locating, computing, and prediction of orbital flight, linked with SPADATS. Any object in space as it passes over entire southern border of the U.S. must move through a radar-wave screen transmitted from ground stations. When an object pierces this screen at two or more points, computers triangulate its position and compute data on the orbit. "Unassociated triangulation" indicates either that a new object is orbiting, or that the predicted orbit of a known satellite has been modified into a new orbit. See **SPADATS.**

NUCLEAR FUEL. Fissionable material of reasonably long life, used or usable in producing energy in a nuclear reactor.

NUCLEAR–HEATER PROPULSION. Propulsion by means of nuclear heat acting upon a working fluid.

NUCLEAR PROPULSION. Propulsion by means of atomic energy. Nuclear propulsion may utilize nuclear energy to produce heat, which may in turn be converted to mechanical energy. Nuclear propulsion may theoretically use a flow of nuclear particles. See **ion engine.**

NUCLEAR RADIATION. The emission of neutrons and other particles, and electromagnetic radiation, from an atomic nucleus as the result of nuclear fission or thermonuclear fusion.

NUCLEAR REACTOR. An apparatus in which nuclear fission may be sustained in a self-supporting chain reaction. Commonly called "reactor."

NUCLEAR ROCKET. A rocket in which the energy for the exhaust stream derives from nuclear fission or fusion.

NUCLEUS. The positively charged core of an atom with which is associated practically the whole mass of the atom but only a minute part of its volume. (A nucleus is composed essentially of one or more protons and an approximately equal number of neutrons.)

NULL CIRCLE. Theoretical point in space where the gravitational attraction of one planet balances that of another planet; there can be no real null point, circle, or region because the solar system is dynamic, parts of it always moving in relation to other parts. See **neutral point.**

O

OAO. See **Orbiting Astronomical Observatory.**

OBSERVATIONAL TWILIGHT. That part of the twilight period during which the horizon may be observed as a sharply defined line and during which the navigational stars may be seen; the light diffused during this period.

For computation purposes, this twilight begins or ends when the middle of the sun is at a point about 10° below the horizon.

OCCULTATION. The disappearance of a body behind another body of larger apparent size. (When the moon passes between the observer and a star, the star is said to be occulted.)

OCEAN RANGE VESSEL (ORV). Ship fitted with extensive instrumentation and radar equipment to track and gather performance data on missiles, booster vehicles, and orbital spacecraft. These ships function as "floating range stations."

OCULO–AGRAVIC ILLUSION. Also: *perceptual illusion*. During subgravity and zero-g states, luminous objects seen in the sky or in space appear to move and to be displaced in an upward direction.

OCULOGRAVIC ILLUSION. The apparent displacement of an object in space caused by the difference which may exist between the direction of the vertical and that of resultant *g*. Encountered under test conditions on centrifuge runs or in the constant turning motion of a high-speed aircraft.

OCULOGYRAL ILLUSION. The apparent movement of an object in the same direction as that in which one seems to be turning when the semicircular canals of the inner ear are stimulated. The observer on a centrifuge, staring at a lighted bar, for example, sees the bar as moving steadily to one side when in reality it remains in its fixed position relative to the observer.

"OFFICE." An aircraft cockpit or spacecraft cabin; specifically, the exact area or position where the pilot or astronaut is located to control his vehicle.

OGO. See **Orbiting Geophysical Observatory.**

ONBOARD PILOT–OBSERVER CAMERA. Remote-control camera for orbital missions which takes motion pictures including the astronaut's shoulders and head and a rough determination of the area at which the astronaut is looking. The exposed film is recovered and then developed and studied. This is unlike the Soviet system, which includes both an onboard pilot-observer camera and several onboard pilot-observer television cameras which relay live transmissions during the flight.

ONIONSKIN ATMOSPHERE. The layer of breathable or useful atmosphere, considered to be approximately 2 miles high. The term derives from the comparison of this 2-mile layer to the diameter of the earth—7,926 miles.

OPEN LOOP. A control system in which there is no self-correcting action as there is in a closed-loop system. See **closed loop.**

OPPOSITION. The situation of a celestial body with respect to another celestial body (especially the sun) when it lies in a direction 180° from the direction of the reference body (e.g., the sun), as viewed from the earth. For example, Mars is in opposition when the earth is between Mars and the sun. Mars is in *conjunction* when the sun is between it and the earth.

OPHTHALMIC FILTER. A filter to control the transmission of high energy to provide protection for pilots' and astronauts' eyes while permitting optimum cockpit/cabin visibility under the wide range of operational conditions that may be encountered in extremes of atmospheric and space-flight operations.

OPTICAL STAR TRACKER. A navigational device that locks onto the light of a particular celestial body, and is used in navigation or astrogation.

ORB. A spherical body, but especially a celestial sphere such as the earth, moon, any planet or a spherical artificial satellite.

ORBIT. The path described by a celestial body or artificial satellite in its revolutions around another body, while under the influence of a gravitational or other force. For instance, the orbit of a celestial body is its path relative to another body around which it revolves. (Illustrations, page 138.)

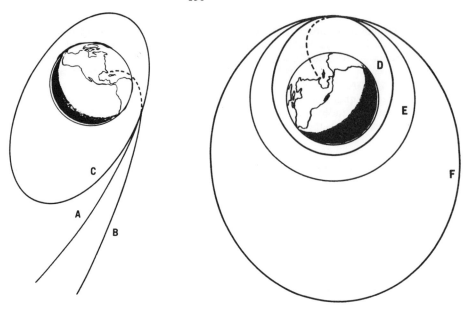

Diagrams of various ORBITS. A, Escape velocity orbit. B, Orbit at greater than escape velocity. C, Orbit at less than escape velocity. D, Orbit at less than circular velocity. E, Circular velocity orbit. F, Orbit at greater than circular velocity

Heliocentric ORBIT of Ranger III (period: 406.4 days). Orbits of several different types are shown in this representation

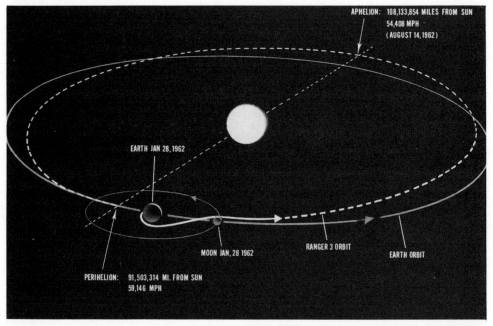

ORBITAL BOMBER. A projected military aerospace vehicle with the capability of orbital or near-orbital speeds, to allow circling of the earth one or more times at very high altitudes and then gliding under manned directional control back to a landing site.

ORBITAL CONFIGURATION. The final design, including external shape and internal arrangements, of any spacecraft when in orbit.

ORBITAL CONFIRMATION. Mathematical confirmation, on the basis of all tracking and other data, that orbit of a payload has been successfully achieved.

ORBITAL CURVE. An imaginary track on a primary body's surface traced by a satellite orbiting about it more than, or less than, once a day, in a direction other than due east or west, each successive track being displaced to the west by an amount equal to the degrees of rotation of the primary body between each orbit.

ORBITAL DIRECTION. The direction that the path of an orbiting body takes. Most satellite or manned spacecraft vehicles are launched from west to east. Satellites orbiting the earth from east to west are known to be in a *retrograde orbit.* See **inclination; orbital curve.**

ORBITING ASTRONOMICAL OBSERVATORY (OAO). First satellite being built under contract by Grumman; this company is also building the Apollo LEM (Lunar Excursion Module)

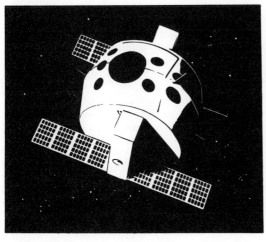

ORBITAL DOCKING. The mating of two spacecraft in orbit after rendezvous has been made, in order to bring the two vehicles together as a single unit and to secure them so that they will continue to orbit together.

ORBITAL ELEMENTS. A set of 7 parameters defining the orbit of a satellite.

ORBITAL INJECTION. Also *injection into orbit.* That moment when power is shut down and orbit is achieved.

ORBITAL PARAMETERS. Scale of vehicle height in miles, orbital velocity, and orbital period:

Altitude (miles)	Velocity (mph)	Period (minutes)
120	17,449	87.8
200	17,238	91.1
300	17,035	94.4
400	16,839	97.7
500	16,649	101.1
600	16,466	104.5
800	16,116	111.3
1,000	15,788	118.5

ORBITAL PERIOD. Time required for one full orbit about the earth. For example, a Mercury capsule in nominal orbit of 150-mile apogee and 100-mile perigee would require approximately 88.5 minutes for one complete orbit.

ORBITAL RENDEZVOUS. The maneuvering of a spacecraft in orbit in order to "close in" and to rendezvous with another orbiting spacecraft. Both vehicles must be matched in all orbital parameters—velocity, angle, equatorial inclination, etc.

ORBITAL VELOCITY. The velocity of a body in its orbit about its primary. For Mercury, approximate nominal orbital velocity at perigee is 17,500 mph—295 miles per minute.

ORBITAL WEIGHT. The specific weight of a spacecraft in orbit, as payload, distinctive from its weight at launch and its weight at time of recovery. Also: the total weight of any booster-spacecraft system as specifically distinguished from the payload weight. Total weight placed in orbit.

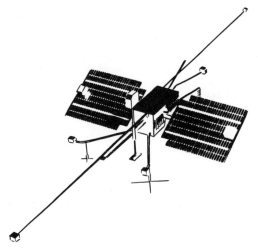

ORBITING GEOPHYSICAL OBSERVATORY (OGO)

ORBITING ASTRONOMICAL OBSERV-ATORY (OAO). An advanced astronomical laboratory with a payload of 3,500 lbs. to be boosted into a high orbit by the Saturn C-1 booster system. Two large telescopes will form the heart of the payload. The first flight is scheduled for late 1963 or early 1964. (Illustration, page 139.)

ORBITING GEOPHYSICAL OBSERVA-TORY (OGO). A 1,000-lb. satellite with advanced instruments for extensive geophysical measurements of the earth. Intended for launch with the Thor-Agena B, Atlas-Agena B, and Centaur booster systems. POGO is the code name for polar orbiting OGO satellites, and EGO is the code name for eccentric orbiting satellites of the series. First flight is scheduled in 1963.

ORBITING SOLAR OBSERVATORY (OSO). An intricate satellite weighing approximately 460 lbs. and 36 inches high, containing extensive instrumentation to measure solar electromagnetic radiation in the ultraviolet, X-ray, and gamma-ray regions of the spectrum. The OSO permits extensive studies through a wide range of solar radiation spectra, especially enhanced by the fact that the OSO is located in orbit beyond the absorbing and distorting effects of the atmosphere.

ORBITING SOLAR OBSERVATORY (OSO)

ORIENTATION IN SPACE. *Subjective spatial orientation* is awareness of position in space. *Objective spatial orientation* is awareness of position relative to other objects, the most important of which is the center of the earth. Orientation with respect to the center of the earth is entirely based upon gravity. Either or both forms of such orientation are the result of precise central integration of stimuli emanating from three systems represented in the *orientation triad* which consists of: (1) the visual apparatus with its nervous connections; (2) the vestibular apparatus with its nervous connections; (3) the kinesthetic apparatus consisting of receptors situated in muscles, skin, viscera, etc., with their nervous connections. See **equilibrium and orientation.**

ORION. Also: *Project Orion.* A proposal to develop a space platform weighing several thousand tons and orbiting the earth. Thrust is achieved by a succession of small nuclear explosions which react against the vehicle.

OSCAR. A "home-built" satellite produced by engineers on their own time with private resources; a 10-lb. satellite in the form of a 6-by-10-inch gold-plated magnesium box, with transmitters to investigate radio propagation phenomena in the two-meter (144–146 mc.) portion of the radio frequency spectrum. Oscar is orbited within the Agena-B upper stage of the Discoverer satellite.

OSCILLATION. A periodic moving or swinging from one extreme position or attitude to another; any such uncontrolled swinging back and forth of an aircraft or spacecraft, such as *uncontrolled* or *violent oscillations*. Also, a recurring periodic disturbance.

OSO. See **Orbiting Solar Observatory.**

OTOLITH. A small calcareous concretion located in the inner ear which plays a part in the mechanism of orientation. See **equilibrium and orientation.**

OUTER SPACE. A definition much abused and whose specific meaning is widely misunderstood. As commonly used, outer space is that area of space beyond the influence of the earth's atmosphere. More accurately, the term refers to space beyond the limits of the solar system.

OUTGASSING. The evolution of gas from a solid under vacuum conditions. See **vacuum evaporation.**

OVERRIDE. A manual system by which the astronaut can override—take command away from—automatic systems.

OXIDIZER. A substance that combines with another to produce heat and, in the case of a rocket, a gas. In the case of a rocket, the oxidizer usually contains oxygen, or is itself oxygen, but it may be another substance, such as fluorine as used in one exotic fuel combination. See **hypergolic fuel; liquid oxygen.**

OXIMETER. A photoelectric instrument for measuring the oxygen content of the blood; used in experimental work, and also as a device incorporated in flight-vehicle hypoxia-warning systems. See **hypoxia.**

OXYGEN EXCESS. Just as abnormally low oxygen supply in the breathable air produces the harmful effects of **hypoxia** (q.v.), so an excessive exposure in time to one atmosphere (14.7 psi) of pure oxygen can bring on serious and harmful effects. These are characterized by eventual lung inflammation; respiratory disturbances such as pulmonary

congestion, gasping, and coughing; nausea; numbness of fingers and toes; and various heart symptoms. If the oxygen pressure exceeds one atmosphere, the effects become more pronounced and serious—extreme discomfort, growing nervousness, severe irritation of the eyes leading rapidly to almost complete blindness, nausea, convulsions, and unconsciousness.

OXYGEN LACK. An all-encompassing term to represent a condition of scarcity or absence of oxygen in the atmosphere, as at high altitudes or in a confined space unsupplied by oxygen; a deficiency of oxygen in the body of a person brought on by exposure to this condition. See **anoxia; hypoxia.**

OXYGEN MASK. A rubberized mask with a system of straps to achieve a secure seal over the mouth and nose. Oxygen flows from an aircraft or spacecraft source through an oxygen hose to the mask, allowing pilot to breathe in oxygen when exposed to dangerously low atmospheric pressure and oxygen content.

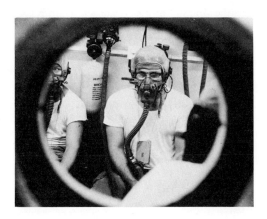

OXYGEN MASK

OXYGEN MASK, CONTINUOUS FLOW. A gaseous-supply oxygen-mask system is used generally in troop and cargo aircraft because of trouble-free characteristics and simplicity of equipment. The oxygen flow is continuous. A regulator connects through a bayonet-type connector with a rubber tube running to the neck of the bag at the base of the facepiece, which seals against the face.

The oxygen inflates the bag with about a pint of oxygen, the norm for a single inhalation. The continuous-flow system is limited by factors of temperature and crew activity to 25,000 feet for routine use and 35,000 feet for emergency use.

OXYGEN MASK, DEMAND. The demand system delivers oxygen to an airman "on demand"—the process initiated by inhalation. Inhalation closes a valve in the mask and opens a valve in the oxygen regulator (exhalation reverses the operation of the valves). The movements of inhalation and exhalation automatically start and stop oxygen flow, preventing excessive oxygen consumption. A diluter-demand regulator contains a diaphragm which opens the valve at the slightest suction and closes it at the slightest push. It contains also a reducing valve which reduces oxygen pressure in the line from the oxygen cylinders down to atmospheric pressure in the mask proper. Between the outside air and the mask is an aneroid (see **altimeter**), or evacuated bellows. This permits an air inlet to dilute the oxygen at sea level so that the airman breathes mainly atmospheric air. With a rise in altitude and a decrease in barometric pressure, the aneroid gradually closes the air inlet until at about 34,000 feet the airman receives 100% oxygen; simultaneously the ambient air valve is sealed. This auto-mix device operates automatically unless the airman switches his equipment to a position marked "100% oxygen," when he receives 100% oxygen flow no matter what the barometric pressure. The 100% oxygen flow below 34,000 feet permits denitrogenation for prevention of bends and chokes, or other needs. The "oxygen mask, demand" system is effective to 40,000 feet, with a normal use limited to altitudes below 35,000 feet. Above this altitude, pressure demand is required. See **denitrogenation; dysbarism; oxygen mask, pressure demand.**

OXYGEN MASK, PRESSURE DEMAND. The "oxygen mask, demand" system is satisfactory for air-crew use to 35,000 feet, to 40,000 feet for limited operations, to 43,000 feet for critical emergencies. Above this altitude even 100% oxygen is ineffective to meet airman needs. To provide for routine use to 42,000 feet and emergency use briefly

to 50,000 feet, the "oxygen mask, pressure demand" is used. This is the system of *pressure breathing,* which raises the pressure of the oxygen delivered to the lungs to slightly above that of ambient air. The overpressure within the mask system is only ½ lb. psi, but this small difference is critical to the body and brain oxygen needs at this high ambient air altitude. Normal breathing requires slight muscular effort to expand the chest and draw in air; relaxation of the chest muscles pushes out the air without direct effort (see **breathing, process of**). Pressure breathing adds sufficient pressure to the breathing atmosphere within the oxygen-mask system to inflate the lungs automatically. The airman receives complete inhalation without effort. He must make a specific exertion to exhale. This system forces a *reversal* of the muscular action involved in the respiratory process, but assures that the airman under extreme-altitude ambient conditions always receives sufficient oxygen to meet his needs. The system is necessary because at altitudes exceeding 43,000 feet, without pressurization of the body or the cabin, the ambient air pressure is insufficient to permit sufficient minimum oxygen to be brought into the lungs, despite the use of 100% oxygen.

OXYGEN SYSTEMS, FLIGHT CREWS. Military oxygen systems for high-altitude flight are basically identical in "oxygen plumbing"—from the source of the oxygen to the regulator. Fighter and bomber aircraft use a liquid-oxygen system; cargo and transport aircraft use a gaseous-oxygen system. The liquid-oxygen system contains vacuum-insulated converters for storing and converting the liquid oxygen to gaseous oxygen. Oxygen amounts are indicated by quantity gauges, calibrated in liters of liquid oxygen. The liquid-oxygen converters are shatter-proof; they may rupture, but will neither explode nor fragment even if penetrated. Liquid-oxygen breathing systems have the exceptional advantages of high-density storage for great quantities of oxygen within the smallest possible space. Extensive experience with this system has made it readily adaptable to aerospace craft.

OXYGEN TENSION. The faculty or capacity of oxygen at a given pressure and in a given amount to extend itself into the cells

OXYGEN MASK. Pilot wearing pressure demand mask

of the lungs, or into the blood and tissues of the body. Said of oxygen in the atmosphere, in the lungs, blood, etc. See **alveolar air; breathing, process of; oxygen mask, pressure demand; respiration.**

OZONE LAYER. Layer in the atmosphere about 20 miles above sea level which strongly absorbs solar ultraviolet radiation; absorption of energy not only converts molecular atmospheric oxygen into ozone but heats the atmosphere and produces a high-temperature layer, a little above the ozone layer.

OZONOSPHERE. See **ozone layer.**

P

PAD. Area from which rocket is launched. Usually "pad" refers to the immediate launch site, while "complex" includes entire facility for launching the rocket, including pad, blockhouse, etc.

PAD CHIEF. The individual charged with co-ordinating over-all operations on the launch pad.

PAD DELUGE. A deluge of water sprayed upon certain launch pads during the launch of a rocket vehicle so as to reduce the temperatures of critical parts of the pad or rocket engines.

PAD SAFETY OPERATIONS. That portion of launch safety operations concerned with rocket operations in the area of the launch pad. This includes the exercising of precautionary measures involving the fixed launch facilities, ground handling gear on the pad, and the rocket vehicle itself up to the point of liftoff.

"PANIC BUTTON." Any control button, switch, or other device for use in a dire emergency. See **chicken switch.**

"PANIC RACK." An explosive ejection seat.

PARA–BALLOON. A combination of a parachute and balloon in which the parachute sprouts around the center of the balloon; a device used for ballistic-flight recovery of camera capsules, instrumentation packages, etc.

PARABOLIC ORBIT. An orbit shaped like a parabola, the orbit representing the least eccentricity for escape from an attracting body. Unlike the circle or ellipse, the parabola does not return into itself, but extends to infinity. It has an eccentricity of one, and thus represents the minimum value for an escape orbit. (The parabolic orbit is such that a body has escape velocity at every point along it; also known as *parabola of escape.*)

PARACHUTE. A contrivance that opens out somewhat like an umbrella and catches the air so as to retard or slow down the movement of a body attached (usually by nylon shroud lines) to the main parachute canopy. *Parachute assembly* is the complete parachute assembled together or ready for wear, consisting of the canopy folded and placed in the parachute pack, and the harness. *Parachute canopy* is that part of the parachute that opens up and is deployed to catch the air, consisting usually of silk or nylon fabric. *Parachute harness* is the part that fits about the body and to which the parachute canopy is attached, by use of shroud or suspension lines. The *ripcord* is the cord or cable which, when pulled, opens the parachute pack in a free fall. This causes springs to eject a small *pilot chute,* which inflates and is pulled out by the airstream, in turn deploying the main canopy. The *vent,* or *canopy vent,* is a distensible opening in the apex of the parachute canopy designed to relieve excess pressure and to stabilize the parachute in descent. There are three types of personnel parachutes—back, chest, and seat packs.

PARACHUTE EFFECTIVE ALTITUDE. The maximum height above the earth at which a parachute will open is determined by the need of a certain pressure differential between the inside and outside of the canopy to achieve inflation. The magnitude of any pressure differential depends upon the impact (dynamic) pressure, with minimum values for canopy deployment and inflation established at approximately 0.05 lb. per square foot. This minimum creates a balanced force system sufficient to assure parachute inflation and to provide tension to retain inflation. The maximum altitudes where the parachute inflates evenly and sustains its form lie between 200,000 and 350,000 feet, the exact height a variable of speed and density. The *effective altitude* of the parachute, however, may be computed only on the basis of when the inflated parachute begins to decelerate and stabilize the body attached to the parachute system. (Parachute partial or full deployment and inflation is possible at greater heights due to inertial forces or induced rotation of the canopy. Such deployment and inflation is

PARACHUTE. Pilot in correct descent position in parachute harness, legs together, knees flexed, hands grasping risers for directional control

ineffective in respect to stabilization and deceleration and is even potentially dangerous, since the parachute may begin to stream, squid, twist, and get into a wraparound snarl. Unless there is sufficient impact pressure as a result of velocity/air density, aeroelastic effects could create extremely high and dangerous parachute forces.)

PARADOXICAL EFFECT. A transitory relapse in a patient who has suffered from lack of oxygen even though adequate oxygen is again being breathed by him. See **hypoxia.**

PARAGLIDER. See **flexwing.**

PARALLAX. The apparent displacement of an object, or the apparent difference in its direction of motion, when viewed from two different points.

PARAMEDIC. A doctor or medical corpsman qualified to participate in parachute drops for the purpose of rescue and recovery. Paramedic crews are assigned to astronaut recovery forces, and the personnel involved usually are qualified scuba divers as well.

PARAMETER. A constant having a series of particular and arbitrary values, each value characterizing a member in a system or family of expressions, curves, surfaces, functions, or the like—such as orbital parameters.

PARAWING. See **flexwing.**

PARESTHESIA. A condition of swelling, rash, cold or hot sensations, etc., brought on by the formation of gas bubbles in the tissues, especially those tissues directly beneath the skin. See **creeps; dysbarism.**

PARKING ORBIT. An orbital technique used in deep-space probes to increase the accuracy of the probe. A booster vehicle propels an upper-propulsion stage with the attached payload into a low earth orbit—approximately 95 to 110 miles perigee; when the vehicle reaches a precisely calculated point along the orbit and the attitude

of the vehicle in thrust-line is as required, the rocket engines are restarted to begin a new trajectory outbound from the earth, usually at escape velocity.

PARSEC. A unit of measure for interstellar space equal to 3.26 light years. A contraction for "parallax second." A parsec indicates the distance at which the mean radius of the earth's orbit would subtend an angle of one second of arc. Each parsec—3.26 light years—is equal to 19.15 trillion miles.

PARTIAL PRESSURE SUIT. See **pressure suit—partial.**

PARTIAL PRESSURE SUIT TEST. A physiological stress test in which the subject is placed in a pressure chamber and taken to a simulated altitude of 65,000 to 70,000 feet in a partial pressure suit. The test lasts one hour and produces severe discomfort and confinement. The test measures reaction to these factors, as well as the efficiency of the heart system and breathing at low ambient pressures.

PASSIVE PASSENGER. Occupant of a spacecraft assigned to a backup rather than a primary pilot control function; a passenger in a spacecraft where flight is maintained and controlled by automatic and/or remote command devices.

PASSIVE SATELLITE. Generally, a satellite without instrumentation. More specifically in the sense of communications satellites, reflecting a signal without transmission originating from within or boosted from within the satellite. Contrasted to "active satellite."

PASTE FOOD. Food—meat, fruit, and other substances—reduced to a paste form to be contained in squeeze-tube bottles or soft metal or plastic containers for eating under conditions of weightlessness. Common term for paste food by astronauts is *goop.* (Illustration, page 146.)

PATRICK AIR FORCE BASE (PAFB). Headquarters of the Air Force Missile Test Center (which administers the Atlantic Missile Range), located on Highway A1A

PASTE FOOD

approximately 18 miles south of Cape Canaveral on Florida coast.

PAUSE. A boundary at the upper limit or limits of one of the atmosphere's strata, where the character of the stratum (as defined by a given function) disappears. Used as a combining form, as in *aeropause, mesopause, stratopause,* and *tropopause.*

PAYLOAD. The useful—or working—cargo of a space mission. Payload is that net weight placed into orbit for specific mission results. Payload is distinct from the weight of the carrier rocket that in certain types of missions also goes into orbit but does not function as a vehicle to carry out specific missions.

PEAK ALTITUDE. Synonymous with apogee.

PERCEPTUAL ILLUSION. See **oculoagravic illusion.**

PERCEPTUAL MOTOR LEARNING. The learning of a motor skill with special reliance upon sensory discrimination. (Perceptual learning is involved, for example, in tightrope walking, where the sense of sight

is used to discriminate or judge a distance or an angle.)

PERI–. A prefix meaning near, as in *perigee.*

PERIGEE. That part of the orbit of a natural or artificial satellite that comes the closest to the surface of the earth.

PERIHELION. That point on a planet's, comet's, or spacecraft's orbit that comes nearest the sun. (The earth's perihelion is about 91,500,000 miles from the sun.)

PERISCOPE. A visual-aid device on a spacecraft that permits astronaut vision on that side of the spacecraft away from his hatch. Swivels through 360° for maximum possible field of vision. Also: an optical instrument, used by those remaining within the protection of a blockhouse, which enables them to watch a missile launch as from the relatively close proximity of the top of the blockhouse.

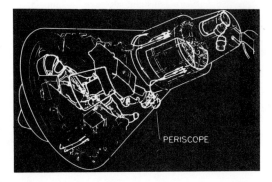

PERISCOPE mounting in Mercury spacecraft

PEROXIDE DUMP. In a Mercury spaceflight, the sequence when the astronaut jettisons all hydrogen peroxide remaining in the capsule, during descent beneath the main landing parachute.

PERTURBATION. A disturbance in the regular motion of a celestial body, the result of a force additional to that which causes the regular motion; also, as this applies to an artificial satellite of the earth or any other spatial body. The perturbations of

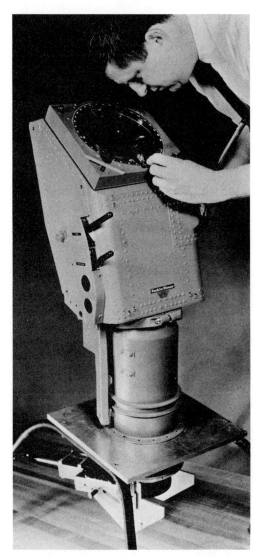

PERISCOPE designed for Mercury spacecraft gives the astronaut a view of the earth below and provides him with navigational data. Its wide-angle objective lens system extends and retracts through the skin of the vehicle. Using wide-angle, low-power magnification, the astronaut would see an area of the earth more than 1,700 nautical miles in diameter

planets are due to their attraction to each other. The *periodic* perturbations of planets are oscillations of short period, dependent on their mutual positions; *secular* perturbations are slow changes in their orbits.

PHARYNGEAL PRESSURE MANEU-VER. The exercise designed to open or assist in opening the Eustachian tube. See **Valsalva maneuver.**

PHOBOS. The inner of the two moons of Mars. Revolves in an orbit 3,700 miles from the planet with an orbital period 7 hours 40 minutes. Diameter is about 10 miles. See **Deimos.**

PHOTIC SPACE ENVIRONMENT. The extremes and patterns of solar light irradiation (or solar illuminance) with regard to vision and to the utilization of light in photosynthetic recycling of metabolic material in the closed ecological system of the space cabin. The environmental extreme for the latter is that point where solar illuminance, dropping with increasing distance from the sun, finally falls below the effective minimum required for photosynthesis; this minimum is believed to be reached somewhere in the region of the asteroid belt, between the orbits of Mars and Jupiter. In respect to vision, at one astronomical unit from the sun (distance of earth from the sun), the unprotected eye in space can receive retinal burns in less than 10 seconds. It is believed that the retina-burning power of the sun may extend as far as the orbit of Saturn.

PHOTIC STIMULATION. Also known as **flicker vertigo.** Photic stimulation is a rare form of epilepsy that affects an unknown number of pilots, usually with fatal results if the stimulation occurs during solo flight; it is rarely detectable before its occurrence. A man subjected to photic stimulation is in an *altered state of consciousness.* Sometimes the result is complete unconsciousness, or a complete lack of balance, and sometimes a trancelike state in which the individual seems to be mesmerized. Photic stimulation can be brought about in several ways, but regardless of the specific source it is a response to a psychovisual stimulus. Most frequently photic stimulation is caused by the rhythmic interruption of a steady light source—such as occurs when a pilot stares through a slowly turning propeller or rotor blade into a bright light. If there exists a steady light flicker at a frequency of 4 to 20 cycles per second, or "blinks per second," the frequency may match the subject's alpha-wave pattern, producing photic stimulation. It has occurred fairly often, for example, in the case of pilots in single-engine airplanes landing into the setting sun. The reactions were *immediate* and included one or more of the following: convulsion, nausea, unconsciousness, or complete vertigo. Photic stimulation is considered a hazard in aerospace operations because of the wide range of possible encounters with a 4 to 20 cycles-per-second light source. An anti-collision light, for example, operates at 30 blinks per minute, or a half-cycle per second. If it speeds up to 4 cycles per second or more, and the airman susceptible to photic stimulation stares at the light, "flicker vertigo" is the instantaneous result.

PHOTON. A quantum of radiant energy. According to the quantum theory, the photon is the elementary quantity, or *quantum,* of radiant energy. Although they have "zero mass," photons have certain other discrete properties similar to particles in motion. Photons theoretically may be harnessed to power a spacecraft. See **photon engine.**

PHOTON ENGINE. A design-status type of reaction engine in which thrust would be obtained from a stream of electromagnetic radiation. Although the thrust would be minute, it may be possible to apply the thrust for a greatly extended period of time. Under "deep space" conditions where no resistance is offered by air particles, it is theoretically possible to build up extremely high speeds. See **electrical engine; ion engine; photon.**

PHOTOPIC VISION. The reaction of the eye to high levels of illumination. At average brightness levels, visual acuity increases markedly as the amount of light is increased. The maximum gain in visual acuity appears to be set at a limit of 1,000 foot-candles.

PHOTOSPHERE. (1) The outermost luminous layer of the sun's gaseous body. (2) The intensely bright portion of the sun visible to the unaided eye.

PHOTOSYNTHESIS. A process found in green plants in which carbohydrates are formed under the influence of light with chlorophyl serving as a catalyst. See **algae; closed ecological system.**

PHUGOID OSCILLATION. A slow- or long-period longitudinal oscillation of a flightborne (aerodynamic) vehicle.

PHYSICAL COMPETENCE TEST. See **ergometer; treadmill maximum workload.**

PHYSIOLOGICAL ACCELERATION. The acceleration experienced by a human or an animal test subject in an acceleration vehicle.

PICKET SHIP. An ocean-going vessel carrying radar and electronics equipment, forming part of a "picket fence" beneath the flight line of an airborne or spaceborne vehicle. See **ocean range vessel.**

PICKET SHIP. Ocean-borne tracking and communications vessel on station in the Atlantic

PICKOFF. A sensing device, used in combination with a gyroscope in an automatic pilot or other automatic or robot apparatus, that responds to angular movement to create a signal or to effect some type of control.

PICKUP. A device that converts a sound, view, or other form of intelligence into corresponding electric signals (e.g., a microphone, a television camera, or a phonograph pickup).

PICO–. A prefix meaning divided by one million million.

PICTURE WINDOW. A large viewport or window, circular, oval, rectangular, or other shape of a size sufficient to permit ease of vision during flight.

PIGTAIL. A short, coiled connecting wire, or a short bundle of connecting wires, such as an igniter connection for rocket booster vehicles.

PILOT CHUTE. A small parachute that initiates the opening sequence of the major parachute canopy. The release of springs in the parachute pack ejects the small pilot chute; this fills immediately. Inflated to full diameter by the airstream, it pulls the main parachute canopy and shroud lines from the pack into the airstream.

PIONEER. Deep-space probes identified as Pioneer series, beginning with the early Project Mona of 1958, to place payloads in the vicinity of the moon. The first Pioneer satellites were in the shape of a double toroid with a maximum height of 30 inches and a diameter of 29 inches. Spacecraft weight after jettisoning eight small vernier motors for course correction was approximately 75 lbs. Booster for first shot in Project Mona (no designation given to the payload), and for second and third shots, was Thor-Able three-stage rocket. First Pioneer-series shot was August 17, 1958, and a failure; second shot (Pioneer I) went up to 70,700 miles after launching on October 11, 1958; third Pioneer shot (Pioneer II) was launched on November 8, 1958, and failed when Stage III did not ignite. Pioneer III and IV used the Juno-II booster, and the new Pioneer payload was a cone weighing 12.95 lbs. for Pioneer III (Pioneer IV weighed 13.5 lbs.). Pioneer III on its launching of December 6, 1959 reached a height of 63,580 miles. Pioneer IV on March 3, 1959 reached escape velocity, passed by the moon at 37,000 miles, and entered solar orbit. Pioneer V was a sphere 26 inches in diameter (and was also known as Project Able IV), with large solar cells that extended in the same manner as on the Explorer VI earth-orbiting satellite. On March 11, 1960 the Pioneer V was boosted by a Thor-Able booster to a velocity of 36,500 feet per second, and went into solar orbit. The probe transmitted signals

Three **PIONEER** lunar probe satellites were fired by the U.S. Air Force in 1958 in Project Mona, with Thor-Able rockets

PIONEER IV space probe throwing off anti-spin weights to slow down spin rate imparted by upper stages during firing into solar orbit

until it reached a separation from the earth of approximately 22,500,000 miles. The next Pioneers were part of the Atlas-Able IV (Project Able IV), continuing the effort to place satellites in the lunar vicinity. The first Atlas-Able booster exploded in September 1959 in a static test at Canaveral; the second and third failed in ascent; the fourth exploded in ascent.

PIONEER V. Deep-space probe that broadcast data to earth from distance of 17,500,000 miles, was tracked to 22,500,000 miles from earth before contact was lost

PIP. Signal indication on the scope of an electronic instrument, produced by a sharply peaked but short pulse of voltage. Also called *blip*.

PITCH. The movement of a booster, spacecraft, or other vehicle about an axis that is at once perpendicular to the missile's longitudinal axis and horizontal with respect to the earth. The movement of an aircraft or spacecraft about its lateral axis; i.e., movement of the nose up and down from the horizontal.

PITCH-. Of a rocket booster or vehicle: *pitchover*—to turn from a vertical direction; *pitchup*—to turn toward a vertical direction, as in the case of an ascending booster that corrects its trajectory from a non-vertical to a vertical.

PITCHOVER. The programmed maneuver or turn from the vertical that a rocket booster takes as it describes an arc and points in a direction other than upward.

Also: the point-in-space of this action, as during programming. See **Atlas-D flight plan; Atlas-D guidance system.**

PLAGES. Clouds of calcium or hydrogen vapor that show up as bright patches on the visible surface of the sun.

PLANET. A spatial body that revolves about the sun or other star, but excluding the comets and meteors and the asteroids. The larger of such bodies are sometimes called *principal planets* to distinguish them from asteroids, planetoids, or minor planets, which are comparatively very small. An *inferior planet* has an orbit smaller than that of the earth; a *superior planet* has an orbit larger than that of the earth. The four planets nearest the sun are called *inner planets* (Mercury, Venus, Earth, Mars); the others, *outer planets* (Jupiter, Saturn, Uranus, Neptune, Pluto). The four largest planets are called *major planets*.

PLANETARY BIOLOGY. See **astrobiology.**

PLANETOCENTRIC. In astronautics, pertaining to a planet as the center of a system.

PLANETOGRAPHY. The study and analysis of conditions found on celestial bodies. See **exobiology; planetology; spatiography.**

PLANETOLOGY. The study of planets and their natural satellites, especially in regard to the interpretation of their surface markings, i.e., the *canali* of Mars.

PLASMA. An electrically conductive gas comprised of neutral particles, ionized particles, and free electrons, but which, taken as a whole, is electrically neutral. A plasma is formed when an electrically charged gas or body of gas is subjected to extreme temperatures.

PLASMA ENGINE. A reaction engine using magnetically accelerated plasma as a propellant. See **electrical engine; ion engine; plasma; plasma generator.**

PLASMA GENERATOR. A machine, such as an electric arc chamber, that generates very high heat fluxes to convert deuterium or other gas into plasma.

PLASMA ENGINE

PLASMA JET. A magnetohydrodynamic (MHD) rocket engine in which the ejection of plasma generates thrust. The high-temperature jet of electrons and positive ions is heated and ionized by the magnetohydrodynamic effect of a strong electrical discharge. See **magnetohydrodynamics; plasma.**

PLASMA SHEATH. An envelope of ionized gas that surrounds a body moving through an atmosphere at hypersonic velocities. See **ionized layer; re-entry profile.**

PLOTTING BOARD. A board on which the movements of an object or objects are shown with reference to given co-ordinates or to fixed objects. A plotting board consists usually of a chart mounted flat on which movement is shown by markers; or it may consist of a vertical screen that displays movement by electronic means. A plotting board would be used, for example, to display the exact position and movement of all units of a spacecraft recovery force.

PLUS COUNT. During a countdown and launch, the count in seconds that immediately follows T-Time, used to maintain a check on the sequence of events after the action of the countdown has ended, and lasting until the powered portion of the booster flight has ended. For example: "Separation of the escape tower occurs at T plus 151 seconds. . . ."

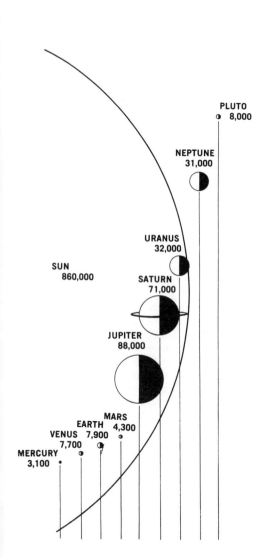

How the sun and PLANETS compare in diameter (figures show diameters in miles)

PNEOSTENOSIS. A condition resulting from any obstruction of the normal flow of air into and out of the respiratory passages.

PNEUMOHYPHYNEMIA. A condition in which the total surface area available for gas diffusion through the gas-blood barrier in the lungs is reduced. See **alveolar air; alveoli; breathing, process of; hypoxia; respiration.**

PNEUMONECTASIS. The condition of swelling caused by the presence of air in the intra-alveolar tissue of the lungs. See **alveolar air; alveoli.**

POLAR ORBIT. A satellite orbit running north and south so that the satellite vehicle orbits over both the North and South Poles. U.S. polar-orbit satellites are launched from Vandenberg Air Force Base, California.

PORT CANAVERAL. Harbor area just south of Cape Canaveral used for logistics support of AFMTC operations.

POSIGRADE ROCKETS. In Project Mercury, the 3 small solid-propellant rockets which are used in a cluster to separate the manned spacecraft from the Atlas booster after booster burnout and injection into orbit. Each rocket is 14.5 inches long, 3 inches in diameter, and weighs 5 lbs. As a cluster they fire with a thrust of 1,250 lbs.

POSITIVE g. Force exerted on the human body in a gravitational field or during an acceleration, when the body is so positioned that the force of inertia acts on it in a head-to-foot direction (as in the seat of a fighter aircraft), i.e., the footward inertial force produced by a headward acceleration. See **positive-g tolerance; transverse acceleration; transverse g.**

POSITIVE–g TOLERANCE. Reaction in the positive-g field varies with the individual. Generally, however, the following results apply. At 2g, the individual is "pressed down" as though by a strong, sustained, and invisible force. At 3g, movement of the arms and legs is accomplished only with difficulty; the corners of the eyes, mouth, and jowls sag greatly. Eyesight dims out between 3.5

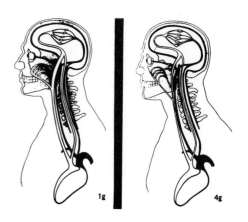

POSITIVE-g TOLERANCE

and 5g positive (dimout; grayout). From 4g to 5.5g positive, there is vision blackout, distinctive from blackout or unconsciousness due to lack of oxygen. Under positive-g vision blackout, the individual loses all vision but is still conscious. A 4.5 to 6g positive maintained for 3 to 5 seconds causes loss of consciousness. Vision blackout occurs because of (1) the extreme sensitivity of the retina to lack of oxygen, and (2) the body fluid shift of the positive-g field that drains blood from the head. Between the heart and the brain is a column of arterial blood about 12 inches in height. At 5g positive, the downward pull of the blood column equals the ability of the heart to push the blood toward the brain. The blood pressure in the legs where blood is pooled because of the positive-g fluid shift reaches 240 (mm Hg*). The result of the variation from the normal blood pressure of 120 in the arterial blood column between the heart and the brain, and that of the legs, is a serious impairment of circulation. If the positive-g field continues, the brain and retina fail to receive blood and fresh oxygen, and they begin to break down, as the heart pumps itself dry because of blood accumulation in the lower extremities. At 4g, however, the blood pressure in the brain is actually down to about 30. The blood already in the brain and retina area yields its total oxygen within about 3 seconds and if the g force continues, vision blackout oc-

* Millimeters of mercury.

curs. Soon afterward the airman becomes unconscious. If the positive-*g* field at 6*g* continues for some minutes, the result is death due to circulation failure.

POTASSIUM SUPEROXIDE. A relatively unstable chemical compound which in the presence of water liberates free oxygen, forming potassium hydroxide, which in turn absorbs exhaled carbon dioxide from the air. Of special consideration for emergency spacecraft and extraterrestrial base needs.

POUNDS THRUST. A measurement unit of the reaction force generated in a jet or rocket engine and available for propulsion.

POWER LANDING. Spacecraft landing in which the thrust of its motors is used as a deceleration device; i.e., as a brake.

PRANG. To crash or crash-land, but not necessarily with fatal results. See **auger in.**

PRECESSION. The change in the direction of the axis of rotation of a spinning body or of the plane of the orbit of an orbiting body when acted upon by an outside force.

PRECOUNT. First half of a split countdown. It is separated by a built-in hold from the second half, or final count, of the countdown. See **split countdown.**

PREOXYGENATION. The breathing of pure oxygen prior to flight to high altitudes and sharply decreased ambient air pressure. See **denitrogenation.**

PRESSURE BREATHING. Technique in which oxygen is injected inside the respiratory ducts through a pressure higher than the ambient barometric pressure. See **oxygen mask, pressure demand.**

PRESSURE CHAMBER. A sealed chamber from which the air may be exhausted to produce conditions similar to that of high-altitude flight, in order to test oxygen, pressure, and other equipment, and to provide pilot and astronaut training in pressure-breathing and suit equipment. See **altitude chamber; decompression chamber.**

PRESSURE CHAMBER

PRESSURE DIFFERENTIAL. The difference between the air pressure within a sealed cabin or capsule and the pressure of the ambient air immediately outside the cabin or capsule. A normal aircraft cabin pressure altitude of 15,000 feet is maintained at a flight altitude of 50,000 feet. The atmospheric psi at 50,000 feet is 1.69; at 15,000 feet it is 8.24. The atmospheric psi of 1.69 is 6.55 psi less than the 8.24 psi of 15,000 feet; therefore 6.55 psi is the pressure differential of the pressurized cabin.

PRESSURE FRIER. A modification of the familiar pressure cooker to permit cooking of foods under space-vehicle conditions. Temperatures suitable for complete cooking of foods under space-flight conditions are possible with a pressure cooker because the internal air pressure of the cooker is great enough to permit greater temperatures; the same is true of a "pressure frier." Such cooking is done by electrical heat rather than open-flame appliances.

PRESSURE SUIT—FULL. A form-fitting garment that completely encloses the human body, providing it with an environment above ambient pressure so that respiratory and circulatory functions may continue normally, or nearly so, under low-pressure or zero-pressure conditions, such as are met at extreme altitude or in space. To be used in the absence of a functioning pressurized cabin. The full pressure suit is distinguished from the partial pressure suit, or pressurized suit which inflates, although it is usually fitted with inflating parts that tighten the garment as ambient pressure decreases. See **pressure suit—partial.**

PRESSURE SUIT—PARTIAL. A skintight suit that encloses all of the body except the hands and feet, and which is capable of exerting pressure on the major portion of the body in order to counteract an increased intra-pulmonary oxygen pressure. It is worn at any time an aircraft exceeds 50,000 feet above sea level. The helmet delivers oxygen to the lungs under pressure (see **oxygen mask, pressure demand**) as in pressure breathing. Counter-pressure is applied over the torso, arms, and legs to equalize the internal and external pressures, preventing overinflation of the lungs, stagnation of the blood, and shock—which would result if pressure were applied to the lungs alone. The partial pressure suit prevents boiling of the blood (see **blood, boiling of**). The partial pressure suit also is known as the three-in-one suit. It incorporates

Engineer models space helmet of PRESSURE SUIT under test for lunar missions in Project Apollo

the pressure-demand system for regular use at oxygen-mask altitudes; the *g*-suit system (see **g-suit**); and protects the wearer against sudden loss of cabin pressure at physiologically hazardous pressure altitudes. The suit has been successfully worn under ambient barometric pressure of 198,-000 feet altitude. Fabric-covered rubber tubes (capstans) within the suit extending along the side of the arms, torso, and legs are attached to the suit by crossing tapes; when the tubes inflate they act on the tapes as pneumatic levers, drawing tight the fabric. Bladders in the suit inflate to apply pressure to the remainder of the body. In the partial pressure suit, the hands and feet are not pressurized, although suit modifications for space-research flights provide for such pressurization. The partial pressure suit is also known as the *pressurized suit*. See **pressure suit—full.**

PRESSURE SUIT, PROJECT MERCURY. The full pressure suit consists of five basic parts: suit torso, helmet, gloves, boots, and undergarment.

The torso is a closely fitted coverall tailored for each astronaut individually, covering all of the body except for the head and hands. The torso section is of two-ply construction: an inner gas-retention ply of neoprene and neoprene-coated nylon fabric and an outer ply of heat-reflective, aluminized nylon fabric.

The helmet is attached to the torso section by a rigid neck ring; a tiedown strap is provided on the neck ring to prevent helmet rise when the suit is pressurized. Torso straps permit individual-comfort adjustment and prevent suit from ballooning when pressurized. All zippers (one extends diagonally across the front of the torso from the left shoulder down to the waist, and there are two frontal neck zippers and a circumferential waist zipper) are pressure-sealing. The pressure-suit ventilation system is integral with the torso section. (See **Mercury capsule pressure-suit control system** for suit ventilation and oxygen-supply details.) A conical rubber neck dam is attached to the torso neck ring and is designed to prevent water from entering the suit in event of egress into water with the helmet removed. The neck dam is rolled and stowed on the

outside of the neck ring disconnect; for suit watertight condition the astronaut unrolls the neck dam until it provides a neck seal (see **neck dam**). The helmet consists of a resinous, impregnated Fiberglas hard shell; an individually molded crushable impact liner; a ventilation exhaust outlet; a visor sealing system; and a communications system.

The suit gloves attach to the suit torso at the lower forearm by means of a special "detent" ball-bearing lock, and provide maximum comfort and mobility. The gloves have curved fingers so that when pressurized the gloves assume the contour of the hand controller. Miniature needle-like red finger lights are provided on the index and middle fingers of both gloves. Battery-powered, the lights provide instrument-panel and chart illumination before the astronaut is adapted to night vision.

The boots are lightweight, of aluminized nylon fabric, with tennis-shoe-type soles (flexible friction soles) to aid in spacecraft egress.

The undergarment is a one-piece, lightweight cotton garment with long sleeves and legs. Ventilation spacer patches of tri-lock construction on the outside of the undergarment assure ventilation gas flow over certain critical areas of the body.

Gloves for PRESSURE SUIT, PROJECT MERCURY

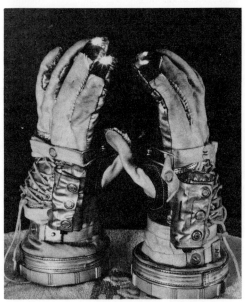

PRESSURE SUIT, PROJECT MERCURY, in fully inflated condition

PRESSURIZED. Containing air, or other gas, at a pressure that is higher than the pressure outside the container.

PRESSURIZED CABIN. A sealed cabin in any aerospace vehicle that is capable of maintaining an internal air pressure great enough to permit normal respiratory and circulatory functions of persons or animals within the cabin, without need of other protective means, i.e., a **pressure suit.**

PRESSURIZED CAPSULE. A capsule that maintains an internal gaseous pressure greater than the ambient pressure; for example, a pressurized capsule may be maintained as part of a satellite payload for specific scientific experiments in which it is necessary to keep instruments under pressures higher than that of the ambient air or space conditions.

PRESSURIZED SUIT. See **pressure suit—full; pressure suit—partial.**

PRESTAGE. Prelaunch engine combustion sequence in which a partial flow of propellants (usually by gravity) is started, and combustion chamber ignition occurs. Main stage follows as propellant pumping systems "ram" fuel under maximum pressure into the combustion chamber. Also: *preliminary stage*. See **main stage.**

PRIMARY. The spatial body or central force field about which a satellite or other body orbits, or from which it is escaping, or toward which it is falling. The primary body of the moon is the earth; the primary body of the earth is the sun. A lunar orbital vehicle is one that changes its primary body; it escapes the earth to take up orbit about the moon.

PRIMARY COSMIC RAYS. High-energy particles originating outside the earth's atmosphere; the primary cosmic rays appear to come from all directions in space. See **cosmic radiation.**

PRIMARY VOICE LINK. In a spacecraft in which there are several frequencies employed for voice communications, that radio transceiver promising the most efficient voice communications under all conditions. Usually VHF (Very High Frequency).

PROBABILITY. In statistics, the chance that a prescribed event will occur, represented as a number greater than zero but less than one. The probability of an impossible event is zero, and that of an inevitable event is one.

PROBE. Any device inserted in an environment for the purpose of obtaining information about the environment; specifically, an instrumented vehicle moving through the upper atmosphere or space, or landing upon another celestial body in order to obtain information about the specific environment. See **lunar probe.**

PROGRAM. To put into an electronic guidance unit or other electronic sequencer a particular *event* or *action,* as in "to program a roll maneuver," or "to program the flight for an early thrust cutoff."

PROGRAMMED ROLL. An automatically controlled roll of a vertical ascent booster vehicle, usually executed during the vertical ascent prior to pitchover. See **pitchover.**

PROGRAMMED TURN. The turn of a ballistic rocket booster from vertical motion, after liftoff, to a curved path approximating the desired powered flight trajectory prior to the initiation of guidance. Control signals are normally provided by a device in which nominal values for thrust, propellant mass flow, specific impulse, aerodynamic loads, winds, and other trajectory-disturbing influences are mechanized. Correction for off-nominal performance is not provided.

PROGRAMMING. Movement of a booster vehicle through assigned trajectory maneuvers in flight, as when a booster launches from a vertical position, then programs over toward horizontal flight.

PROJECT 7969. A 1956 Air Force "Manned Ballistic Rocket Research System" study, with the specific task of recovering a manned capsule from orbital conditions. By early 1958 seven major industrial firms under Air Force contract had developed advanced plans for an orbiting manned capsule, and the Air Force and NACA (National Advisory Committee for Aeronautics) began to work together on the program. By June 1958, with full and official cognizance of ARPA (Advanced Research Projects Agency, Department of Defense), the vehicle configuration was well established. The Air Force proposal was to boost a man into orbit with an ICBM (plus a suitable upper stage), observe the man's capacity to withstand the environment and function effectively, and then recover him by ballistic re-entry, to be initiated with a retro-rocket and final landing by parachute. The finally accepted plan called for a biocapsule to support a man in orbit for at least 24 hours. The development program called for the recovery from orbit of small satellites as part of the Discoverer program; mice and primates were to be included in these small recoverable packages. Intermediate-size satellites with large primates would then be orbited, followed by the full-size ballistic-shaped biocapsule. This man-size vehicle would be orbited first with instruments, then with large primates, and, finally, with a man aboard. At this time and as the program progressed rapidly, NASA (National Aeronautics and Space Administration) had not yet been created. The manned space capsule was built in mockup form, life-support system contracts were awarded, NACA conducted aerodynamic data tests, full-scale water impact tests, full-scale airdrops of the capsule and parachute system, and developed the formed-couch (contour couch) pilot support system. In August of 1958 NASA was created by law. A joint ARPA-NASA Manned Satellite Panel was established, and on October 7, 1958, the NASA Space Task Group was formed. This group took over the Air Force program, and Project Mercury was established.

PROJECT MERCURY. See **Mercury, Project.**

PROJECT MONA. See **Mona, Project.**

PROMINENCE. A filament-like protuberance from the visible portion of the sun.

PRONE POSITION. Prone position for pilots was a feature tested to determine in-crease of pilot tolerance to high g forces of aerial maneuvers. Increased tolerance resulted, but the position proved excessively uncomfortable over long mission times, and program was abandoned.

PROPAGATION. In astronautics terminology, the term to describe the manner in which an electromagnetic wave, such as a radar signal, timing signal, or ray of light, travels from one point to another.

PROPELLANT. Any one of the separate ingredients that go into a liquid mixture of fuel and oxidizer or additive. Also, the mixture of fuel and oxidizer or additive, either in a liquid or solid state, which when ignited in a combustion chamber changes into hot gases with a large increase in pressure. These gases, when released by means of a nozzle into a jet stream, cause a reaction opposite in direction to that of the jet stream, thus propelling the vehicle attached to the nozzle in the direction of the reaction.

PROPRIOCEPTIVE STIMULATION. Stimulation originating within the deeper structures of the body (muscles, tendons, joints, etc.) for sensing body position and movement, and by which muscular movements can be adjusted with a great degree of accuracy and equilibrium can be maintained. See **equilibrium and orientation.**

PROPULSION SECTION. That part of a rocket or spacecraft vehicle that contains the propulsion system.

PROSPECTOR. A robot-controlled lunar-landing logistics vehicle (third in the robot exploration lunar series, following the Ranger and Surveyor series) designed to land many different cargo and instrument payloads. Intended for establishing on the moon a small depot of supplies and equipment, including surface transportation and small rocket vehicles with re-entry capability to be sent under automatic control back to earth. Also intended as an emergency lunar shelter during intense radiation storms in space.

PROTON. A subatomic particle having a positive charge equal to the negative charge of the electron but of 1,837 times the mass; a constituent of all atomic nuclei.

PROTOTYPE. A model of a vehicle (booster rocket, staging rocket, capsule, aerospace craft) that is suitable for complete evaluation of form, design, and performance. A prototype model utilizes approved parts and is representative of the final equipment. It usually follows an experimental model and precedes the production model.

PROVING STAND. A test stand for reaction engines, especially rocket engines.

PROXIMA CENTAURI. One of the two nearest known stars to the earth, about 4.3 light years distant. The other nearest star, **Alpha Centauri,** is in the same constellation.

PSI. Pounds per square inch. Used especially as a measure of ambient air or closed cabin air pressure. Sea level atmospheric pressure is normally 14.7 psi.

PSYCHOMOTOR ABILITY. Ability in muscular action ensuing directly from a mental process, as in the co-ordinated manipulation of the reaction control jet system of a spacecraft; also applies to ability in the co-ordinated manipulation of aircraft controls such as stick, rudder pedals, and throttle.

PULMONARY FUNCTION TEST. A physiological test to determine an individual's lung capacity and breathing efficiency, by measuring the amount of oxygen the individual breathes normally and during periods of exercise.

"PUNCH OUT." Pilot expression meaning to actuate the explosively propelled ejection seat of an aircraft to abandon the aircraft. See **ejection; ejection seat.**

PURGE. To rid a line or tank of residual fluid, especially fuel or oxygen remaining in the tanks or lines of a rocket after a test firing or simulated test firing, or after the scheduled firing of a booster, already fueled for firing, is scrubbed or postponed.

PU SYSTEM. Propellant Utilization System. The automatic electromechanical system for rocket booster vehicles that precisely controls the mixture ratio of the liquid propellants—oxidizer to fuel—as these propellants are consumed during the thrust period.

PYROLYSIS. Chemical decomposition through the action of heat. See **closed ecological system.**

Q

q. q = dynamic pressure. See **max** *q.*

Q-BALL. A spherical air-data sensor mounted in the nose of an aerospace vehicle (such as the X-15) that measures angles of attack and sideslip while the high-speed (hypersonic) vehicle is leaving or re-entering the earth's atmosphere. Air data are sensed through orifices in a movable sphere which is "servomechanismed" to face

Q-BALL

the relative wind (the air into which the vehicle moves directly) at all times. The pilot is thus advised of frictional heat danger arising from certain angles of attack, and is able to prevent excessive heat loads on any part of the vehicle by carrying out corrective flight maneuvers.

QUANTIZATION. The process of converting from continuous values of information to a finite number of discrete values.

QUANTUM THEORY. The theory (first stated by Max Planck in 1900) that all electromagnetic radiation is emitted and absorbed in discrete units called *quanta*. A quantum thus is a unit of radiant energy absorbed or emitted by an unrestricted atom. (An atom may absorb energy if subjected to outside radiation, an increase in temperature, electrical stimulation, or impingement by another particle.)

QUICK–DISCONNECT FITTING. In an aerospace-vehicle booster or manned-vehicle system, any electrical or other fitting designed for ready disconnection and connection, for example, oxygen-hose equipment, biosensor plug-in units, **umbilical cords.**

R

R & D. Research and Development.

RADAR. Radio Detection and Ranging. Any of certain methods or systems of using beamed and reflected radio-frequency energy (radio waves) for detecting and locating objects, for measuring their distance, azimuth, or altitude, or for other purposes such as navigating or homing. Also: the electronic equipment, sets, or devices used in any such systems; a radar set.

RADAR PROBING. The action of obtaining data on distant objects, especially spatial bodies, by means of radar signals, in which the radiated energy is reflected from the body under observation, but originates on the earth. Also: *radar astronomy.* See **radar.**

RADIAL ACCELERATION. The force imposed upon an airman attempting to abandon a stricken aircraft that has fallen out of control into a spin, in which the centrifugal force of the radial acceleration hampers and sometimes prevents movement of the airman. A force of $1.5g$ radial acceleration greatly hampers escape; $2.5g$ completely immobilizes the individual.

RADIAL VELOCITY. The velocity of approach or recession between two bodies, especially between an observer and a source of radiation.

RADIANT ENERGY. Energy that travels as a wave motion, such as radio waves, infrared waves, visible light, etc.

RADIATION. Common term for "electromagnetic radiation," "nuclear radiation," "solar radiation," etc. Specifically, the emission and propagation of energy or matter.

RADIATION BELT. See **Van Allen radiation belt.**

RADIATION INTENSITY. The rate at which ionizing radiation is being absorbed. Usually measured in roentgens per unit time.

RADIATION MEDICINE. A special branch of aerospace medicine that is concerned with the protection of health and life from the effects of radiation encountered in the upper atmosphere and space.

RADIATION PARTICLE. A particle of matter, such as an atomic nucleus, that has been radiated at high velocity from a given source.

RADIATION PRESSURE. Generally, the pressure exerted upon a body by electromagnetic radiation incident upon the body. The pressure of the sun's radiation upon the earth, for example, is small, about 2 lbs. to the square mile. See **solar sail.**

RADIATION REFLECTOR. Anything that *reflects* radiation, as contrasted to a radiation shield that may reflect and/or absorb radiation to protect a given object or area. See **radiation shield.**

RADIATION SCATTERING. The diversion of radiation—thermal, electromagnetic, or nuclear—from its original path as a result of interactions (or collisions) with atoms, molecules, or larger particles in the atmosphere or other media between the source of radiation and a point at some distance away. As a result of scattering, radiation (especially gamma rays and neutrons) will be received at a given point from many directions instead of only from the direction of the source.

RADIATION SHIELD. Loosely, any device used to protect bodies from the harmful or undesired effects of radiation, nuclear, thermal, cosmic, or the like. A nuclear radiation shield absorbs rather than reflects nuclear particles and radiations. More specifically: a device used on certain types of instruments to prevent unwanted radiation from biasing the measurement of a quantity.

RADIATION STORMS. Storms of electrical particles hurled out by the sun during solar disturbances, raising radiation levels in space to the extent of possible serious radiation injury to astronauts.

RADIATOR. (1) Any source of radiant energy, especially electromagnetic radiation. (2) A device that dissipates heat from something, as from water or oil, not necessarily by radiation only. (Generally, the application of the term *radiator*—in sense 2—or *heat exchanger* to a particular apparatus depends upon the point of view: if the emphasis is upon merely getting rid of heat, *radiator* is most often used, or sometimes *cooler;* if the emphasis is upon transferring heat, *heat exchanger* is used—but these distinctions do not always hold true.)

RADIO ASTRONOMY. The study of celestial objects through observation of radio frequency waves emitted or reflected by these objects.

RADIOBIOLOGY. A branch of biology concerned with the effects produced on living organisms by radiation.

RADIO COMMAND. A radio signal transmitted to a vehicle in flight or orbit to which the vehicle will respond, either in terms of specific equipment, flight maneuver, or any other response.

"RADIO EAR." Slang expression for a radio telescope. See **radio telescope.**

RADIO FIX. The determination of a navigational position by an aircraft or aerospace craft by ascertaining the direction of radio signals received from two or more sending stations, the locations of which are known.

RADIO FREQUENCIES. Normally expressed in kilocycles per second (kc/s) at and below 30,000 kc/s, and megacycles per second (mc/s) above this frequency:

Very Low Frequency (VLF)	Below 30 kc/s
Low Frequency (LF)	30 to 300 kc/s
Medium Frequency (MF)	300 to 3,000 kc/s
High Frequency (HF)	3,000 to 30,000 kc/s
Very High Frequency (VHF)	30,000 kc/s to 300 mc/s
Ultra High Frequency (UHF)	300 to 3,000 mc/s
Super High Frequency (SHF)	3,000 to 30,000 mc/s
Extremely High Frequency (EHF)	30,000 to 300,000 mc/s

RADIO–INERTIAL GUIDANCE. Rocket booster guidance system divided into (1) the onboard guidance and flight-control system, and (2) a ground-located guidance station. See **Atlas-D guidance system.**

RADIOMETER. Any instrument that detects and measures the intensity of thermal radiation, especially infrared radiation.

RADIOMETRIC STAR TRACKER. A tracker attuned to the thermal radiation of the celestial body being tracked.

RADIO SUN. The sun as revealed by a **radio telescope,** its limiting boundary being indefinite, not sharp, and in diameter about twice that of the visible sun.

RADIO TELESCOPE. A radio receiving station for detecting radio waves emitted by celestial bodies or by artificial bodies in space, especially deep-space probes. See **Jodrell Bank; radio astronomy.**

RADIO TRANSMITTER. An electromagnetic device that transmits electric impulses at frequencies below those normally used in radar or television. The impulses may be excited by non-auditory instruments, as in the minitransmitters of an earth satellite, by the voice, or by other sounds.

RADIO WAVE. An electromagnetic wave with a frequency from 10 to more than 30,-000,000 kilocycles, or a length of from 30 kilometers to less than 1 centimeter. The radio wave travels with the velocity of light, and differs from a light wave in being of greater length. Radio waves penetrating the atmosphere range in length from more than 20 meters to less than a centimeter. Were our eyes sensitive to these wave lengths, the sun would appear more than twice as large in diameter.

RADOME. A protective dome or domelike covering for a radar antenna and sometimes for other radar equipment, such covering being pervious to radio-frequency radiation. Radomes are used extensively in ground-based and flight systems.

RANGE OF INDIFFERENCE. The extent to which departure occurs from originally or initially tolerated standards of operation (as in reading an instrument dial or gauge). Also: a manifestation of fatigue, an operator's tolerance of, or indifference to, errors.

RANGER. A series of elaborate scientific probes for the study and investigation of characteristics of the moon as observed both from space and from the lunar surface. Launch vehicle is the Atlas-Agena B. The Ranger vehicle weighs between 650 and 800 lbs. in various configurations and is generally a cone that is formed by struts and braces atop a hexagonal base, with large solar panels extending from the base. In "orbital flight configuration" with solar panels and antenna extended, it is 13 feet high and 17

feet in diameter through the panels. The Ranger series, the second in extensive lunar studies following the early Pioneer satellites of Project Mona begun in 1958, are providing information for future and more complicated missions by investigating control and navigation, guidance systems, cosmic rays, magnetic fields, communications, dust particles, radiation, and other areas of study. Some Rangers are to carry a 25-inch balsawood lunar capsule and retro-rocket to be rough-landed on the lunar surface to transmit seismographic data back to earth. Some Rangers will also carry television cameras for closeup studies of the lunar surface.

The Ranger program has suffered critical failures in its first five missions. In late 1962 a Ranger Inquiry Board initiated drastic management changes in the Ranger program, with cancellation of Ranger VI; three Ranger shots are now scheduled for 1963.

RANGE SAFETY OFFICER (RSO). The individual in the main control room of Central Control at Cape Canaveral (or a similar position at any launch site) who is charged with insuring that a booster vehicle will not

RANGE SAFETY OFFICER (RSO)

during its flight present a hazard to any person or persons, or structures, as a result of deviating from its preassigned flight path. If the booster in flight fails to remain on prearranged flight path, the RSO sends a radio command signal to detonate explosive charges in the booster to (1) immediately cease powered flight, and (2) destroy the booster in flight.

RANGE SURVEILLANCE. The surveillance of a ballistic vehicle (missile or space booster) range by means of electronic and other equipment.

RAPID DECOMPRESSION. See **explosive decompression.**

RATE RECEIVER. A guidance antenna that receives a signal from a rocket booster or other inflight vehicle as to its rate of speed.

RATE TRANSMITTER. A guidance antenna that signals the desired rate of speed for a rocket booster or other inflight vehicle.

RATION DENSE. Foods which, through processing, have been reduced in volume and quantity to a small compact package without appreciable loss of food value, quality, or other minimum basic values, with a high yield in proportion to space occupied, such as dehydrates and concentrates. Especially valuable in manned space missions and in survival kits.

RAT'S NEST. A specified area within a rocket or spacecraft vehicle which is unusually crowded with complicated circuitry and electronic equipment. See **clunge.**

RCS. Reaction Control System.

REACTION CONTROL JETS. Jets used to control the attitude of a craft such as the Project Mercury capsule or X-15 when outside the atmosphere. The Mercury capsule has 16 fixed and movable nozzles through which steam generated by the decomposition of hydrogen peroxide within the capsule is ejected under pressure. Reaction to these jet forces provides attitude movement and con-

trol of the capsule. Also termed *altitude control jets; reactor jets; steering jets; thrusters.*

REACTION ENGINE. An engine that develops thrust by its reaction to ejection of a substance from it; specifically, such an engine that ejects a jet or stream of gases created by the burning of fuel within the engine. A reaction engine operates in accordance with Newton's third law of motion, i.e., to every action (force) there is an equal and opposite reaction. Both rocket engines and jet engines are reaction engines.

REACTION TIME. The time interval between the command to launch and the actual time of launch of a rocket booster vehicle. Also: the time interval between the demonstrated need to initiate a control sequence maneuver as determined by a pilot, and the moment when he responds to the need.

READOUT. The action of a radio transmitter sending data either simultaneously with the acquisition of the data, or by the playing of a magnetic tape upon which the data have been recorded.

READOUT STATION. A recording or receiving radio station where data are received from a transmitter in a manned spacecraft, satellite, probe or other spacecraft.

READY LIGHTS. Lights on an instrument or launch-control console, a range-readiness control, or any other control board, console, or panel, that signify that a certain event or series of events is ready to happen; green lights signify that all is clear for an operation or event to proceed.

READY ROOM. A room in which a pilot or astronaut receives final attention to flight needs before beginning a mission. See **Hangar S.**

REAL–TIME OPERATION. The time actually involved in human or machine performance of an activity, exclusive of preparation, rest periods, adjustments, etc. In Project Mercury, during the critical phases of a manned flight—liftoff, ascent, and preparation for re-entry—the Goddard Space Flight

Center computer facility works on a *real-time* basis. All mission flight data are computed down to half-second intervals. The system receives, moves, analyzes, predicts, transmits, and displays data so quickly that control personnel can follow events within seconds of their actually taking place.

REBOUND. A passive communications satellite system with the first launching scheduled for 1963, using the Atlas-Agena B as the booster. A joint USAF–NASA project with a system of three rigidized, low-orbit mylar balloons, each of approximately 135-foot diameter (Echo II type).

RECEPTOR. A sensory nerve ending that receives physical and chemical stimuli. See **mechanoreceptor.**

RECIRCULATORY SYSTEM. In a closed spacecraft, the special devices and equipment, chemicals, and processes which reuse human waste products to grow food and provide pure drinking water.

RECOMPRESSION. The process by which a person who has suffered decompression undergoes a controlled increase in air pressure, as in returning from flight under low ambient air pressure conditions.

RECOVERY. The procedure or series of actions occurring when the whole of a satellite, spacecraft, or other vehicle, or a section, instrumentation package, or other part of a rocket or satellite vehicle, is recovered after a launch; the result of this procedure.

RECOVERY AIDS. Devices employed to assist search and recovery units in locating a spacecraft down at sea or on the land. Include flashing lights, radio homing beacons, dye markers, flares, **sofar** bombs, smoke bombs, and other devices to draw attention to the spacecraft.

RECOVERY FORCES. The men, ships, planes, helicopters, amphibious vehicles, and all equipment related to a task force at sea, on the land, and airborne that is used to track, search for, and recover a manned spacecraft. The recovery force is active from the moment of launch until both the crew and the spacecraft are safely recovered.

RECOVERY FORCES. Sikorsky HSS amphibious helicopter recovering Mercury capsule

RECYCLE. To reschedule a countdown in time, to an earlier phase of the count; e.g., recycling from T minus 60 minutes to T minus 100 minutes.

REDOUT. A condition produced by sustained negative *g* that results in high neck arterial blood pressure and pooling of blood in the eyes, resulting in a literal condition of seeing red and a loss of normal vision. See **negative-g tolerance.**

REDSTONE. A short-range ballistic missile modified for space-vehicle test flights and manned suborbital space flights. Redstone had 78,000 lbs. thrust, and propelled capsules to slightly over 5,000 mph, to a height of approximately 115 miles and a range of 300 miles. Astronauts Alan B. Shepard and Virgil I. Grissom made Redstone-boosted suborbital flights. The Redstone is now phased out of manned space-flight tests, and the launch gantry system at Canaveral has been dismantled. (Illustration, page 164.)

RE-ENTRY. The event occurring when a spacecraft or other object comes back into the sensible atmosphere after being rocketed to altitudes above the sensible atmosphere, either as a vehicle in a ballistic trajectory or in orbit; the action involved in this event. See **re-entry profile.**

REDSTONE carrying Mercury capsule being readied for suborbital flight of Alan B. Shepard, Jr., May 5, 1961

RE–ENTRY BODY. That part of an orbiting spacecraft designed safely to re-enter earth's atmosphere and descend to the surface.

RE-ENTRY CORRIDOR. See **re-entry window.**

RE–ENTRY PROFILE. The complete spectrum of all events relating to re-entry. For the Mercury spacecraft, the re-entry maneu- ver requires a distance of approximately one-quarter orbit. As the capsule approaches the U.S. West Coast· (3-orbit mission), retro-rockets fire to reduce velocity by approximately 350 feet per second. Retropack then jettisons and capsule assumes re-entry attitude angle of 2° from the horizontal. Capsule begins to encounter more dense atmosphere over southern U.S., near Georgia-Florida region, at altitude of 55 miles. At this point temperatures begin to rise sharply on ablative heat shield. On nominal mission, peak shield heating of 3,000°F. will occur at 37 miles altitude with descending velocity of 15,000 mph. Peak temperature—maximum heat pulse—is sustained approximately 5–6 minutes. Between 46 miles and 12 miles altitude, over a slant range of 460 miles, capsule decelerates from 17,000 mph in 3 minutes to 1,350 mph. See also **retropack, retrorockets; shock wave.**

RE–ENTRY VEHICLE. A space vehicle designed to return with its payload to earth through the sensible atmosphere without injury or damage to the payload.

RE–ENTRY WINDOW. The area at the limits of the earth's atmosphere through which a spacecraft in a given trajectory can pass to accomplish a successful re-entry. Also: **re-entry corridor.**

REFRACTORY CERAMICS. A coating or outer surface for the re-entry body of a space vehicle or probe. Refractory ceramics, such as the oxides of aluminum, silicon, and zirconium, resist oxidation and retain strength until near their melting points, around 2,700°C.

REFRACTORY–LIKE STATE. A biologic condition in which the nervous and muscular systems become less responsive to stimuli.

REGENERATIVE COOLING. The cooling of a part of an engine by the propellant, as it is delivered to the combustion chamber or nozzle, being circulated around the part to be cooled, prior to its combustion.

RELATIVISTIC. In general, said of material, such as a subatomic particle, moving at speeds which are an appreciable fraction of the speed of light.

RELATIVITY. A principle that postulates the equivalence of the description of the universe, in terms of physical laws, by various observers or for various frames of reference.

RELAY. An active repeater experimental communications satellite to be placed in a low orbit. Booster is Thor-Delta; first launching was made in late 1962, with additional

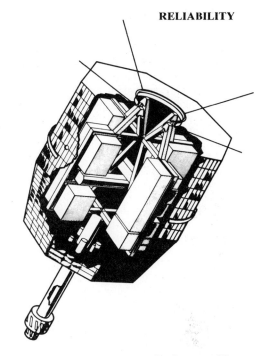

RELAY. Cutaway of communications satellite system to replace original Telstar satellite

launchings scheduled for 1963. The 150-lb. satellite is spin-stabilized, and carries two complete and separate communications transponders, each of which is capable of handling a standard TV channel. Ground stations are in Britain, France, Brazil, and Germany.

RELIABILITY. A quality or property built into, or inherent in, a thing that indicates that the thing will probably perform its specified function without failure under given conditions for a specified period of time. Reliability is measured in terms of its degree of probability. For example, the Atlas-D booster has some 300,000 parts, including all components and subsystems. For a successful flight every part must work perfectly. Engineers provide a comparison of the reliability to achieve complete success in a single firing with the operation of the modern automobile. To operate with the reliability of the Atlas-D booster as it functioned in the flights of Astronauts John Glenn, Scott Carpenter, and Wally Schirra, a car would have to run 24 hours a day, 7 days a week, without maintenance, without any parts wearing out, and operating under the worst conditions at the highest possible speeds and with a continuous but fluctuating acceleration. If this could be done with an auto for 30 years, day and night continuously, without breakdowns—then we would achieve reliability comparable to that attained in the astronauts' flights.

RELIABILITY TESTING. Testing aimed at achieving a high degree of reliability in the functioning of the object being tested.

RELIEF TUBE. A facility provided in aircraft and spacecraft for urine disposal for male pilots during extended flight within a limited-area cabin or cockpit. Used also during orbital flights as standard medical equipment for urinalysis samples. (During the MA-6 mission of Astronaut John Glenn, a urine sample of 800 cubic centimeters was taken just prior to retrofire. Physiological action in the weightless state was "completely normal.")

REMAINING BODY. That part of a rocket booster vehicle or spacecraft system that remains after the separation of the fallaway section. See **fallaway section.**

REMOTE VELOCITY. The velocity of an object taken as a whole relative to the surrounding fluid, as distinguished from the local velocity of any of its parts, i.e., a comparison of the airspeed of an aircraft as separate from the velocity of the propeller tips of an aircraft.

RENDEZVOUS. The event of two or more objects meeting at a preconceived time and place. A rendezvous would be involved, for example, in servicing or resupplying a space station—in this instance the activity is more specifically *rendezvous and docking.*

RENDEZVOUS RADAR. Radar modified for use in orbital rendezvous and docking. The rendezvous radar system is carried in the seeking vehicle. At a distance of approximately 250 miles from the target vehicle, the rendezvous radar "locks on" to a transponder located externally on the target vehicle. Information from the radar data feeds into a computer system with immediate visual readout to provide angles, ranges, and

range rates for guidance to assure rendezvous and then docking.

RESEARCH. A process of scientific investigation prior to and during development. It has for its aim the discovery of new scientific facts, techniques, and natural laws; more specifically, an extension of the "state-of-the-art."

RESEARCH, APPLIED. Research aimed at specific application of scientific laws, principles, and phenomena. In contrast to basic research, the prospect of practical application of the results is a primary motive for applied research. Frequently even the methods to be used are identified before work commences.

RESEARCH VEHICLE. Any contrivance that carries something used to obtain new data or to confirm established data, especially data about the environment through which the vehicle passes. See **probe.**

RESERVE LANDING SYSTEM. In Project Mercury, a second—standby—main parachute of 63-foot diameter which the astronaut can deploy manually in event of failure of the primary main parachute. See **landing parachute.**

RESOLUTION. Distinguishing among and rendering visible separate parts; to resolve lines in the spectrum. Resolution is expressed as a factor that approaches 100 for perfect resolution in photographs (as broadcast from a space vehicle or received aboard a space vehicle), astronomical observations, etc.

RESPIRATION. The exchange of oxygen and carbon dioxide between an organism and the gases in its environment. Oxygen is taken into the body and utilized in the combustion of food. It is from this oxidization that energy is derived to operate the entire mechanism which keeps the body alive and active. The principal end product of this combustion is carbon dioxide; its elimination completes the process of respiration. In the mammalian body, two divisions of respiration are recognized—external and internal. *External respiration,* with which aerospace physiology is primarily concerned, involves the exchange of gases between the blood in the capillaries of the lungs and the external atmospheric environment, as represented by air in the air sacs of the lungs. *Internal respiration* is the exchange of gases between the body's tissue cells and the blood, as the blood passes through the minute capillaries permeating every tissue. See **alveolar air; alveoli; breathing, process of.**

RESPIRATORY PHYSIOLOGY. See **basic medical sciences.**

RESPONSER. An electronic device used to receive an electronic challenge and to display a reply thereto.

RESTRAINT HARNESS. A system of webbing and/or straps that secure a pilot's body to a rigid assembly of his craft, in order to restrain the body and limbs from any dangerous movements during periods of acceleration or deceleration, or severe oscillations or buffeting.

RESULTANT FORCE. See **force.**

RETINAL ADAPTABILITY. The ability of the retina to adapt to various field brightnesses; the physiological process by which the retina adapts to a large range of brightness in order (1) to maintain a high degree of constancy of the visual sensation at varying levels of illumination; (2) at a specific brightness level, to increase retinal sensitivity to the contrasting sensation (red and green, black and white, blue and yellow, etc.); and (3) to keep to a minimum visual discomfort (and possible disability) resulting from overexposure to extreme brightness fields. Retinal adaptability is of major concern in flight at extreme altitude and in space where brightness contrasts are most pronounced.

RETROGRADE MOTION. Orbital motion opposite in direction to that normal in spatial bodies within a given system. A retrograde satellite of the earth would orbit from east to west.

RETROGRADE SATELLITE. A satellite that orbits the earth in a westerly direction, i.e., from east to west.

RESTRAINT HARNESS. Boeing hammock-seat restraint system

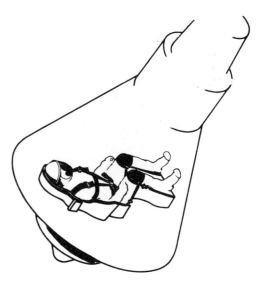

RESTRAINT HARNESS in semi-supine contour couch system of Mercury capsule

RETROPACK. A package of rockets, attached to a spacecraft, which can be fired to provide thrust in a direction the same as the craft's direction of flight, and thus to reduce its speed and so initiate descent from orbit. In Project Mercury, the rocket package is at the base of the Mercury capsule, strapped across the front of the heat shield. It contains 3 posigrade rockets and 3 retro-rockets. The retropack is jettisoned from the capsule after retro-rocket fire. In emergency, re-entry may be made with the retropack still fastened, as happened during the re-entry of Mercury-Atlas 6 on February 20, 1962.

RETRO-ROCKET. A rocket fitted on or in a spacecraft, satellite, or the like to produce thrust opposed to forward motion. In Project Mercury, 3 small retro-rockets are mounted at the blunt-end base of the Mercury capsule, and secured to the heat shield by metal straps. Each rocket burns for 10 seconds with individual thrust of 350

Mercury capsule RETRO–ROCKETS firing simultaneously

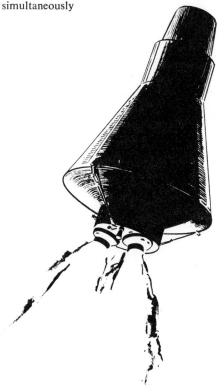

lbs. The retros are fired in ripple fashion at 5-second intervals; actual burning time (MA-6) is 22 seconds total. They decelerate the capsule by 350/400 feet per second (depending upon angle of fire, etc.). Time from retro firing until impact into ocean is approximately 20 minutes.

RETROSEQUENCE. The entire sequence of required events necessary to initiate retro-rocket fire for spacecraft re-entry from orbit. The retrosequence involves checking of all calculations for time-sequence activities; setting timer clocks and automatic controls; aligning spacecraft attitudes; activating automatic sequencers; firing the retro-rockets; establishing re-entry attitude; jettisoning spent rockets; beginning re-entry.

RETROTHRUST. The thrust of rockets in the direction of flight of an orbiting spacecraft in order to decelerate that spacecraft to begin re-entry.

REVOLVE. To move in a path about a focal point, as the earth revolves about the sun; the revolution of a body about a focal point or primary.

RIFT. Reactor In Flight Test. A nuclear rocket engine system programmed for flight test with the Saturn C-1 vehicle in the late 1960's.

RIFT. Reactor In Flight Test

RINGSAIL PARACHUTE. A Northrop-developed recovery parachute system for the Mercury capsule and other heavy weights for atmospheric descent at controlled speed. The basic Ringsail design is a series of concentric cloth rings, joined by radial tapes. The canopy differs from the standard Ringslot type in that the co-ordinates are modified to provide a higher average angle of attack in each ring. This gives the inflated canopy a sawtooth profile with sharp edges pointing downward instead of the smooth curve of conventional canopies. The Ringsail thus achieves a 35% increase in drag over the standard parachute. See **parachute.**

RISERS. Fabric straps connected to the shroud lines of a parachute. Manipulation of the risers during parachute descent enables the jumper to direct his flight, his positioning, and speed of descent. See **parachute.**

RJ-1. A liquid fuel with a higher density than the kerosene-based fuel RP-1, and with greater energy yield. See **RP-1.**

ROCKET. A thrust-producing system, or a complete vehicle which receives its thrust from the ejection of hot gases generated from material carried within the system, not requiring intake of any gaseous or liquid substances. Rockets may be of the liquid- or solid-propellant types.

ROCKET ENGINE. A rocket propulsive device that is relatively complicated in its workings, as distinguished from a rocket motor. The liquid-fuel engine with its elaborate pumping equipment, pressure chambers, fuel lines, electrical connections, etc., is more appropriately called an engine than the solid-fuel motor.

ROCKET ENGINE IDENTIFICATIONS, U.S. ADVANCED BOOSTERS. *H.1 Engine:* 165,000 and 188,000 lbs. thrust ratings, for Saturn C-1 first-stage propulsion. *J.2 Engine:* 200,000 lbs. thrust ratings, for upper stages of Saturn C-5 and Nova vehicles. *F.1 Engine:* 1,500,000 lbs. thrust ratings, for Saturn C-5 and Nova first-stage propulsion. *M.1 Engine:* 1,200,000 lbs.

F.1 ROCKET ENGINE for Saturn

thrust ratings, for second and intermediate stages of Nova booster vehicles. *A.3 Engine:* 15,000 lbs. thrust ratings, for upper stage of Centaur and Saturn C-1.

ROCKET MOTOR. Specifically, a rocket utilizing a solid propellant. See **rocket engine.**

ROCKET PROPELLANT. Any agent used for consumption or combustion in a rocket and from which the rocket derives its thrust, such as a fuel, oxidizer, additive, catalyst, or any compound or mixture of these.

ROCKET PROPULSION. Reaction propulsion wherein both the fuel and the oxidizer, generating the hot gases expended through a nozzle, are carried as part of the rocket engine. Specifically, rocket propulsion differs from jet propulsion in that jet propulsion utilizes atmospheric air as an oxidizer whereas rocket propulsion utilizes nitric acid or a similar compound contained within the vehicle as an oxidizer.

Human test subject undergoing severe decelera-tion load on ROCKET SLED

ROCKET SLED. A steel sled mounted on special slippers that grip railroad tracks, and propelled at very high speeds by solid-and/or liquid-propellant rockets. Rocket sleds are used for acceleration-and-decelera-tion and windblast tests on human subjects, animals, and equipment. On one rocket-sled test run, Air Force Colonel John Paul Stapp reached a speed of 632 mph. The sled then crashed into a water barrier, and from this 632-mph speed, Colonel Stapp slammed to a full stop in 1.4 seconds.

ROCKETRY. The art and science of de-signing, developing, building, testing, and launching rockets, rocket missiles, rocket boosters, or rocket vehicles (including their subsystems), and of guiding and controlling them during launch, flight, orbit, space flight, re-entry, or impact.

ROENTGEN. The international unit for measuring a quantity of X- or gamma radia-tion, based on the ionization of air.

ROLL. The rotational or oscillatory move-ment of an aircraft, spacecraft, or similar body which takes place about a longitudinal axis through the body—called *roll* for any amount of such rotation.

ROLL CONTROL. The exercise of control over an aircraft or spacecraft so as to make it roll to a desired degree or at a desired rate, to a specified point at which the roll motion about the longitudinal axis stops.

ROPE. Reflectors of electromagnetic radia-tion consisting of long strips of metal foil. A small parachute or other device is some-times attached to each strip to reduce the rate of fall. See **chaff.**

ROTATING ROOM. A unique training and flight-simulator device at the U.S. Navy's School of Aviation Medicine at Pensacola, Florida, for advanced human disorientation studies. The rotating room is a 13-foot room built on the hub of a large centrifuge; the hub is a 22-ton flywheel. Set into spinning motion, it forms a very stable platform, much like a gyro. The room is equipped with complete living facilities for its oc-cupants to remain in motion for several days. Tests with this room have raised extremely serious problems as to the feasibility of creating "artificial gravity" through the spinning motion of a manned space station or vehicle—using rotation motion as a sub-stitute for gravity. The room occupants are visually isolated in that vision beyond the room is not possible. The direction of rota-tion at first is known to the occupants, and the rotation is quite slow—usually about six rpm. Soon after the rotation commences, the occupants no longer are conscious of any movement whatsoever. The room is so stable that there is no sensation of move-ment. Everything is fine "until one starts to move his head, and then some of the most devastating symptoms occur," explained one test subject. Those symptoms are described as "frightening." The validity of this term is explained thus: "They are frightening be-cause of the triviality of action on your part that is required to produce such devastating symptoms as nausea, vomiting, vertigo, and general malaise." Under the particular con-ditions of the room there is a major conflict between the visual sense of "no motion" and the sensations experienced by the vestib-ular apparatus of the inner ear. The stimuli which are normally suppressed or dominated by vision then have full sway, with "pretty severe" results. Some test subjects (experi-enced pilots) in the room for only 10 minutes became violently ill, and did not recover fully for *several days*. Other people who remained in the room for 2 or 3 days finally overcame their acute discomfort and illness and adapted to the room; but upon cessation of the rotation they had to back out through the same cycle of discomfort and sickness all over again. A position of sitting rest, *without any head movements*, permits essential comfort. But the slightest movement of the head can produce extreme nausea and vomiting and, at times, incapacitation.

ROTI. Recording Optical Tracking Instrument

ROTI. Recording Optical Tracking Instrument. A motion-picture camera that takes photographs at the rate of 6,400 frames per second. It is invaluable in recording vital flight-performance data on all types of boosters and flight vehicles. With a 500-inch focal length telescope, it can photograph a missile at 12,000 mph, 100 miles away. Its precision is great enough to photograph in flight a baseball hit by a batter standing 8 miles from the camera.

ROVER. *Project Rover*—a program to develop a nuclear rocket engine for deep space probes.

RP-1. Rocket Propellant, Type 1. A super-refined kerosene fuel for rockets and aircraft. Used as a rocket fuel with liquid oxygen.

RSCS. Rate Stabilization Control System. A manual-automatic control linkage of the Mercury spacecraft control system. RSCS uses a combination of manually controlled stick positions and the computing components of the automatic system (ASCS) to provide rate control of the spacecraft. RSCS senses and commands the rates of motion of the spacecraft within specified degrees, usually at a preset rate of movement of plus or minus 3° per second. See **Mercury capsule control system.**

ROTATING ROOM. At Pensacola, Florida, Astronaut John H. Glenn, Jr., tosses tennis ball into wastebasket during disorientation exercise

ROTATION. Turning of a body about an axis within the body, as the daily rotation of the earth.

RUMBLE. A form of combustion instability, especially in a liquid-propellant rocket engine, characterized by a low-pitch, low-frequency rumbling noise; the noise made in this kind of combustion.

S

SABOT. Lightweight carrier in which a sub-caliber projectile is centered to permit firing the projectile in the larger-caliber weapon. The carrier fills the bore of the weapon from which the projectile is fired; it is normally discarded a short distance from the muzzle. By extension, a device installed in the neck of the Mercury spacecraft, and used, combined with a piston, forcibly to eject the parachutes of the spacecraft during the lower atmospheric part of re-entry and descent.

SAFETY PIN. A thin metal pin or rod that is inserted into any equipment—such as an explosive seat-ejection system—to prevent inadvertent actuation of the system, by blocking a firing pin from striking a detonator. Any device used to prevent inadvertent actuation of a system prior to the moment when it is desired to "arm" or to activate the system.

SAINT. Satellite Inspector. A remote-controlled and monitored satellite of approximately 4,000-lb. payload to be directed to the immediate vicinity of potentially unfriendly satellites for identification and inspection while in orbit. Atlas-Agena B is the booster. Advanced Saint models will have satellite-destruction capabilities. (In late 1962 a "critical review" reduced the Saint program to study-development status, phasing it out as a planned operational weapon space system.)

SAMOS. Formerly known as Sentry. An advanced reconnaissance-systems military satellite carrying extensive camera and other surveillance equipment. The research Samos satellites weigh 4,100 lbs., are launched by the Atlas-Agena B. The satellite has a jettisonable camera package which is ejected from orbit and recovered by the air-snatch system, as tested in the Discoverer program. Scheduled to become operational in late 1962 or early 1963.

SARCOPHAGUS installation in centrifuge at USAF Wright Aeromedical Laboratory, Dayton, Ohio

SARCOPHAGUS. A mummy-case-shaped tank in which a test subject is immersed in water on a semi-supine couch for increased tolerance of positive-g forces. See **water-cushion principle.**

SARAH BEACON. A radio homing transmitter device in the Mercury capsule that is activated at 10,000 feet during the atmospheric descent.

SATELLITE. (1) An attendant body that revolves about another body, the primary; especially, in the solar system, a secondary body, or moon, that revolves about a planet.

S-48 SATELLITE, designed to measure electron density distribution in ionosphere from 188 to 250 miles high. A typical scientific satellite

(2) A man-made object that revolves about a spatial body, such as Explorer I, Sputnik, or the Mercury spacecraft orbiting about the earth.

SATELLOID. A vehicle that revolves about the earth or other body, but at such altitudes as to require sustaining thrust to balance drag. The thrust would be of a low order, but maintained constantly.

SATELLOID FLIGHT. Powered satellite flight at altitudes below mechanical borders of the atmosphere.

SATURN. Advanced, high-energy, heavy-payload booster systems for U.S. manned and instrumented space missions for earth orbit, lunar, and planetary missions. Code identifications include *C* for entire vehicle (as C-1, C-5), and *S* for separate Saturn stages (as S-I, S-IVB). *SA* refers to a particular production item (as SA-8, SA-9). The first 10 Saturn C-1 assemblies will be known as SA-1 through SA-10. Beginning with the 11th vehicle, Chrysler-built, the operational Saturn C-1 vehicle coding begins, using three-digit codes, being SA-111 rather than SA-11. See succeeding entries.

SATURN C-1. Two- or three-stage rocket booster vehicle for: heavy-payload manned earth-orbital flights; **boiler plate** (q.v.) Apollo orbiting and high-energy re-entry tests; heavy payload scientific-satellite missions to moon and planets. As earth-orbiting vehicle, C-1 has S-I first stage of 1,500,000 lbs. thrust, S-IV second stage of 90,000 lbs. thrust. As lunar and interplanetary probe vehicle launch system, C-1 adds the S-V third stage of 30,000 lbs. thrust.

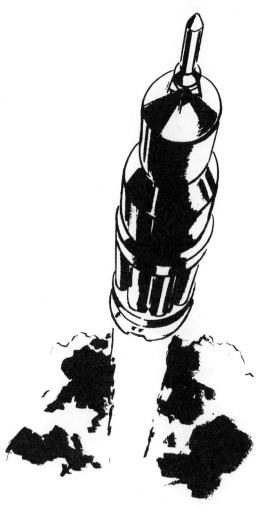

SATURN C-1 two-stage booster ascends for earth-orbiting tests of Apollo Command and Service Module units

SATURN C-1B. The Saturn C-1 as an advanced version for greater flexibility in Apollo and other missions. The C-1B mounts the fixed aerodynamic fins on the S-I booster as on the initial operational vehicle, but the upper stage—S-IV—is replaced by the S-IVB stage, with a single J.2 200,000-lb. thrust engine. Saturn C-1B has an orbital payload capacity of 29,000 lbs., 9,000 lbs. greater than C-1. The C-1B vehicle will be used for experimental work in rendezvous and docking techniques and procedures with the Apollo lunar landing program.

SATURN C-2, C-3, C-4. Booster-vehicle configurations employing varied staging "building blocks" for advanced manned and unmanned space missions. The C-2, C-3, and C-4 vehicles were abandoned early in 1962 in favor of the C-1 and C-5 boosters, when the NASA decision was made to proceed from the 1,500,000 lbs. thrust first-stage C-1 vehicle, directly to the Saturn C-5 with a first-stage thrust of 7,500,000 lbs.

SATURN C-5. Also known as *Advanced Saturn*. An advanced three-stage booster vehicle intended for heavy-payload (120 tons) low earth orbit (300 miles) missions, and for boosting Apollo spaceship-module systems to the moon. S-IC first stage has 7,500,000 lbs. thrust; S-II second stage has 1,000,000 lbs. thrust; S-IVB third stage has 200,000 lbs. thrust.

SATURN S-I. First stage of Saturn C-1 launch vehicle booster. Eight H.1 engines of planned 188,000 lbs. thrust each for orbital missions, with S-I stage launch thrust of 1,500,000 lbs. (Initial tests are with H.1, burning kerosene/liquid oxygen, rated at 165,000 lbs. thrust each, for S-I stage thrust of 1,300,000 lbs.) Eventual development of 8-H.1 engine configuration for S-I stage is launch thrust of 2,000,000 lbs.

SATURN S-1C (1). Saturn C-5 first-stage vehicle with 4 F.1 engines developing total thrust of 6,000,000 lbs. Production tooling and work for 25 S-IC stages had begun when NASA uprated the stage to 5 F.1 motors for total stage thrust rating of 7,500,-000 lbs.; the 5-motor first-stage vehicle is known as the S-IB. In hopes of keeping down

the confusion of these designations, NASA in mid-1962 reverted to the S-1C designation for the 5-engine vehicle.

SATURN S-1C (2). Saturn C-5 first-stage vehicle, finalized in designation coding as having 5 F.1 engines, with total stage thrust of 7,500,000 lbs., and assigned to Apollo Lunar Orbital Rendezvous missions (LOR). See **Apollo.**

SATURN S-II. Second stage of Saturn C-5 launch vehicle. S-II stage has 5 J.2 engines burning liquid oxygen/liquid hydrogen, each of 200,000 lbs. thrust, for S-II stage rating of 1,000,000 lbs. thrust.

SATURN S-IV. Second stage of Saturn C-1 launch vehicle. Six A.3 liquid-oxygen/liquid-hydrogen engines, each of 15,000 lbs. thrust for S-IV stage total of 90,000 lbs. thrust.

SATURN S-IVB. Third stage of Saturn C-5 launch vehicle. One J.2 engine, burning liquid oxygen/liquid hydrogen, developing 200,000 lbs. thrust. Also, second stage for C-1B.

SATURN S-V. Second stage of Centaur booster vehicle adapted for Saturn C-1 program. A.3 engines burning liquid oxygen/liquid hydrogen for total stage thrust rating of 30,000 lbs. S-V stage forms third stage of Saturn C-1 vehicle for lunar and planetary probe missions.

SCALE HEIGHT. A measure of the relationship between density and temperature at any point in an atmosphere; the thickness of a homogeneous atmosphere which would give the observed temperature or pressure.

SCINTILLOMETER. A precision instrument that measures radiation levels and intensities by counting the light flashes emitted by the impact of radiation particles against the scintillometer.

SCORE. The successful satellite orbiting of December 18, 1958, consisting of the entire Atlas 10-B booster vehicle plus 167 lbs. of instruments for a communications-satellite test program. Over-all vehicle (in orbit) was 85 feet, diameter 10 feet, orbital weight 8,750 lbs. The equipment of Score was the

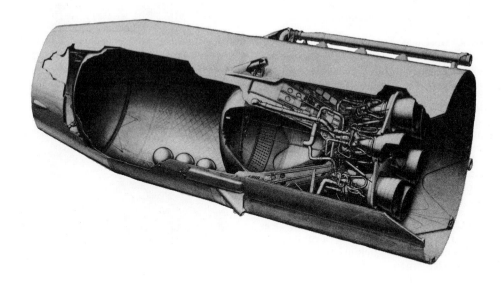

SATURN S-IV stage

SATURN S-IVB seen in artist's conception during rendezvous mission

first to transmit a recorded human voice from space to the earth's surface.

SCOTOPIC VISION. The reaction of the eye to low levels of illumination.

SCREAMING. A form of combustion instability, especially in a liquid-propellant rocket engine, of relatively high frequency and characterized by a high-pitched noise.

SCRUB. The term that denotes cancellation of a space mission for any reason before or during the countdown.

"SEAL THE BLOCKHOUSE." Command to close all doors, vents, and other openings of blockhouse as the final stage of a countdown gets under way.

SEASAVE BEACON. A radio homing beacon used in Mercury capsule, aircraft, and unmanned recovery satellites that activates automatically when carrier vehicle impacts on the ocean surface.

SEAT KIT. A carefully packed kit of medical and emergency survival equipment and supplies, used by the pilot in flight as a seatpack, but which is attached to his parachute harness and/or pressure-suit garment.

SECONDARY COSMIC RADIATION. The energetic nuclear debris and electromagnetic radiation produced by the collision of primary cosmic ray particles with atoms and molecules of the upper atmosphere. See **cosmic radiation; primary cosmic radiation.**

SECOND OF ARC. An astronomical measure of an angle, $\frac{1}{60}$th of a minute.

SECOR. Sequential Collation of Range. (1) An electronic tracking system employing several ground stations and a transponder in the flight vehicle, i.e., rocket booster, to measure positions of the vehicle in flight. (2) A 20-inch sphere weighing 36 lbs., orbited to provide range calibration data of world tracking nets.

SEEING. A blanket term long used by astronomers for the disturbing effects produced by the atmosphere upon the image quality of an observed astronomical body.

"SEAL THE BLOCKHOUSE"

SEAT KIT, located beneath parachute

SELENOCENTRIC. Relating to the center of the moon; referring to the moon as a center.

SELENOGRAPHIC. (1) Of or pertaining to the physical geography of the moon. (2) Specifically, referring to positions on the moon measured in latitude from the moon's equator and in longitude from a reference meridian.

SELENOID. A lunar satellite.

SELENOPHYSICS. Studies and charting of the lunar surface.

SEMICIRCULAR CANALS. Tubes located in the inner ear which play a part in the mechanism of balance and orientation. See **equilibrium and orientation.**

SEMISATELLITE. A missile, orbital glider, or other object that attains such velocity as to become subject to some of the conditions of an orbiting body without, however, achieving an orbit itself. A semisatellite would be capable of completing a flight that encompassed the entire planet, but part of that flight would be well within the atmosphere. Not to be confused with suborbital.

SEMI–SUPINE POSITION. A modification of the supine position in which the subject is lying face-up with the legs elevated to a position slightly higher than the torso, in order to increase positive-g tolerance. In the Mercury spacecraft, the semi-supine position for the astronaut is with the head and back raised 12° from the horizontal and hips and knees flexed at approximately 90° angles. See **contour couch; supine position.**

SENSIBLE ATMOSPHERE. That part of the atmosphere that offers resistance to a body passing through it. See **aerothermodynamic border; effective atmosphere.**

SENSOR. A technical means to extend man's natural senses; equipment which detects and indicates natural and man-made objects and activities by means of energy emitted or reflected by such objects and/or activities. The energy may be nuclear, electromagnetic, including the visible and invisible portions of the spectrum, chemical, biological, thermal, or mechanical, including sound, heat, and earth vibration. Also: the component of an instrument that converts an input signal into a quantity which is measured by another part of the instrument. In the latter sense, also called *sensing element.*

SENSORY DEPRIVATION. A condition in motion or other simulators or training devices, or a condition in atmospheric or orbital flight, under which the normal body senses for purposes of balance are denied their "normal stimuli" such as visual perception, light, hearing, touch, gravity, etc., resulting in a loss of equilibrium and orientation. See **equilibrium and orientation.**

SENSORY ISOLATION EXPERIMENT. The subject is immersed in an 8-foot-deep tank of warm water. The tank ("dog dip") is within a small airtight room with steel walls 8 inches thick, and built so as to be soundproof, lightproof, odorproof, vibration-proof, and humidity-proof. The experiment provides for the greatest possible deprivation of the five basic senses, and the test subject has "nothing" to see, hear, taste, touch, or smell. The water temperature is controlled to match body temperature, and water submersion simulates to some extent a weightless condition. The test exerts very strong impact in creating sensations of being deaf and blind and without sense of touch, taste, or smell. A common reaction is for the subconscious mind to "take over" normal thought processes and for the test subject to lapse into "uncontrollable hallucinations."

SEPARATION. The discarding of a rocket booster stage while the remaining stage(s) continue(s) in flight; also, the time when this occurs. With the Atlas missile, the main booster section stages—separates—about 130 seconds after launch. The term generally applies to the separation of any two parts of a vehicle, or the payload from the booster.

SEPARATION ROCKET. A small rocket, usually solid-propellant, installed in groups of two or more on a second or higher stage (as with Titan), and operated when its stage needs additional thrust to accelerate away, at separation, from the preceding stage.

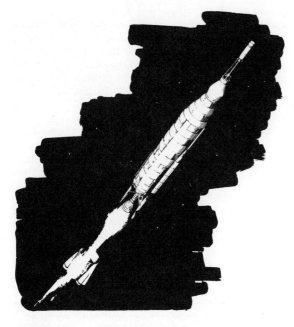

SEPARATION. Atlas booster jettisons two-chambered booster section; sustainer engine continues firing

SEPARATION VELOCITY. The velocity at which a space vehicle is moving when some part or section is separated from it; specifically, the velocity of an earth satellite at the time of separation from the carrier, usually at orbital velocity.

SEQUENCER. A mechanical or electronic device that may be set to initiate a series of events and to make the events follow in a given sequence.

SER. SNAP Experimental Reactor. See **SNAP.**

SERT. A satellite maintained at a high rate of spin while in orbit, and carrying electric-propulsion engines for in-space environmental tests.

SERVICE TOWER. See **gantry.**

SERVOCONTROL. The servomechanism of any manned aerospace vehicle to operate an auxiliary control device or control surface that by mechanical or aerodynamic relay takes over part of the load in operating a larger control device or surface.

SERVOMECHANISM. A mechanism in which control of position, attitude, speed, power output, control rates, etc., is effected by a device or devices that automatically change or correct, or help to change or correct, such position, attitude, speed, power, control rates, etc., in accordance with a predetermined setting, value, or manipulation. In general use, often referred to as a *slaving mechanism.*

SHADOW. The dark region behind an illuminated body. Umbra is shadow which receives no light at all. Penumbra is a portion of a shadow which receives some light from the source.

SHAKE–TABLE TEST. A laboratory test in which an instrument component is placed in a vibrator that simulates one of the conditions during the launch of a booster vehicle.

"SHEDDING HER SKIRT." When a booster vehicle is fueled, and then liquid oxygen is fed to the lox tanks, a covering of ice surrounds the portion of the booster containing the lox tanks. During engine ignition and liftoff, the vibration of the booster breaks free the ice, which in thousands of glittering particles sprays off to the side of the climbing booster—"shedding her skirt."

"SHEDDING HER SKIRT"

SHIELD. Short for *heat shield, radiation shield,* etc.

SHIRT–SLEEVE ENVIRONMENT. An advanced spacecraft system in which the spacecraft is intended for extended flights, during which personnel comfort is of pri-mary consideration; the spacecraft environment would be maintained with sufficient pressure, humidity control, oxygen content, heating and cooling, etc., to permit the removal of pressurized-suit equipment and permit sustained safety without pressure equipment, i.e., in "shirt sleeves."

SHOCK BANDS. Also: *shock lines.* Slim, fluctuating bands of gray light sweeping sharply back from the wingtips, and broad, stiff bands of gray light sweeping back from the nose section of an aerospace vehicle moving at high supersonic speeds. The bands vary and fluctuate in intensity, width, and tone, sometimes intermeshing in their patterns. They are clearly visible—the manifestation of **shock waves** resulting from the compression of air at supersonic speeds across the surfaces of the vehicle.

SHOCK DIAMONDS. Diamond-shaped shock waves visible in exhaust of rocket or jet aircraft flame.

SHOCK WAVE. Also: **bow wave.** Re-entry of any blunt-shaped capsule object into atmosphere at orbital speeds creates a tremendous shock wave ahead of that vehicle. In re-entry of the Mercury capsule the temperature of the shock wave ahead of the blunt heat shield reaches as high as 11,000°F. This shock wave rides ahead of the heat shield, and actually aids re-entry by acting as an insulation layer about the forward edge of the capsule.

SHOT. An act or instance of firing a rocket, especially from the earth's surface.

SHROUD LINE. One of a number of nylon lines connecting the periphery of a parachute canopy with the harness. See **parachute.**

SHUTDOWN. See **shutoff.**

SHUTOFF. Cessation of operation of booster engines of a space vehicle, either by automatic systems operation or at a command signal from the ground. Also, the moment when the engines cease operation. Also **shutdown, cutoff,** or **Brennschluss,** signifying cessation of thrust.

SIDEREAL. Of or pertaining to the stars; a measurement of time. One sidereal day is the time required for the earth to accomplish a complete rotation measured from the stars. A sidereal day is 4 minutes shorter than the normal day, which is a solar day as measured from the sun.

SIDEREAL PERIOD. The time required for a planet (or any spatial satellite) to complete one revolution about its primary as seen from the primary and as referred to a star.

SIGHTING. Actual visual contact with a spacecraft or other object. Does not include other contacts, which must be reported by type; e.g., radar and sonar contacts.

SIGNAL STRENGTH. The specific intensity or strength of a radio transmission, or signal, as it is measured at the receiver.

SIGNAL–TO–NOISE RATIO. The ratio of any information-bearing signal to the unavoidable interfering or disrupting noise that accompanies the transmission of the signal. Perfect information transfer has a ratio of 100, and complete noise—enough to block out all information in the signal—has a ratio of 0.

SILICA GEL. Commercial trade name for a drying agent composed of a mixture of silicic acid and silicon dioxide in a colloid form, which can absorb large amounts of water. Of special value to closed ecological systems.

SILICON MONOXIDE. An oxide of silicon used as a thin film on the surface of a spacecraft or satellite to reflect thermal and infrared radiations.

SIMULATOR. Any training instrument or device that is used to simulate a specific or general condition of atmospheric or orbital flight. Example: a centrifuge, which simulates accelerations of flight. See **centrifuge.**

SINKING SPEED. The descent speed of any flightborne object that moves downward vertically or laterally, but expressed in vertical downward speed, and referring to the object or vehicle that descends under control, as opposed to the falling speed of an object or vehicle which falls without control.

"SITTING FAT." Generally: "Orbit achieved, everything is okay."

SIZE–DISTANCE ILLUSION. The size-distance illusion occurs usually under conditions of darkness, and results from staring at a point of light which approaches and recedes from the observer; it is thus of paramount importance in orbital rendezvous and docking procedures. In the absence of additional distance clues, accurate depth perception is extremely difficult. Instead of seeing the light advancing and receding, the observer (pilot or astronaut) has the illusion that it is expanding and contracting at a fixed distance from him. This illusion may be dispelled by shifting eye fixation continually. See **autokinetic movement.**

SKID STRIP. The 10,000-foot runway at Cape Canaveral. It is called the "skid strip" because of its original use to recover radio-controlled SM-62 Snark missiles that were landed on skids.

"SKIN TRACKING." The tracking of an object by means of radar.

SKIP–GLIDE BOMBER. Winged vehicle that is boosted above the atmosphere by large rocket-powered stages and turned into a somewhat circular orbit before thrust cut-off. From this point, the manned extraterrestrial bomber follows an undulating trajectory, glancing or skipping off the upper regions of the atmosphere through induced limited-re-entry atmospheric lift as it travels around the earth to complete its mission. See **boostglide vehicle.**

SKIRT FOG. The cloud of steam and water that surrounds the engines of a missile being launched from a wet emplacement, including the most visually obvious element, the bluish-white vapors arising from liquid-oxygen fueling.

SKIRT FOG seen in prelaunch photos of Juno II lunar probe (*left*) and Thor missile (*right*)

SKY COLORATION. Under normal seeing conditions, the sky as seen from the surface of the earth is blue. Sunlight penetrating the atmosphere is scattered by air molecules, with blue light scattered much more than red. Thus the sunlight is reddened, and instead of appearing white it becomes yellow to the human eye; the blue light taken from it is reflected back from molecules in all directions of the sky. With increasing height and decreasing air density there are fewer air molecules. Scattering of sunlight becomes much less pronounced and the sky assumes a dark blue appearance, this color deepening into the dark purple and then finally becoming black at a point where there are insufficient air molecules to sustain the light-scattering effect.

SKYHOOK BALLOON. A plastic, constant-volume, stratosphere balloon research vehicle. The plastic used is flat polyethylene sheets. The balloons range in size from 73 to 110 feet in diameter, and carry payloads varying from a few to several hundred pounds, lifting these payloads to heights exceeding 130,000 feet. They provide a long-duration, stable platform for extensive aeromedical tests. See **constant-volume balloons.**

SKY OBSCURATION. Visual factor in launching of any manned space vehicle. Flight safety factors require that good optical clarity be provided for a major chain of tracking and camera sites. The percentage of sky obscuration that prevents any launch is determined by the visual resolution obtained by these various sites. Usually a five-tenths cloud obscuration of the sky will prevent the launch.

SKY SCREEN. An element of equipment used by the Range Safety Officer. The sky screen (either electronic or optical, but usually the former) provides a positive indication to the Range Safety Officer whenever the missile deviates from its planned trajectory. In operational use, one sky screen is used to monitor vertical programming.

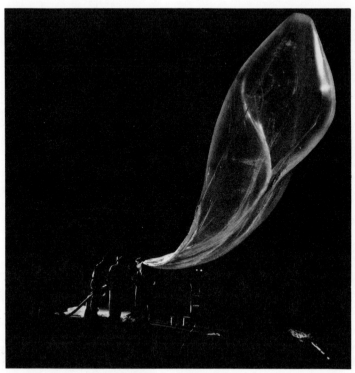

SKYHOOK BALLOON

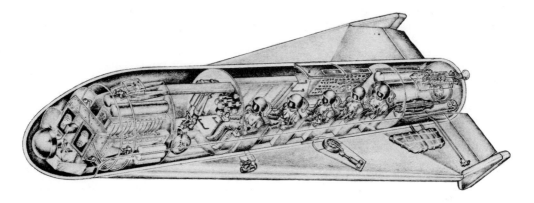

SLOMAR

SKY SEARCH. A developed means of maximum possible visual acuity in seeking out objects or actions. It is a common misconception that the eye "takes a picture" of everything within its field of view. (Pick out any word in this sentence and then move your eye to the next and then the next. You will discover that you can no longer read the first word after having moved your eye about 5°.) The individual sees best in daylight with the cones in the center of the eye, and the eye sees by moving in short jumps. It is not a sweeping motion, but rather a jerking motion, with which the individual best sees details (and this is of utmost importance in sighting other aircraft at a distance in the sky). Experiments have shown that the eye sees nothing in detail while it is moving. It sees only when it pauses and fixes an object on its retina. In scanning the sky, the individual who uses the wide, sweeping glance has poor visual resolution. The most efficient method of seeing is to cover an area with short, regularly spaced movements of the eye.

SLANT RANGE. The distance of a booster at any given moment from its launch site, measured directly from the launch pad to the missile in flight. It is distinctive from altitude above the surface and the distance over the earth's surface to a point directly below the booster.

SLAVED GYRO. A gyro that is controlled by a magnetic force through a transmitter, as in a gyrosyn, in which the gyro is synchronized to a magnetic force.

SLOMAR. An advanced "orbital tug and ferry" vehicle, under Air Force development since early 1960, as an earth-to-orbit-to-earth logistics, maintenance, supply, and crew-transfer vehicle. It is an aerodynamic-lift configuration vehicle under piloted control, with high-speed glider landing and descent capabilities.

SLOSHING. The back-and-forth splashing of a liquid fuel in its tank, creating problems of stability and control in the vehicle.

SLUG. A unit of mass; the mass of a free body which if acted upon by a force of 1 lb. would experience an acceleration of 1 foot per second per second.

SLURRY. A suspension of fine solid particles in a liquid, as in a liquid fuel.

SMART. An Air Force study of space systems using manned satellites and recoverable vehicles to carry out maintenance and repair operations in space. Tied in closely with the SLOMAR project. See **SLOMAR.**

SNAFU. Situation Normal, All Fouled Up. A "normal" state of confusion, hectic and harassed.

"SNAKEBITE." An accident. Slang at Cape Canaveral in allusion to the snakes that inhabit the Cape area.

SNAP. Systems for Nuclear Auxiliary Power. Nuclear power systems developed for advanced space missions to meet long-term power requirements. Three SNAP reactor projects are programmed for early orbital flight testing. These include the 500-watt SNAP 10A; the 3-kilowatt SNAP 2; and the 30–60-kilowatt SNAP 8 systems. Under accelerated development are advanced systems capable of producing hundreds of kilowatts with extension into the megawatt range with less than 5 lbs.-per-kilowatt specific weight. The heat source for SNAP 10A, SNAP 2, and SNAP 8 is a high-temperature, homogeneous, thermal, fully enriched, metal-cooled nuclear reactor. The fuel moderator is uranium-zirconium hydride, which has the property of containing as much hydrogen at high temperatures (1,500°F.) with sub-atmospheric pressure as ordinary water has at room temperature. This high hydrogen content gives the reactor extreme compactness, and the low pressure permits a high-temperature coolant (1,000° to 1,300°F.) to be used with lightweight vessels, piping, and components. Each of these three systems is designed with an orbital lifetime of one year. SNAP 10A unshielded weight is 525 lbs.; SNAP 2 is 750 lbs.; and SNAP 8 is 1,500 lbs. Flight schedules call for orbiting of SNAP 10A in 1963, SNAP 2 in 1964, and SNAP 8 in 1965.

SNAP 10A. One of a series of nuclear power systems for advanced spacecraft; cutaway reveals reactor and plumbing system

SNAP 2 is designed for maximum operational life in orbit of one year, producing a thermal power of 50,000 watts and a design net electrical power of 3,000 watts. By comparison for space power supply, *500,000 lbs. of batteries would be required to produce 3,000 watts of electricity in space for one year—or about 10,000 lbs. per week.* Approximately 1,500 square feet of unoriented solar cells, about the size of an average home, would be required to provide the same power output as a SNAP 2 system.

SNAPSHOT. Orbital flight test program of SNAP systems. See **SNAP.**

SOFAR. Sound Fixing And Ranging. In Project Mercury, when the main 63-foot parachute deploys at 10,000 feet during descent, a SOFAR charge ejects into the air. This falls into the ocean and sinks. At a preset depth it explodes as a miniature depth charge. Navy listening apparatus aboard ships can hear this blast from many miles away and pinpoint its location by an intersection of several "fixes."

SOFT DOCKING. In the process of orbital rendezvous and docking, the bringing together in the same orbital proximity of two spacecraft, and achieving a link between the two craft by means of a nylon line, lanyard, cable, or other such device, without actual mechanical coupling of the two vehicles. The two vehicles might be placed in orbit alongside each other, with crew transfer by means of hand-over-hand pulling motions along the line. The two vehicles never actually touch. See **docking; hard docking.**

SOFT LANDING. A landing on the moon or other spatial body at such slow speed as to avoid a crash or destruction of the landing vehicle. Soft landings on the moon are anticipated by use of retro-rockets (or landing rockets) for slowdown of the landing vehicle; soft landing on Mars may be accomplished by partial use of the Martian atmosphere (believed to be equal at the Martian surface to the pressure at 50,000 feet altitude above the earth).

SOLAR ATMOSPHERIC TIDE. Vertical motion of the atmosphere due to thermal or gravitational action of the sun.

SOLAR CELL. A photovoltaic device that converts sunlight directly into electrical energy; used often in satellites to provide low-energy, long-term power for miniaturized transmitting equipment.

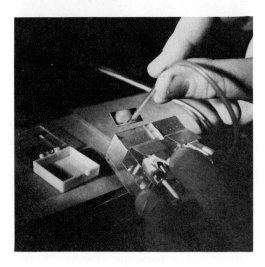

SOLAR CELL

SOLAR CONSTANT. The rate at which solar radiation is received on a surface perpendicular to the incident radiation and at the earth's mean distance from the sun, but outside the earth's atmosphere.

SOLAR CORPUSCLES. Particles, usually protons, sprayed out into the solar system by disturbances on the sun. If the earth intercepts one of these sprays, the particles react with the earth's magnetic field and produce ionospheric disturbances.

SOLAR CORPUSCULAR RAYS. Cosmic radiation originating from the sun. See **corpuscular cosmic rays.**

SOLAR FLARES. Violent and sudden disturbances on the surface of the sun, resulting in fierce floods of high-energy particles that inundate the earth and the space around the earth. These radiation storms in space are considered a serious danger to the safety

of men who may at that time be in orbit. See **magnetic storm.**

SOLAR NOISE. Electromagnetic radiation from the atmosphere of the sun at radio frequencies, causing interference with radio communications on these affected frequencies.

SOLAR RADIATON. The total electromagnetic radiation emitted by the sun.

SOLAR RADIATION PRESSURE. Particles (photons, protons, etc.) emitted from the sun at fixed velocities and momenta, as expressed as the sum total of the momenta of the particles entering a given area at a given instant of time is the radiation pressure at that moment.

SOLAR SAIL. A very large and lightweight surface planned for future manned spacecraft for deep-space missions through the solar system to nearby planets, such as Mars, Venus, Mercury. The great sails for these "ships of space" would be so designed as to receive their thrust from **solar radiation pressure.**

SOLAR SYSTEM, PLANETS. The solar system includes 9 major planets (Mercury, Venus, Earth, Mars, Jupiter, Saturn, Uranus, Neptune, Pluto), 31 moons or planetary satellites, thousands of minor planets or asteroids, scores of comets, and unnumbered millions of meteors.

The *average distance* of the planets from the sun in millions of miles is:

Mercury	36	Jupiter	483
Venus	67	Saturn	886
Earth	93	Uranus	1,783
Mars	141	Neptune	2,793
		Pluto	3,670

The *average distance* of the planets from the sun *as compared to earth* is:

Mercury	.38	Jupiter	5.20
Venus	.72	Saturn	9.54
Earth	1.00	Uranus	19.19
Mars	1.52	Neptune	30.07
		Pluto	39.46

The *diameter at the equator* of each planet is:

Mercury	3,100	Jupiter	88,770
Venus	7,700	Saturn	74,200
Earth	7,927	Uranus	32,400
Mars	4,220	Neptune	30,900
		Pluto	3,600?

The *known moons* of each planet are:

Earth	1	Saturn	9
Mars	2	Uranus	5
Jupiter	12	Neptune	2

The *period of revolution* about the sun of each planet as expressed in earth day and year measurements is:

Mercury	88 days	Jupiter	12 years
Venus	225 days	Saturn	29 years
Earth	365 days	Uranus	84 years
Mars	1.9 years	Neptune	165 years
		Pluto	248 years

(For planetary escape velocities, see **escape velocities, solar system.**)

SOLAR TIME. Time measured by reference to the *apparent* motion of the sun about the earth.

SOLAR WIND. A stream of protons constantly moving outward from the sun.

SOLENOID. (1) A coil of closely wound turns of wire which, when electrified, acts as an electromagnet. (2) Such a coil surrounding an iron rod or bar which is free to move under the magnetic influence of the coil. (3) In sense 2, the solenoid is often used for the remote control of aerospace-vehicle equipment, such as valves, radar antenna, optical tracking systems, etc.

SOLID PROPELLANT. A rocket propellant in solid state consisting of all the ingredients necessary for sustained chemical combustion. A fast-burning compound of fuel and oxidizer mixed to produce desired chemical and physical properties. Solid propellants are usually in plastic-like, caked form. They burn on their exposed surface, generating hot exhaust gases to produce a reaction force.

SOLID-PROPELLANT ROCKET MOTOR during test firing

SOLID–PROPELLANT ROCKET MOTOR. A rocket motor using a solid propellant. Such motors consist essentially of a combustion chamber containing the propellant, and a nozzle for the exhaust jet, although they often contain other components, such as grids, liners, etc. See **rocket engine.**

SOLID ROCKET FUEL. See **solid propellant.**

SOLSTICE. See **spatial references.**

SONIC. *Sonic speed* is the speed of sound through the air. At sea level with a temperature of 59°F. this is approximately 762 mph. It varies with air density and pressure. The speed of sound at 35,000 feet, for example, is approximately 660 mph. Thus the speed of sound is expressed as Mach 1—the speed of sound at any altitude for any atmospheric conditions. Here are other Mach number speed references:

Subsonic	below Mach 1
Transonic	Mach .9 to Mach 1.2
Supersonic	Mach 1 to Mach 5
Hypersonic	Mach 5 and above; also considered as 3,500 mph or greater.

SONIC BOOM. An explosion-like sound heard when a shock wave, generated by an aircraft (or a rocket) traveling at supersonic speed, reaches the ear. The principal shock waves are approximately conical in shape and originate at the front and rear of the aircraft or rocket (or other object). The shock-wave cone angle depends upon vehicle speed and the speed of sound in the surrounding medium. To the observer, who senses the shock wave with his ear, the arrival of each pressure wave is manifested as a booming sound, sometimes so intense as to be capable of causing extensive physical damage to structures.

SONIC SPEED. The speed of sound. When an object travels in air at the same speed as that of sound in the same medium it has reached sonic speed.

SOPHISTICATED. Specifically in reference to space vehicles and systems: complex and intricate; making use of an advanced art or state of the art; requiring special skills to operate.

SOUNDING BALLOON. Meteorological- and physiological-experiment balloon vehicles which carry instruments, animals, spores, and research equipment to altitudes approximately 140,000 to 150,000 feet above sea level.

SOUNDING ROCKET. A rocket designed to explore the atmosphere within 4,000 miles of the earth's surface.

SPACE. The expanse which surrounds the celestial bodies of the universe; considered impossible of precise definition. The characteristics of various parts or areas of space differ from one another. For example, near earth, gas particles that form the "air" or "atmosphere" are close together and the earth's gravitational attraction is comparatively strong. Elsewhere in space are other environments in which other forces and other conditions exist. Environments vary with regard to the other planets in our solar system and to other systems in the universe.

In relation to earth, the environment popularly regarded as *space* is found to be

SOUNDING ROCKET. Nike-Cajun rocket carrying grenades timed to explode at intervals during flight as part of a study of atmospheric winds and temperatures at great altitudes

at different distances from the earth's surface, depending upon the nature of the study or activity. Therefore, no one can say, except arbitrarily, where the "air" ends and "space" begins in relation to earth. "Air" and "space" form an indivisible operational medium, a continuum best described as aerospace. Certain distinctions, however, do hold valid. The flight of a vehicle through the atmosphere is sustained through aerodynamic lift; at a point where such lift no longer is generated despite the velocities achieved, that aircraft must resort to centrifugal force in order to prevent falling back to the earth's surface or to denser atmosphere. But at heights still above that where aerodynamic lift fails, there is yet sufficient pressure of gases to affect through friction the passage of a body moving with high velocities. In this context, then, the earth's atmosphere is considered to end when that atmosphere no longer is able to affect the passage of any vehicle, despite its velocity, and at that region or zone, space begins. Above this region or zone, however, there are layers or zones of "electrical atmospheres." These do not appreciably affect, even over a period of decades, the passage of an orbital vehicle, but they do constitute a specific barrier against which radio waves may be reflected for purposes of communications.

In terms of man, the space-equivalent region begins at different altitudes above the earth's surface where he must be supplied with some elements of an artificial environment in order to survive. In respect to the movement of vehicles at increasingly high velocities, a former widely held concept was that once atmospheric considerations were left behind, space was a total emptiness—a whole and complete vacuum. In terms of the atmosphere, this is essentially true, but today we tend to regard space as a *radiation environment* in which—although invisible to man's physiological senses—great forces are at work and interplay. Not only are there tides, floods, storms, winds, and currents of different types and magnitudes of radiation, but there is also the extraordinarily complex fabric of gravitational effects and forces. Again—the definition of space must be one that is arbitrary.

SPACE–AIR VEHICLE. See **aerospace vehicle.**

SPACE BIOLOGY. A branch of biology concerned with life as it may exist in space.

SPACE BOMBER. Any vehicle that operates in the space environment with the capability of directing weapons against a specific target or series of targets on the surface of the earth; a vehicle with which to effect bombardment of terrestrial targets from space.

SPACEBORNE. (1) Of a person or thing: supported in space by velocity. (2) Of an operation or actions: carried out or conducted with spacecraft or with missiles that travel through space.

SPACE CABIN. A pressurized and climatized cabin for use in flight through space; a cabin with a complete and wholly self-sustained life-support system.

SPACE–CABIN SIMULATOR. A completely closed chamber in which the changes of the intracabin climate produced by the presence of the occupants, as in a spacecraft cabin, are recorded and controlled. It permits the study of the reactions of the occupants to confinement, isolation, and day-night cycling of events. See **simulator; space environmental chamber.**

SPACE CADET. A hot pilot or astronaut; a pilot or astronaut in training for an unusual mission.

SPACE COOKING. Preparation by heat of food under space-flight and weightlessness conditions. See **pressure frier.**

SPACECRAFT. Devices, manned and unmanned, which are designed to be placed in an orbit about the earth or in a trajectory to another celestial body.

SPACECRAFT VARIABLE WEIGHTS. The weight of a spacecraft is a variable, depending upon the time of any mission. During the mission, certain elements of the spacecraft (such as an escape tower, retropack, clamp rings, fairings, etc.) are jettisoned, and certain internal stores are consumed. There are five specific weight factors: at launch, insertion into orbit, retrograde, landing, and recovery. As an example, the MA-6 Mercury spacecraft weighed 4,265 lbs. at launch, 2,987 lbs. at insertion into orbit, 2,970 lbs. at retrograde, 2,493 lbs. at landing (splashdown), and 2,422 lbs. at recovery.

SPACE ENVIRONMENT. The area of space; or an area where conditions close to that of the space environment are encountered, such as extremely low atmospheric pressure, absence of breathable gases, a zone of acoustic silence, etc. Specifically, the environment in space is characterized by the absence of a life-supporting, life-protecting, and flight-supporting atmosphere.

SPACE ENVIRONMENTAL CHAMBER. A sealed chamber in which air may be exhausted to simulate near-vacuum conditions, as well as extremes of heat, cold, humidity, and other conditions. For purposes of advanced research, it is usually equipped with spacecraft instrumentation, controls, and other devices.

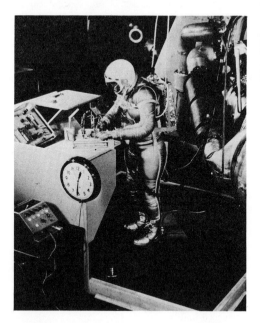

SPACE ENVIRONMENTAL CHAMBER. An engineer wearing a pressure suit is performing a series of mechanical and electrical operations in an environmental test

SPACE EQUIVALENCE. A postulation or principle that a condition or conditions within the atmosphere may be virtually identical with a condition or conditions in outer space. (Space equivalence is a postulation; a space equivalent is a particular condition. See **space equivalent.**)

SPACE EQUIVALENT. A condition within the earth's atmosphere that is virtually identical, in terms of a particular function, with a condition in "outer" space. For example, at 50,000 feet the extremely low air pressure and the absence of breathable oxygen create a condition, so far as respiration is concerned, that is equivalent to a condition in outer space where no oxygen is present; thus, a physiological space equivalent is present in the atmosphere, and physiological aids to respiration must be provided.

SPACE FERRY

SPACE FERRY. An aerospace vehicle intended for use as a ferry between the earth's surface and other vehicles in orbit. To be used for men, equipment, supplies, and other materiel.

SPACE FIREFLIES. See **luminous particles.**

SPACE FIXED REFERENCE. An oriented reference system in space independent of earth phenomena for positioning.

SPACE LABORATORY. (1) A space vehicle carrying sensing and measuring instruments, recording equipment, radio transmitting equipment, and other related instruments, used as a means of obtaining scientific information on conditions in the upper regions of the earth's atmosphere or in space. The vehicle may be unmanned or manned. (2) A vehicle that simulates the conditions of a space vehicle; i.e., a space simulator.

SPACE LABORATORY. A 24-foot diameter inflatable space station under current design study by NASA

SPACEMAN'S TATTOO. Small tattooed dots on the skin of an astronaut that mark permanently the location sites of biomedical sensor electrodes for physiological monitoring during flight.

SPACE MEDICINE. A branch of aerospace medicine concerned specifically with the health of persons who make, or expect to make, flights into space beyond the sensible atmosphere.

SPACE PLATFORM. Large satellite with both scientific and/or military applications, conceived as a habitable base in space. The proposed space platform would contain such things as housing facilities, power supplies, gravity simulation, provisions for transferring personnel and cargo to and from other space vehicles, scientific instruments, weapon systems, controlled atmosphere, communications systems, and emergency escape and survival systems.

SPACEPORT. Popular name for Cape Canaveral Missile Test Annex, rocket, missile, space-vehicle launch site. See **CCMTA.**

SPACE PROBE. See **probe.**

SPACE PROPULSION. Any means of propelling a vehicle through space.

SPACE REFERENCE GYRO. See **free gyro.**

SPACE SATELLITE. Any man-made vehicle that orbits the earth, moon, or other spatial body.

SPACE SCIENCES PROGRAM. The NASA program, fundamental to all manned space-flight activities. It provides the basic scientific knowledge essential to the development of specific uses of the space environment. It includes the use of instrumented satellites and space probes to measure and record the scientific properties of the atmospheric and ionospheric regions, nearby and outer space, and to help to determine the origin, composition, and environment of the moon and the planets.

SPACESHIP. A spacecraft, generally one that is manned.

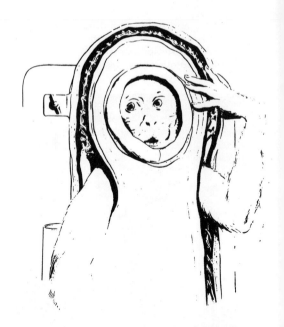

Instrumental in developing SPACE MEDICINE capabilities have been extensive tests run with animals in space flights. Monkey in partial pressure suit was placed in sealed cabin, fired into space at 10,000 mph within missile nose cone, recovered safely

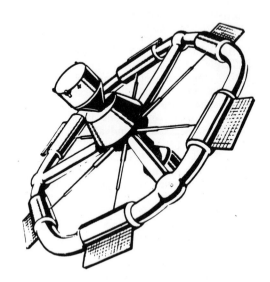

Wheel-type SPACE PLATFORM, with two Apollo spacecraft docked top and bottom in hub ports

SPACE SICKNESS. Dizziness and nausea due to sustained flight under zero-gravity conditions with attendant disturbance of the vestibular apparatus. See **equilibrium and orientation; motion sickness.**

SPACE SIMULATOR. A closed chamber, or cabin that can be hermetically sealed, in which human or animal subjects can be studied at ground level in artificially maintained cabin environments and conditions of complete isolation that simulate as closely as possible the conditions to be found in spacecraft (excepting weightlessness and true cosmic radiations).

SPACE SNOWFLAKES. See **luminous particles.**

SPACE STATION. A facility placed in orbit about the earth (or any other spatial body), by means of which, or from which, space flight or space exploration may be further effected.

SPACESUIT. Common-usage term for fully enclosed pressure suit which provides com-

SPACESUITS

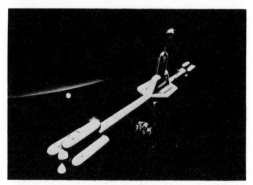

Manned Satellite Observatory, another SPACE PLATFORM design

SPACE PLATFORM

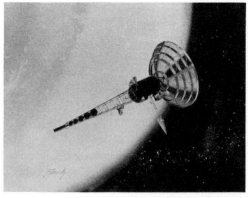

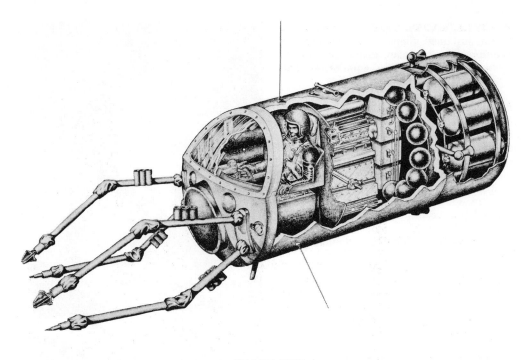

SPACE TUG

plete life support in a vacuum, exclusive of all other life-support systems. See **pressure suit—full.**

SPACE TASK GROUP (STG). Original NASA organization to prosecute the man-in-space program; now the Manned Space-craft Center at Houston, Texas.

SPACE TOOLS. Manual/mechanical tools designed specifically for use in weightless-and-vacuum environment of flight in space. They include such devices as a spunfit (space union and fitting wrench) which consists of a holding wrench and spin tool for standard fittings; the unit has adjustable handles for various space-suit inflation pressures. A modification, the semi-remote spunfit, allows a repair or service operation to be carried on at some distance from the repair area, especially where limited access is a problem. Another tool is a special nut-and-bolt tool which is a reactionless ratchet-drive device with which a pressure-suited astronaut can tighten or remove nuts and bolts on flanges. It is operated manually or through a power system.

SPACE TUG. A compact vehicle designed for use in orbit about the earth for moving equipment, metals, rocket hulls, etc., to facilitate construction work of manned space stations. Manually controlled, the space tugs are intended for orbital operations only.

SPACE WARFARE. Warfare, unmanned and/or manned, conducted by use of weapons brought to bear upon earth targets from space, or brought to bear upon targets in space.

SPADATS. Space Direction and Tracking System. Headquarters are at NORAD (North American Air Defense Command), Colorado Springs, Colorado. SPADATS ties in all U.S. tracking stations and systems, feeding data into computers, to maintain highly precise tracking, record, and prediction of location and movement of any artificial object in space.

SPATIAL. Pertaining to space.

SPATIAL BODY. Any body or aggregate of matter that exists in space and behaves in accordance with astronomic or astrophysical law. (This term includes the earth as well as celestial bodies.) See **celestial body.**

SPATIAL DISTANCES. Examples of distances traveled at light velocity, 186,271 miles per second (5.88 trillion miles per year):

(1) Sun to earth—93,-000,000 miles	8 minutes
(2) Sun to Pluto—3,-680,000 miles	5.25 hours
(3) Sun to Proxima Centauri, closest star to our solar system—25,000,000,000,000 miles	4.5 years
(4) Sun to center of Galaxy	26,080 years
(5) Center of Milky Way Galaxy to center of galaxy that contains the great nebula Andromeda	2,262,000 years

SPATIAL REFERENCES. Standing on the earth's surface at night, the sky appears to the observer as a vast, hollow half-globe. The rim of the globe always sits on the horizon, and the observer is in the very center of the globe. The *Zenith* is the position exactly overhead; the *Nadir* is the position exactly below. The distance of any star above the horizon is the stellar *altitude*. The Celestial North Pole is the star *Polaris*. Imaginary lines from True North through Zenith, True South, Nadir, and back to True North are *meridians*. When a star crosses a meridian it is said to *culminate*. Two successive culminations of a star constitute a *sidereal* or *star day*. Due to the earth's rotation around the sun, the *sidereal day* is 4 minutes shorter than the *solar day* and therefore marks most accurately the period of true rotation of the earth in relation to the stars.

Points of rising and setting of the stars are equally distant from the horizon's North point, e.g., a star rising due NE sets due NW. The *Great Circle* dividing the celestial globe into a Northern and Southern Celestial Hemisphere is the *Celestial Equator* and circles drawn parallel to the Celestial Equa-

tor are called *Parallels of Declination*. The Celestial Equator has a declination of zero degrees and the declination of each star is measured therefrom in degrees, minutes, and seconds. While the altitude of a star changes as it rises and sets, its declination always remains the same. The *Hour Circle* of a star is one half of a Great Circle from True North, through that star to True South. When an Hour Circle coincides with a meridian, all stars on the Hour Circle culminate at the same time even though their declinations may vary. There are 24 Hour Circles, counted eastward on the Celestial Equator, starting from a Zero Point in *Pisces* (a Constellation) which is called the *Vernal Equinox*. Hour Circles and Parallels of Declination define the place of a star on the celestial globe; however, the astronomer gives the *Right Ascension* (R.A.) of a star which is the arc on the Celestial Equator measured eastward from the Vernal Equinox to the point where the star's Hour Circle crosses the Celestial Equator. It is expressed in hours, minutes, and seconds. If the observer erects a perpendicular in the center of the plane created by the orbit in which the earth travels around the sun in one year, he finds that the axis of the earth through its poles deviates from this perpendicular by 23.5°, hence the celestial axis also deviates 23.5°. When the observer looks from the earth toward the sun with the stars as a background, he finds that the "apparent path" of the sun among the stars, which is called the *ecliptic,* in the course of one year leads through 12 constellations. This group of constellations is called the *Zodiac* (in their order of appearance, these constellations are: *Aries, Taurus, Gemini, Cancer, Leo, Virgo, Libra, Scorpio, Sagittarius, Capricorn, Aquarius, Pisces*). Since the Celestial Axis deviates by 23.5°, the Celestial Equator is also tilted at an angle of 23.5° with respect to the ecliptic. The point of intersection of the Zero Hour Circle, the Celestial Equator, and the ecliptic in the constellation Pisces is called the Vernal Equinox or Spring Equinox. The sun, as seen from the earth, crosses this point on March 21. The point of intersection of the 12th Hour Circle, the Celestial Equator, and the ecliptic in the constellation Virgo is called the Autumnal Equinox or Fall

Equinox. The sun, as seen from the earth, crosses this point on September 23. During the Equinoxes, day and night are of equal length. Due to the tilt of 23.5° of the Celestial Equator with respect to the ecliptic, one half of the Celestial Equator is above and one half is below the ecliptic. The Turning Points (where the Celestial Equator reaches its greatest distance from the ecliptic—23.5°) are called Summer and Winter Solstices. The Summer Solstice comes on June 21 when the sun is in the constellation Gemini, 23.5° below the ecliptic. In the Northern Hemisphere it marks the longest day of the year. The Winter Solstice comes on December 22 when the sun is in the constellation Sagittarius, 23.5° above the ecliptic. In the Northern Hemisphere this marks the shortest day of the year.

SPATIO–. A combining form meaning "space."

SPATIOGRAPHY. The ecological evaluation by space-medicine methods of the basic structural environment of space, especially in the regional and temporal variations. Spatiographic study includes the earth's atmosphere in order to determine where above the earth's surface space actually begins.

SPECIFIC IMPULSE. A performance parameter of a rocket propellant, expressed in seconds, and equal to thrust (in pounds) divided by weight flow (in pounds per second). See **thrust.**

SPECTROMETER. An instrument which measures some characteristics, such as intensity, of electromagnetic radiation as a function of wavelength or frequency.

SPECTROSCOPY. The science that relates the nature of luminous sources to the characteristics of the light they emit.

SPECTRUM. (1) In physics, any series of energies arranged according to wavelength (or frequency); specifically, the series of images produced when a beam of radiant energy, such as sunlight, is dispersed by a prism or reflecting grating. (2) Short for "electromagnetic spectrum" or for any part of it used for a specific purpose, such as the "radio spectrum," which extends to 300,000 megacycles.

SPHERE OF GRAVITATIONAL INFLU-ENCE. See **gravisphere.**

SPIN ROCKETS. Small rockets mounted tangentially on a rocket vehicle, and fired in order to impart a spinning movement to the vehicle for purposes of spin stabilization, to prevent tumbling, gyrating, or any other undesired motions.

SPIN TABLE. A test and training device to which a human subject is strapped. The table is then rotated at high speeds to simulate uncontrolled spinning motion of the human body in a free fall through the air, or aboard a spacecraft that is spinning out of control in orbit. Also: complex types of tumbling can be simulated by mounting the spin table on the arm of a centrifuge. See **centrifuge.**

SPIN TABLE

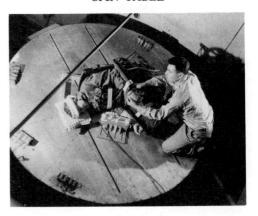

SPLASH. Impact of a manned spacecraft, nose cone, or re-entry vehicle on the ocean surface.

SPLASHDOWN. Impact of a manned spacecraft on the surface of the ocean; moment when this occurs. See **touchdown.**

SPLIT COUNTDOWN. In Mercury-Atlas, a manned orbital mission countdown is performed in two parts. The first part is the *precount,* primarily a check of the various spacecraft systems. Following completion of the precount, there is an approximate 15-hour hold built into the count-

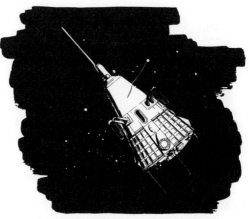

SPUTNIK III, third Russian satellite, launched May 15, 1958, with payload of 2,925 lbs.

SPLASHDOWN of Mercury capsule; moment of impact of capsule with ocean

down for pyrotechnic check, electrical connection, and peroxide system (spacecraft) servicing and surveillance. At the end of the built-in hold, the *final count* is started. See **launch count.**

SPR. Solid Propellant Rocket.

SPUTNIK. Common term for a Russian space satellite of the earth; specifically, one which orbits the earth. A contraction of the full Russian designation of *Iskustvenyi Sputnik Zemli*—"artificial companion of the earth."

SPUTTERING. The loss of atoms from a solid surface, caused by bombardment of the surface with atoms or ions which have kinetic energies of a few electron volts or more. During flights between planetary

bodies corpuscular radiation from the sun will cause sputtering, as will the constant collisions between a spacecraft and the atoms of interplanetary gas. During low-orbit flight about the earth, sputtering will result from collisions of a spacecraft with atoms of the earth's atmospheric fringes and with the particles of the radiation belts (i.e., Van Allen belts) surrounding the earth. Sputtering is considered a prime design caution factor for long-lifetime space vehicles, since it may produce an adverse effect on spacecraft surface materials.

SQUEEZE BOTTLE. A plastic container that contains liquids in a sealed condition with a tube opening; the liquids are released by partially collapsing the bottle through hand-pressure squeezing. See **paste food.**

SQUEEZE TUBE. A plastic or metal tube containing paste food for eating under weightless conditions. See **paste food.**

SQUIB. A small pyrotechnic device which may be used to fire the igniter in a rocket or for some similar purpose. Not to be confused with a detonator, which explodes.

SRO. Superintendent of Range Operations. The over-all director and co-ordinator for the Atlantic Missile Range during a launch operation. He co-ordinates activities in the Operations Room of Central Control on Cape Canaveral. See **CCMTA; Central Control.**

STABILIZATION CHUTE. See **drogue parachute.**

STABILIZED PLATFORM. Major part of an all-inertial guidance system, composed of an assembly of gimbal frames that hold three accelerometers in a fixed position in relation to inertial space. The accelerometers are mounted perpendicular to each other to measure accelerations along the three reference axes. These accelerations can be fed to a computer that will determine instantaneously velocity and position in space.

STAGE. A propulsion unit of a rocket, especially one unit of a multi-stage rocket, including its own fuel and tanks. Stages are numbered chronologically in their order of burning.

STAGE–AND–A–HALF. A liquid-rocket propulsion unit of which only part falls away from the rocket vehicle during flight, as in the case of booster rockets falling away to leave the sustainer engine to consume remaining fuel. The Atlas is a stage-and-a-half booster vehicle. See **Atlas-D propulsion system.**

STAGING. Separation process for booster rocket stages or between booster and payload vehicles. See **separation.**

STAGNANT HYPOXIA. See **hypoxia.**

STAGNATION TEMPERATURE. The temperature created on the leading edges of an aircraft or spacecraft traveling through the atmosphere. Refers to the complete standstill of air molecules on the leading edges of the craft.

STANDARD ATMOSPHERE. A hypothetical vertical distribution of atmospheric temperature, pressure, and density which, by agreement, is taken to be representative of the true atmosphere for purposes of pressure altimeter calibrations, aircraft and rocket design, ballistic tables, etc.

STAR. In its restrictive sense: a self-luminous celestial body exclusive of nebulae, comets, and meteors; any one of the suns seen in the heavens.

STARS (Examples):

Star	Brightness (Sun = 1)	Distance in Light Years
Alpha Centauri	1	4.5
Wolf 539	1/60,000th	7.7
Sirius A, B	23	8.7
Procyon A	6	11.3
Altair	8	16.5
Argo	5,200	180
Deneb	6,600	640
Rigel	23,000	650
Betelgeuse	13,000	650

STAR TRACKER. A telescopic instrument on a rocket vehicle or other airborne or spaceborne object that locks on to a celestial body and gives guidance to the vehicle or object during flight. A star tracker may be optical or radiometric.

STARE VISION. See **autokinetic movement.**

STARTING TRANSIENT. The series of events that take place when a modern liquid-propellant power plant (especially a liquid-propellant rocket engine) is started. This sequence includes: starting the gas generator, bringing the turbopump up to full speed, firing the main pyrotechnic igniters in the thrust chambers, switching over from external feed, initial combustion of limited propellant flow to the thrust chambers, building up of main thrust in a series of steps or by a timed increase, and stabilizing the output of the engine at the specified thrust.

STATE OF THE ART. The level to which technology and science have at any designated cutoff time been developed in a given industry or group of industries, as in "The booster vehicle's capabilities for orbital performance were determined by the state of the art at the time it went into production."

STATIC FIRING. The firing of a rocket engine or rocket motor in a held-down position to measure thrust and to accomplish other tests.

STATIC TEST. Maximum thrust operation of booster rocket engines in gantry or special holddown launch platform, with clamps and/or shackle arms to prevent booster lift-off. Used to completely check out propulsion-system performance prior to flight.

STATIONARY ORBIT. A circular orbit around a planet in the equatorial plane and having a rotational period equal to that of the planet. A body moving in a stable stationary orbit would appear fixed in the sky relative to an observer on the surface of the planet in the hemisphere facing the body. See **synchronous satellite.**

STELLAR MAP MATCHING. A process during the flight of a booster rocket system or a spacecraft by which a map of the stars set into the guidance system is matched with the position of the stars observed through telescopes, so as to provide continuing guidance to the vehicle.

STEROID CONTENT. The complex chemical compounds originating from some of the glands and being mostly fragments of hormones. They provide an index of body functions.

STICK. Short for "control stick." A manual control in an aircraft or spacecraft for the manipulation of aerodynamic or jet reaction controls.

STOVEPIPE. The outside shell of a rocket vehicle.

STRAIN GAUGE. A device for measuring "strain," which is the deformation produced in a solid as the result of stress. Stress is a force acting on a unit area of a solid. For example, the gauge measures the deformation in metal which has been part of a spacecraft, or in the tissue of the human body as a result of force (such as acceleration or windblast).

STREAMER. A parachute that fails to inflate fully when deployed, but trails or streams backward and fails in its life-saving function. A streamer usually connotates fatal impact with the ground.

SUBCORTICAL SYSTEMS. The more primitive portions of the brain and the nervous system which regulate the unconscious, vital functions of the body (respiration, circulation, digestion, etc.), with connections to the more discriminating areas of the cortex. See **cortical activity; cortical rest.**

SUBGRAVITY. A condition in which the resultant ambient acceleration is between 0 and 1g.

SUBORBITAL. A ballistic or dynamic soaring mission into space that does not achieve orbit or is not intended to achieve orbit.

SUBSATELLITE. An object designed to be carried into orbit inside an artificial earth satellite, but later ejected to serve a particular purpose.

SUBSONIC. Speeds less than the speed of sound. See **sonic.**

SUDDEN IONOSPHERIC DISTURBANCE (SID). A complex combination of sudden changes in the condition of the ionosphere, and the effects of these changes.

SUN. A "main sequence" star with an astronomical definition of spectral type G-zero, and a surface temperature of approximately 11,000°F. It is only an "average size" star, yet more than 300,000 times as massive as the earth. The solar diameter is 860,000 miles, and its period of rotation is approximately one complete rotation every 30 earth days. A gaseous body, the sun's density is just under 1.5 times that of water, and parts of the surface move at different speeds. The sun—a mass of incandescent gas—is considered in its energy output (as light and heat) to be extremely constant. It is, in effect, a gigantic nuclear furnace in which hydrogen is built into helium with temperatures of millions of degrees. Every second, four million tons of the sun's matter is converted into energy, a process that has gone on for many billions of years and will continue for many billions more.

Stellar comparisons. Within the "average" range of stars, surface temperatures extend from 5,500°F. to 55,000°F., depending upon the specific type of star. The energy liberation involved in the thermonuclear

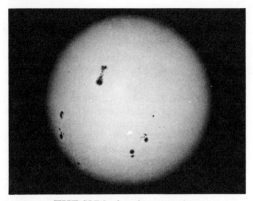

THE SUN, showing sunspots

SUNFLOWER. A NASA study program to develop for orbiting satellite vehicles a power system utilizing solar radiation to supply fixed-level power for one year to the electrical systems of the vehicles.

SUNSEEKER. A solar orientation device. As used in manned spacecraft or robot satellites, the sunseeker "seeks out" the sun by its visual brightness. An automatic pilot notes the position and angle of the sunseeker, and fires reaction jets to keep the spacecraft oriented on the basis of the position of the sun, in relationship to the surface of the earth or another body in space. Specifically, a two-axis device actuated by servos and controlled by photocells to keep instruments pointed toward the sun despite rolling and tumbling of an aerospace vehicle in which instruments are carried.

process of the stars, including our sun, is so enormous that one pound of hydrogen changing to helium liberates energy that is equal to more than 10,000 tons of coal. Stellar energy releases are reckoned in millions of tons of matter per second. Our sun is average in brightness. It is more than 500,000 times brighter than some known stars; at the same time, other known stars are 600,000 times as bright as the sun. The majority of other stars range from 1/10,000th the brightness of our sun, to 10,000 times as bright. The smallest stars—white dwarfs—are about the size of the planets, and with "incredible" density. But the red giant Antares is so huge that its diameter is 390 times greater than that of the sun. (This star is so enormous in size that if it were placed in the same position in our solar system as is the sun, the periphery of Antares would extend several millions of miles beyond the orbit of Mars—and there are other stars that are even larger.)

SUNSPOT. A relatively dark area on the surface of the sun, consisting of a dark central umbra and a surrounding penumbra that is intermediate in brightness between the umbra and the surrounding photosphere.

SUNSPOT CYCLE. A periodic variation in the number and area of sunspots with an average length of 11.1 years, but varying between about 7 and 17 years.

SUPEROXIDE. A relatively unstable chemical compound containing more oxygen than normally exists in the more stable forms of the more reduced compound, thus providing a possible source of additional oxygen for breathing, as in spacecraft or extraterrestrial base situations.

SUPINE POSITION

SUPERSONIC. Pertaining to speeds greater than the speed of sound. See **sonic.**

SUPERNOVA. See **nova.**

SUPINE POSITION. A flight position in which positive acceleration is taken from the chest to the back in order to increase positive-*g* tolerance. The *optimum supine position* consists of a supine position with a back angle of 20° to 25° to the horizontal, the thighs vertical, and the lower legs 5° above horizontal. For pilot comfort it is possible without vital loss of protection to vary the position of the thighs within a range of 20°. See **contour couch; semi-supine position.**

SURCAL. An 8-lb. satellite attached to a final-stage, orbiting rocket booster, used for measurement of the refraction of radio waves in the ionosphere, in order to increase accuracy of tracking nets.

SURFACE TENSION. Tendency of the surface of a liquid to act as a stretched membrane.

SURVEYOR. Follow-on lunar exploration program to succeed **Ranger.** Surveyor vehicles are intended for soft landings on the lunar surface, and subsequent transmissions of data concerning characteristics of the surface and the subsurface environment. Four TV cameras will be carried by Surveyor vehicles, one of which will scan an automatic drill that will penetrate the lunar crust for a depth of 5 feet. The final lunar-landing payload of Surveyor will be 750 lbs., excluding propulsion systems, which will land the vehicle on the moon at 6 mph descent. First launchings are scheduled for 1963. Surveyor A vehicles will be placed in orbit about the moon; Surveyor B vehicles will constitute the "lunar landers."

SURVEYOR

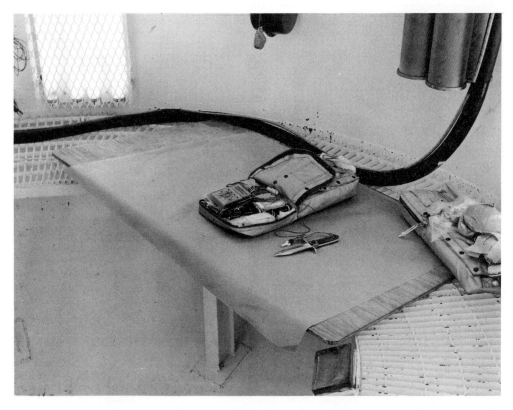

SURVIVAL KIT

SURVIVAL KIT. A spacecraft kit to provide for emergency recovery contingencies. In the Mercury spacecraft, this kit contains: sea dye marker, survival flashlight, shark-chaser chemical, food container, jackknife, sunglasses, pocket waterproof matches, signal whistle, survival knife, signal mirror, zinc oxide, soap, medical injectors (drugs), first-aid kit, Sarah beacon, nylon lanyard, life raft, water container. See **Sarah beacon.**

SUSTAINED FLIGHT VEHICLE. A powered aerospace vehicle deriving most of its lift from aerodynamic forces, but augmented by centrifugal force at altitudes arbitrarily considered to be at 150,000 feet.

SUSTAINER ENGINE. An engine that maintains the velocity of a rocket booster vehicle, once it has achieved its programmed velocity through use of a booster engine. See **Atlas-D propulsion system.**

SUSTAINER ROCKET. A rocket engine used as a sustainer, especially on an orbital glider or orbiting aerospace craft that dips into the atmosphere at its perigee. See **kick rocket.**

SUZANO. An ARPA research, experimentation, and systems study for a space platform which will provide an orbital base for advanced space missions. See **ARPA; space platform.**

SWEAT COOLING. Method of controlling the excessive heating of a re-entering body or an aerospace vehicle flying at hypersonic velocities. With this method, the surfaces that will be subjected to excessive heating are made of a porous material through which a liquid of high heat capacity is forced. The evaporation of this coolant completes the sweat-cooling process.

SWEEP. The motion of the visible dot across the face of a cathode-ray tube (i.e., radarscope), as a result of scanning deflection of the electron beam.

SWIVELING ENGINE. See **gimbal; gimbaled motor.**

SYNCHRONOUS SATELLITE. An equatorial west-to-east satellite orbiting the earth at an altitude of 22,300 statute miles at which altitude it makes one revolution in 24 hours, synchronous with the earth's rotation.

SYNCOM. A NASA communications satellite of advanced design to be placed in orbit synchronous with the rotation of the earth (similar to the military **Advent** program, now canceled). The Syncom satellites will weigh 50 lbs., and will be orbited at an inclination of 33°. Syncom is an active-repeater satellite, and the booster for the 22,300-mile orbit is the Thor-Delta.

SYNERGIC CURVE. A curve plotted for the ascent of a rocket, aerospace vehicle, or space vehicle calculated to give the vehicle an optimum economy in fuel with an optimum velocity. This curve, plotted to minimize air resistance, starts off vertically, but bends toward the horizontal at between 20 and 60 miles altitude.

SYNTHETIC GRAVITY. See **gravity simulation.**

SYSTEMS ENGINEERING. The process of applying science and technology to the study and planning of an over-all aerospace-vehicle system, whereby the relationships of various parts of the system and the utilization of various subsystems are fully planned and comprehended prior to the time that hardware designs are committed.

SYSTEMS MANAGEMENT. During a manned orbital flight, the monitoring of the environmental control, electrical, attitude control, and communications systems.

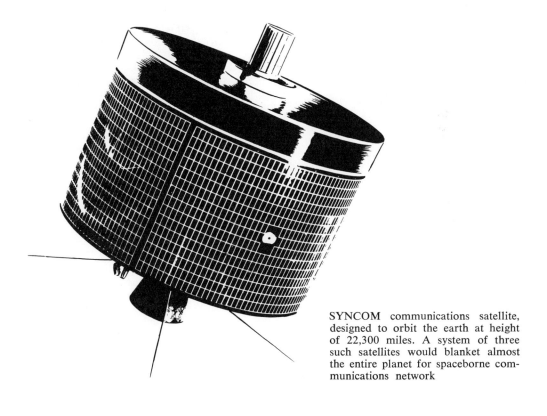

SYNCOM communications satellite, designed to orbit the earth at height of 22,300 miles. A system of three such satellites would blanket almost the entire planet for spaceborne communications network

T

TANGENTIAL ELLIPSE. The most economical of transfer orbits from the orbit of one planet to that of another planet. The tangential ellipse "grazes" the orbits of both planets.

TEARDOWN. The process of tearing down —i.e., completely disassembling—any vehicle—booster, spacecraft, etc.—for a meticulous study, servicing, and reconfirmation of reliability of all components and usually of the system as a whole. Usually performed in a vehicle subjected to malfunction or in which serious malfunction is suspected.

TELELIGHT. An instrument-panel light signal that signifies that an expected event or the initiation of a sequence of events has started as planned. Example: during the re-entry process of a spacecraft, an instrument is provided in the spacecraft to note the first building up of deceleration g forces. Usually this measurement is made at 0.05g. At the moment that this rate is encountered, a signal light flashes to signify the g level, which in turn is noted as a significant moment in the re-entry profile.

TELEMETER. An electronic instrument that senses and measures a quantity or degree, as of speed, temperature, pressure, or radiation, then transmits radio signals to a distant station.

TELEMETERING SYSTEM. A method of taking measured values within an aerospace vehicle and to transmit information to a ground station. See **telemetry.**

TELEMETRY. The science of measuring a quantity or quantities, transmitting the measured value by radio to a distant station, and there interpreting, indicating, or recording the quantities measured. Such values are used to evaluate the performance of a vehicle, its components, and its occupants. Telemetry measures and transmits a rate or a magnitude of certain factors such as velocity, pressure, heart rate, or angle of altitude. Example: a single Atlas ICBM flight test means that information from more than 300

instruments in the missile is telemetered to ground receiving stations over some 50 radio channels. This information, concerning temperatures, pressure, acceleration, stabilization, roll rate, attitude changes, etc., from a single test, requires about 10 miles of magnetic recording tape.

TELSCOM. A single antenna-system installation that permits through the single antenna the ability to carry out, simultaneously, operations in telemetry, surveillance, and communications.

TELSTAR. An active-repeater experimental satellite produced privately by the communications industry (A.T.&T.), and boosted by NASA with the Thor-Delta system into orbits planned for altitudes of 3,000 miles.

TEMPERATURE. The measure of heat intensity on a definite scale. (The theoretical lower limit of temperature is Absolute Zero —approximately 273.16° Centigrade or 459.69° Fahrenheit below zero. No upper limit has been observed.)

TERMINAL COUNT. The final part of a countdown leading directly to launch. Specifically, the final 30 to 60 minutes of a countdown, during which time all blockhouse personnel are at their stations and the firing area has been cleared.

TERMINAL PHASE. The period of flight of a rocket booster, missile, or other vehicle between the end of midcourse guidance and final landing or impact.

TERMINAL VEHICLE. That part of a rocket vehicle that is last to separate, but is itself a carrier of something, as in the case of a lunar probe or earth satellite.

TERMINAL VELOCITY. Hypothetical maximum speed a body could attain along a specified flight path under given conditions of weight and thrust if diving an unlimited distance in air of specified uniform density. In terms of actual flight, the terminal velocity of an aircraft is the maximum possible diving velocity under power before air resistance prevents any further buildup of velocity. Also: the maximum unpowered falling speed of a space capsule before air resistance imposes a sufficient counterforce to prevent further velocity increments. The falling speed of a human body in extended free fall is about 120 to 130 miles per hour in the lower atmosphere, wherein the falling speed is limited by air resistance.

TERMINATOR. The line separating illuminated and dark portions of a non-luminous body such as the moon.

TERRELLA. A small earth in space, i.e., a space capsule containing an environment equivalent, in matters essential to life, to that of the earth.

TERRESTRIAL. Of or pertaining to the earth.

TESTBED. Any flight vehicle for atmospheric or space flight that is used to accommodate or carry along equipment not necessary to its own mission, but which is being tested or developed under actual flight conditions. The Mercury capsule, for example, may carry elements or components of the Gemini or Apollo spacecraft in order to establish their integrity under flight and orbital conditions.

TETHERED CAPSULE. A realistic training device; a spacecraft or aerospace craft designed to simulate vertical descent and landing on the earth, the moon, or other spatial body. The craft is tethered by supporting cables or other restraint system so that it may be suspended safely above the ground, to be lowered under control by landing rockets, the tethering cables kept in standby readiness to prevent an inadvertent fall or plunge to the surface. See **Ugly Duckling.**

THEODOLITE. Basically, an accurate surveyor's transit. At Cape Canaveral, a conventional transit or theodolite is ill adapted to recording booster-vehicle position during flight. Accordingly, the theodolites for range use have evolved into cine-theodolites (see **askania**) and photo-theodolites. The latter differ from cine-theodolites in that the cine-camera is replaced by a precision, fixed (glass) plate camera in which a large field

is viewed and multiple exposures are made on the arc plate showing the rocket vehicle as it moves through the field of view. Whereas a cine-theodolite is a mobile tracking instrument, the photo-theodolite is locked in position during the photographic recordings.

THEORETICAL GRAVITY. The value of gravity at the earth's surface if the earth were a perfect sphere with no variation in mass to induce anomalies. See **gravity anomalies.**

"THE RED BALL IS UP." Signal to personnel at Cape Canaveral that "a bird is live on the pad," "the count is hot," or that "the pigeon is about to fly." A launching is imminent.

THERMAL. Pertaining to heat or temperature.

THERMAL BARRIER. The zone of speed at which friction heat generated by rapid passage of an object through the atmosphere exceeds endurance compatible with the function of the object.

THERMAL HEATING. Aerodynamic heating produced by supersonic and hypersonic travel through the atmosphere; transfer of heat from a laminar or turbulent flow around the nose of a re-entry body as it loses kinetic energy.

THERMAL LOAD. Stresses imposed upon a rocket or spacecraft-vehicle structure because of expansion or contraction (or both) of certain structural elements caused by aerodynamic heating during flight and re-entry, or by cooling effects of liquid oxygen in the oxidizer system. See **creep.**

THERMAL NEUTRALITY. The condition that exists when a nude man is at rest with an ambient temperature of 80° to 86°F., with relative humidity of 50% to 60%. Under these conditions the part of his body circulation which is concerned with the regulation of normal body temperature is in a condition of rest, as are the sweat glands. Environmentally he is wholly unstressed, and his metabolic needs are minimal.

THERMISTOR. A temperature-sensitive resistor with a negative temperature coefficient of resistance.

THERMOCHEMISTRY. A branch of chemistry that treats of the relations between heat and chemical changes.

THERMOCOUPLE. An instrument or device that is composed of two separate metals; when heated, they produce an electrical current. Measurement of this current provides a temperature reading.

THERMODYNAMIC. Pertaining to the flow of heat or to thermodynamics.

THERMODYNAMICS. The study of the relationships between heat and mechanical energy.

THERMONUCLEAR. Pertaining to a nuclear reaction that is triggered by particles of high thermal energy.

THINDOWN. The process by which cosmic rays, atomic particles, meteoroids, or the like lose their identity or their force as they penetrate into the atmosphere.

THROAT. In rocket engines, the most constricted section of an exhaust nozzle. At the throat gas-flow velocities (for supersonic flow rates) always equal sonic velocity. After the throat, the nozzle expands and flow velocities increase to supersonic values.

THROATABLE. Said of a nozzle designed so as to allow a change in the velocity of the exhaust stream through changing the size and shape of the throat of the nozzle.

THROAT CHOKES. A persistent cough without any accompanying chest pain and without labored breathing, sometimes caused by the effect of cold, dry oxygen upon a pre-existing irritation in the throat. *Throat chokes* may or may not be associated with dysbarism or decompression sickness, and are specifically distinguished from chokes. See **chokes.**

THRUST. (1) The resultant force in the direction of motion due to the components of the pressure forces in excess of ambient atmospheric pressure, acting on all inner surfaces of the vehicle propulsion system parallel to the direction of motion. (2) Specifically, in rocketry, the product of propellant mass flow rate and exhaust velocity relative to the vehicle.

THRUST BUILDUP. Sequence of events in starting a large liquid-propellant rocket power plant; begins with the ignition phase, progresses through pre-stage, and is completed when full thrust is obtained at main stage. Main stage is considered obtained when the thrust level reaches 90% of the maximum possible available thrust.

THRUST CHAMBER. A rocket motor or engine.

THRUST CUTOFF. The abrupt cessation of the reaction process in a rocket.

THRUST CUTOFF POINT. The point in a rocket vehicle's trajectory where the guidance system cuts off propulsive power at the desired altitude, speed, and direction. See **Brennschluss; shutoff.**

THRUST DECAY. When the motors of a booster vehicle are cut off, or shut down, the propulsive thrust does not instantly fall to zero, but progressively declines over a fraction of a second. This graduated reduction and loss of thrust is known as "thrust decay."

THRUST EFFECTIVE VEHICLE. The resultant force in the direction of motion of an aerospace vehicle, owing to the components of the pressure forces in excess of the ambient atmospheric pressure acting on all inner surfaces of the vehicle parallel to the direction of motion.

THRUST REVERSE. A device for redirecting a rocket engine's exhaust to the direction opposite to that of flight.

THRUST SECTION. A section in a rocket or spacecraft vehicle that houses or incorporates the combustion chamber or chambers and nozzles. Generally, a propulsion system.

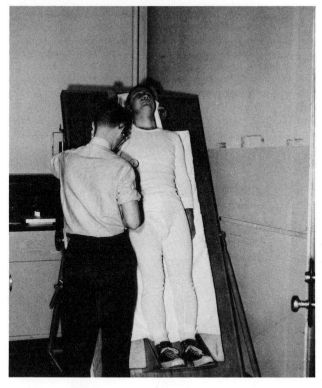

TILT TABLE. The subject is Astronaut Virgil Grissom

THRUST TERMINATOR. A device for ending the thrust in a rocket motor or engine, either through propellant cutoff (in the case of liquids) or through diverting the flow of gases from the nozzle.

THRUST–WEIGHT RATIO. Pounds of thrust per pound of engine weight. A figure used to evaluate engine performance and obtained by dividing the thrust output by the engine weight less fuel.

TILTING CHAIR. A specially mounted chair in which the subject is tilted to different angles and axes, to establish higher efficiency in pilot vision and visual resolution, based on the theory that if the pilot's head is turned to a different angle—to change illumination of the retinas in the eyes—the pilot may see the horizon again more sharply than before.

TILT TABLE. A physiological stress test in which the subject lies on a steeply inclined table for 25 minutes to measure the ability of the heart to compensate for the body's being in an unusual position for an extended time.

TIME DILATION. Relativity effect experienced within bodies moving at very high speeds in which time measured by a clock traveling within the body seems slower than time measured by a clock at rest in the initial frame of reference (such as the earth). In nature, time dilation seems to slow the decay of mesons (cosmic radiation particles) passing through the atmosphere. Time dilation is frequently discussed as a factor for interstellar flight over distances measured in light years at velocities close to that of light, in which the interstellar voyagers could make their journey in only several years of their subjective time while many more years pass on the earth. In theory, such a voyage might encompass 6 years for the interstellar travelers, while 80 years passed on the earth.

TIME HACK. A specific moment in time, especially during a countdown or time mission, that is co-ordinated among all involved operating personnel.

"TIN CAN." The Mercury space capsule. Popular term used by technical and servicing crews—and astronauts.

TIN–CANNING. Sounds made by a large liquid-fueled rocket booster when the booster is fueled and ready for launch. The sounds come from contraction of metal skin, goxing, internal power sources, pressure bleedoffs, etc. Engineers say "the bird is tin-canning; she's alive and talking."

TIROS. A series of elaborate satellites to conduct extensive research tests and TV transmissions of earth cloud cover as seen from space, to develop an advanced meteorological satellite system. During this process of orbiting successive Tiros satellites, data for operational use in meteorological studies and forecasting are provided. The satellite—Tiros IV is the example—is a cylinder 42 inches in diameter and 19 inches high, weighing 285 lbs., and with the top and sides covered with over 9,000 solar cells. Photographs have been excellent in the series, and Tiros is the forerunner of the advanced **Nimbus** and **Aeros** satellite systems.

TITAN II. Two-stage rocket booster to carry two-man Gemini capsule into earth orbit. Uses **hypergolic fuel** (q.v.). Stage I has 430,-000 lbs. thrust; Stage II has 100,000 lbs. thrust. Also, USAF second-generation ICBM.

TITAN III. Titan II booster modified with two large solid-propellant rockets strapped to booster sides. Solid-propellant rockets commence firing on ground, then liquid-propellant Titan system fires in stages. Booster vehicle for Dyna-Soar. See **Dyna-Soar.**

TITANIUM. Strong, heat-resistant metal used for spacecraft structure. Stronger than steel, titanium weighs only 44% of steel.

TIROS I, first of spectacularly successful meteorological satellite series, relayed TV pictures of clouds to ground stations

TITAN II, two-stage booster for Gemini spacecraft. Titan II first stage has 430,000 lbs. thrust; upper stage has 100,000 lbs. thrust. Orbital capability, 8,000 lbs.

TITAN III. First-stage solid-propellant boosters firing

TNT BRICKS. Explosive charges used for the inflight destruction of any rocket booster vehicle; placed so as to rupture the fuel tanks and lines and create an uncontrolled explosion to destroy the vehicle.

TOLERANCE DOSE. The amount of radiation which may be received by the occupant of a spacecraft within a specified period with negligible physiological results.

TOPPING OFF. Replacing, or "topping off," the vapor loss through boiloff of a cryogenic fuel prior to ignition of a rocket booster, or replacing fuel, such as kerosene, as the propellant is consumed during the thrust buildup prior to first motion. Accomplished by the ground fueling system adjacent to the launch stand.

TOPSIDE SOUNDER. A satellite designed to measure ion concentration in the ionosphere from above the ionosphere.

TOTAL IMPULSE. The average thrust times the burning time of the rocket, measured in pound-seconds.

TOUCHDOWN. The landing of any space vehicle under control on the surface of a spatial body by any method except aerodynamic gliding. See **splashdown.**

TRAAC. Transit Research and Attitude Control satellite. The 240-lb. satillite is doorknob-shaped, 43 inches in diameter, 16 inches high, with a tube mounted atop the satellite. Its purpose is to test the accuracy and reliability of a spacecraft stabilization system utilizing as a reference the gravitational field of the earth.

TRACK. To display or record the successive positions of a moving object; also to lock onto a point of radiation and obtain guidance or orientation therefrom.

TRACKING. The process of following the movement of a satellite, spacecraft, rocket, or any other flightborne or spaceborne vehicle by radar, radio, and photographic observations.

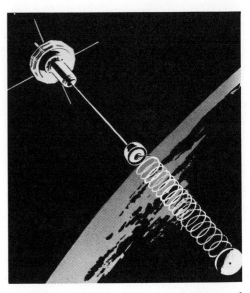

TRAAC satellite in orbit to test spacecraft stabilizing systems based on reference to terrestrial gravity pull

TRACKING STATION. A station set up to track an object moving through the atmosphere or space, usually by means of radar or radio.

TRACKING SYSTEM. Any system used to measure the position, velocity, and direction of an aerospace vehicle in flight.

TRAJECTORY. Path described in flight by a ballistic or space vehicle, moving as a result of externally applied forces. In common usage, also used to mean "flight path" or "orbit."

TRANQUILIZER. An instrument that adds stability to the guidance system of a booster rocket system or a missile.

TRANSDUCERS. End instruments that convert the values of properties to be measured (pressure, temperature, etc.) into equivalent electrical signals. These signals are then fed to the telemetering system for transmission from the vehicle to ground receiving stations.

TRANSFER ELLIPSE. Path followed by a body moving from one elliptical orbit to another. Transfer ellipses which intersect departure and arrival orbits at large angles are most expensive in energy requirements.

TRANSFER ORBIT. In interplanetary flight, an elliptical trajectory tangent to the orbits of both the departure planet and the target planet. See **transfer ellipse.**

TRANSFER VAN. In Project Mercury, the 35-foot-long trailer van, air-conditioned and specially equipped for transfer of astronauts from Hangar S to launch site on Cape Canaveral.

TRANSISTOR. An electronic device that controls an electron current by the conducting properties of germanium or a like material, capable of amplifying signals 100,000 times, but using only a small fraction of the power required for an electron tube. (The transistor is similar to the vacuum tube in uses, but is itself a non-vacuum device.) It is used extensively in space-vehicle equipment.

TRANSIT. (1) The passage of a celestial body across a celestial meridian; usually called meridian transit. (2) The apparent passage of a celestial body across the face of another celestial body or across any point, area, or line.

TRANSIT PROGRAM. A program under auspices of the U.S. Navy to place earth satellites into orbit to serve as a system of extremely accurate aerial and maritime navigation under any weather conditions within the atmosphere. Several of the 200-lb.-plus spherical satellites have been orbited (Thor-Ablestar booster) successfully in the program. (There have also been several failures.) The goal is a system of four satellites in circular orbits.

TRANSLATIONAL MANEUVERS. The maneuvers of positioning, velocity increments and adjustments, and hard docking necessary to accomplish the coupling (mating) of two space vehicles in orbit. Also: the necessary maneuvers to move from a hovering position, using rocket thrust in an

TRANSIT II-A Navy navigational satellite went into orbit with "piggyback" GREB satellite. This made possible two simultaneous research space missions with one booster

airless environment, in order to select a more satisfactory touchdown site on the surface of an airless planet or satellite.

TRANSLATIONAL ROCKETS. Reaction jets or rockets of low-order thrust (25 to 250 lbs.) in a spacecraft, which are to be used for purposes of docking in orbit with another spacecraft. Also called positioning rockets. See **Gemini.**

TRANSLUNAR. Of or pertaining to space outside the moon's orbit about the earth.

TRANSLUNAR SPACE. That part of space conceived as a spherical layer centered on the earth, with its lower limits at the distance of the orbit of the moon, but extending to several hundred thousand miles beyond. (This term is one of distance from the earth, not one of the moon's influence.)

TRANSPONDER. An electronic device that receives a challenging signal and automatically transmits a response. Consists of a receiver to receive the signal impulses, and a responder (transmitter) that returns the impulses to the interrogator-responser. Provides positive tracking and identification signals.

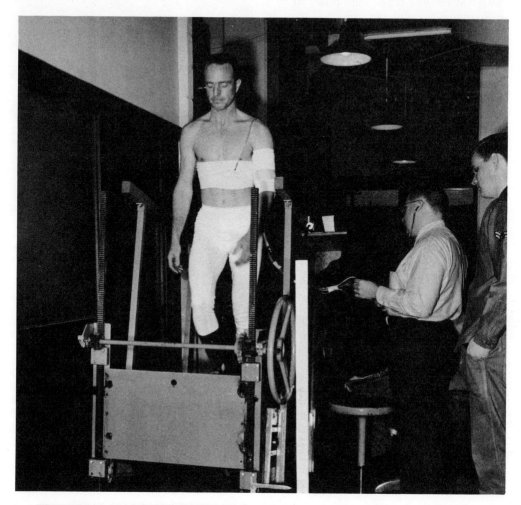

TREADMILL MAXIMUM WORKLOAD test being taken by Astronaut Scott Carpenter

TRANSVERSE ACCELERATION; TRANSVERSE g. The inertial force produced by an acceleration acting across the body, perpendicular to the long axis of the body, as in a chest-to-back direction (i.e., position of the astronaut in the Mercury, Gemini, and Apollo spacecraft). The mild transverse accelerations experienced by the pilot during rapid takeoff of a fighter aircraft or abrupt landing while in the upright seated position, or while in a prone or supine position during a pullout or turn, are conditions of transverse g. See **negative g; nega-** **tive-g tolerance; positive g; positive-g tolerance.**

TRAPPING. The process by which radiation particles are caught and retained in a radiation belt.

TREADMILL MAXIMUM WORKLOAD. A physiological stress test in which the subject walks at a constant rate on a moving platform which is elevated one degree each minute. The test continues until the heart reaches 180 beats per minute. A test of physical fitness.

TROPOPAUSE. The boundary or transition zone between the troposphere and the stratosphere.

TROPOSPHERE. The lower layer of the earth's atmosphere, extending from the surface of the earth to an altitude of approximately 10 miles. Although the composition of the air remains more or less constant, its density decreases rapidly with altitude— 75% of the atmosphere's weight is found in the troposphere. See **atmosphere.**

T–TIME. That moment of a countdown when the booster rocket is to be launched.

TUMBLING. An unsatisfactory attitude situation in which a vehicle continues on its flight, but turns end-over-end about its center of gravity with its longitudinal axis remaining in the plane of flight. Also *tumble.*

TURNAROUND. The initial maneuver executed by the Mercury capsule after separation from the Atlas booster. Automatic pilot dampens out oscillations, then turns capsule 180° so that the blunt edge with the retropack and heat shield face in the direction of flight.

TWO–STEP MASTERS TEST. An exercise test for evaluating the function of the heart muscle by making an electrocardiogram (record of electrical current output of the beating heart) before and after a period of exercise, consisting of stepping up and down a platform two steps high.

U

UGLY DUCKLING. A rocket-vehicle vertical landing and hovering simulator at Naval Ordnance Test Station at China Lake, California. A rocket "vehicle simulator" is tethered to a 160-foot tower, controlled remotely by a pilot on the ground, using an optical scanner that supplies precise altitude of vehicle from the surface. The vehicle simulator has a controllable thrust rocket providing hovering or 4-feet-per-minute descent capability. The rocket vehicle weighs 6,000 lbs., and is being adapted to "free flight" for more realistic control tests to simulate landings on the lunar surface.

A future development of UGLY DUCKLING now under construction by NASA for simulating spacecraft descents to lunar surface

ULLAGE. The amount that a container, such as a fuel tank, lacks of being full.

ULTRA SARAH BEACON. Radio homing beacon contained in survival kit of astronaut for emergency use after landing.

ULTRASONIC. Of or pertaining to frequencies above those that affect the human ear, i.e., more than 20,000 vibrations per second. The term "ultrasonic" may be used as a modifier to indicate a device or system intended to operate at an ultrasonic frequency.

ULTRAVIOLET ALTIMETER. An altimeter for manned atmospheric and space vehicles that uses the ultraviolet spectrum to obtain accurate altitude readings up to 125,-000 feet from the surface.

UNDERDECK SPRAY

ULTRAVIOLET RADIATION. Electromagnetic radiation shorter in wavelength than visible radiation but longer than X-rays; roughly, radiation in the wavelength interval between 10 and 4,000 angstroms. Ultraviolet radiation from the sun is responsible for many complex photochemical reactions characteristic of the upper atmosphere, e.g., the formation of the ozone layer through ultraviolet disassociation of oxygen molecules and recombination to form ozone.

ULTRAVIOLET SPECTROGRAPH. A 35-mm camera equipped with a special quartz lens and prism system for use through the spacecraft window in 2,000- to 3,000-angstrom wavelength band. A demountable reticle is provided for sighting on a particular star. Used in manned orbital missions of Project Mercury.

UMBILICAL CORD. Any of the servicing electrical or fluid lines between the ground or a tower and an upright rocket vehicle and/or spacecraft prior to launch. They are ejected immediately before or during the first instant of launch.

UNCO-OPERATIVE SATELLITE. A passive satellite; one which does not co-operate with the ground environment. More specifically, a satellite in which responsive equipment has failed, rather than a satellite intended specifically to be orbited as a passive satellite without responsive electronic or other equipment.

UNDERDECK SPRAY. That part of a pad deluge in which the water is directed upward from under a rocket vehicle on its launch ring. See **pad deluge.**

UNDERTAKERS. Popular name for underwater salvage crews who dive for parts of missiles, rocket boosters, and rocket assemblies destroyed during abortive launchings, after the parts have fallen into the ocean bordering the Cape Canaveral area.

UNIVERSE. The entire spatial cosmos.

UPPER AIR. The atmospheric region embracing the ionosphere and the exosphere.

UPPER–AIR OBSERVATION. A measurement of atmospheric conditions aloft, above the effective range of a surface weather observation. Also called "sounding" or "upper-air sounding." In this context, upper-air observation goes beyond the specific definition of **upper air** as the atmospheric region embracing the ionosphere and the exosphere, since it involves lower layers of the atmosphere as well.

UPPER STAGE. A second or later stage in a multi-stage rocket.

USEFUL CONSCIOUSNESS. The specific period of time in which a man exposed to explosive decompression under space conditions can function coherently in attempting emergency action to save his life. From 50,-000 feet ambient air pressure into non-atmospheric space, the time of useful consciousness remains generally constant—between 8 and 15 seconds before unconsciousness and death. See **blood, boiling of; explosive decompression.**

V

VACUUM. See **space.**

VACUUM EVAPORATION. The surface of any solid substance always undergoes a process of molecules leaving the surface and other molecules being captured and retained by the surface. Under "normal earth conditions" the dual process balances—there is an equilibrium of exchange. Under vacuum conditions, however, the molecules that escape from a surface have a mean free path of several miles—they are lost forever. Any material in space, then, is constantly losing part of its molecular makeup through evaporation; there is a loss of the equilibrium state and molecules normally captured are absent. The rate of evaporation is dependent upon temperature, surface conditions, and latent heat of vaporization. (The popular expression for this phenomenon is *outgassing*.)

VALID SIGNAL. Any signal which accurately represents an event or action as having literally taken place, as opposed to a false or spurious signal that might arise from malfunctioning equipment.

VALSALVA MANEUVER. Flight personnel breathing pure oxygen under low ambient air pressures often develop severe earache pains hours after descent to the surface. During the period of 100% oxygen consumption, the gas contained in the middle ear has an unusually high oxygen content rather than the normal 21%; this excessive oxygen is absorbed at a higher rate than normal into the middle-ear tissues. The normal body rate of ventilation is insufficient to maintain normal pressure, and there results a reduced pressure or partial vacuum within the middle ear, causing serious pain to develop. The Valsalva maneuver is the action after descent of closing the mouth, holding the nose, and blowing gently. Frequent Valsalva maneuvers prevent continuation of unbalanced pressure, and prevent both pain and possible inner-ear injury to the pilot or astronaut.

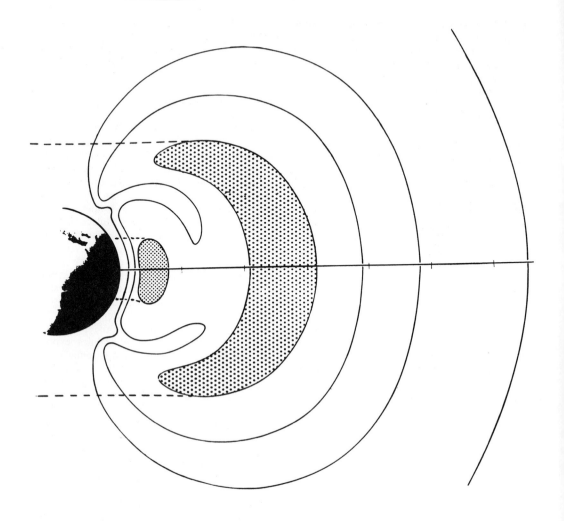

VAN ALLEN RADIATION BELT

VAN ALLEN RADIATION BELT. Two belts of high-energy charged particles trapped in the earth's magnetic field, in the form of doughnut-shaped zones about the planet. These belts ring the earth and constitute a hazard of still fully undetermined danger to astronauts moving through them. Centered at some 2,000 miles above the equator, the inner belt is about 1,000 miles thick. The outer belt is thicker, and fluctuates through peaks and intensities of radiation. Greatest intensity seems to extend from 9,000 to 12,-000 miles above the earth's surface.

VANGUARD. The second program of the United States to launch into earth orbit small scientific satellites. Project Vanguard was carried out originally from its inception date of July 29, 1955 by the U.S. Navy, and then came under the cognizance of NASA. The original plan called for the attempted orbiting of 12 different satellites; the project was to be considered successful if any one satellite went into orbit. Thirteen orbital attempts were made, of which three were successful. The smallest Vanguard satellite, still in orbit, is a small sphere 6 inches in diameter and weighing 3.25 lbs.; with the satellite in orbit is the expended third stage weighing 50 lbs. The next success in the Vanguard series was a spherical satellite 20 inches in diameter and weighing 20.7 lbs. The third Vanguard satellite to orbit represented yet another gain in payload; Vanguard III weighed 50 lbs. This satellite, launched on September 18, 1959, closed out Project Vanguard.

VANGUARD III, last Vanguard satellite placed in orbit; payload of 50 lbs.

VAPORTHORAX. A condition characterized by the existence of large water-vapor bubbles in the intrapleural space between the lungs and the chest wall, occurring when an individual is exposed without protection to altitudes equivalent to 63,000 feet or higher. See **alveolar air; breathing, process of; blood, boiling of.**

VECO. Vernier Engine Cut Off. See **verniers.**

VECTOR. An entity which has both magnitude and direction.

VECTOR STEERING. A steering (guiding) method in which one or more thrust chambers are gimbal-mounted so that the deviation of the thrust force (thrust vector) may be tilted in relation to the center of gravity of the rocket vehicle to produce a turning movement. Two servo actuators, one on the pitch axis and one on the yaw axis, tilt the thrust direction according to signals from the flight control (guidance) system.

VEHICLE. Specifically, in the aerospace sense, a structure, machine, or device, such as an aircraft, rocket, or spacecraft, designed to carry a burden through air or space. More restrictively, a rocket craft. The word has acquired its specific meaning owing to the need for a term to embrace all flight craft, atmospheric or space.

VELA HOTEL. A system of six satellites to detect nuclear explosions in space. Three satellites are to orbit in one plane and three additional satellites in a plane at an angle of 90° to the other three. Orbital heights are planned for 60,000 miles beyond the earth, using the Atlas-Agena B booster system.

VELCRO. Tradename for an adhering material made up of two types of cloth, one with multiple loops, one with multiple hooks, which adhere when pressed together, and are used extensively inside a manned spacecraft (such as the Mercury capsule) for restraining instruments and equipment during zero-g and acceleration conditions.

VELOCITY. (1) A vector quantity that includes both magnitude (speed) and direction relative to a given frame of reference. (2) Commonly used as a synonym of speed.

VELOCITY INCREMENT. An additional measure of speed imparted to a vehicle already moving at a specific velocity. See **kick rocket.**

VELOCITY VECTOR. Combination of two ballistic trajectory values: the speed of the vehicle's center of gravity at a designated point on the trajectory and the angle between the local vertical and the direction of the speed.

VENTILATING SUIT. A protective garment for airmen under conditions of sustained high ambient temperatures. The ventilating suit is a lightweight, quilted, sandwich-type suit made of vinyl plastic. Air is forced between the two layers and jets out through numerous tiny holes inside the garment. The air then picks up the moisture of body perspiration and carries it from the suit. The air is supplied from either an aircraft air-conditioning system or a small portable blower. (Illustration, page 216.)

VENTILATING SUIT being worn in chamber test

VERNIERS. Small rocket engines used for roll control of booster vehicle and for velocity trim requirements. For example, in addition to three main engines, Atlas has two small verniers, each of 1,000 lbs. thrust, for roll control during ascent. After main engine shutdown, the verniers "trim" the booster vehicle velocity to exact value required. After verniers shut down, all power flight of booster ceases.

VERTICAL. The direction in which the force of gravity acts.

VERTICAL ACCELERATOR

VERTICAL ACCELERATOR. A training device at Air Force Aero Medical Laboratories, Wright-Patterson Air Force Base, Ohio, which subjects its human occupant to violent up-and-down vertical movements, while simultaneously swinging from side to side to simulate severe yaw. The vertical accelerator simulates realistically the conditions of violent buffeting and yaw movements of a high-speed vehicle during flight through severe turbulence, or during re-entry from space.

VERTICAL FRONTIER. Popular expression that encompasses the entire extent of activities toward manned space flight; designates the border of the area intended for exploration and control that lies in all directions outward from the earth.

VERTIGO. Complete and total spatial disorientation; total inability to judge any visual references.

VESTIBULAR APPARATUS. The "balance mechanism" of the inner ear, responsive partially to gravity and partially to tangential acceleration or deceleration. See **equilibrium and orientation.**

VIOLET RAY. The shortest ray (385 millimicrons) of the visible spectrum, evoking the color violet in the eye.

VIPS. Voice Interruption Priority System. A flight safety concept developed to an unusual degree of pilot-safety monitoring effectiveness, and tested extensively aboard high-supersonic aircraft; with further development being integrated into spacecraft systems to meet emergency conditions. In terms of current use, VIPS provides continuous monitoring of at least 20 potentially hazardous conditions aboard the aircraft. When strategically located fault switches are activated by an emergency (such as low cabin pressure), a tape-recorded warning message is broadcast through the headset of the pilot and/or the crew. Each message plays 15 seconds and is calculated to provide the most useful information concerning a given emergency. In most cases the message consists of both the warning and remedial procedures. The VIPS warning message repeats until the hazardous condition is corrected or the pilot deactivates the signal. In case additional hazards occur while one voice channel is playing, the system's logic network immediately selects the hazard having the highest priority and "interrupts" the original warning. VIPS is a significant improvement over warning systems employing lights, bells, horns, etc. A visual warning signal must fall within a pilot's 30° cone of vision. The pilot must also *see* the light (a factor which during busy moments is left to chance), and tests have shown that warning lights can go un-

detected for as long as 15 minutes, although the average time for perception is 5 seconds. On the average, a pilot requires a total of 12 seconds to perceive and interpret a visual warning and to take action. With VIPS, wherein emergency information is transmitted immediately to the brain, the total reaction sequence is reduced to about 3 seconds. A woman's voice is used on the prerecorded tapes to assure quick differentiation between the warning voice and the voices of crew members.

VISCOSITY. Measure of difficulty with which molecules of a fluid flow past one another.

VISIBILITY. Also: **visual acuity.** The ease with which an object can be seen. Depends on (1) the angular size of the object, (2) the quantity and direction of illumination of the object, (3) the contrast between the object and its background, (4) the length of time it is seen, (5) the degree of retinal adaptation, and (6) the condition of the atmosphere (when applicable) separating the observer and the object. The visibility of any object increases as the angular size, illumination, contrast, viewing time, retinal adaptation, or atmospheric clarity is increased. See **depth perception.**

VISIBLE RADIATION. Electromagnetic radiation lying within the wavelength interval to which the human eye is sensitive, which is approximately from 0.4 to 0.7 micron (4,000 to 7,000 angstroms). This portion of the electromagnetic spectrum is bounded on the short-wavelength end by ultraviolet radiation, and on the long-wavelength end by infrared radiation.

VISOR. A plasticized, transparent, and curving shield that reduces intensity and glare of the sun. It is mounted on a helmet and may be snapped down in position before the eyes and face of a pilot. Also: *sun visor.*

VISUAL ACCOMMODATION. The ability of the eyes to adjust, or change focus, in order to see objects within about 20 feet (the eyes accommodate little for seeing distant objects).

VISUAL ACUITY. See **visibility.**

V–METER. The specific name of this instrument is the *extinctospectropolariscope-occulogyrogravoadaptometer.* A device used, specifically in the manned orbital missions of Project Mercury, for 16 astronomical and physiological tests in orbit. It can be used for measuring the relative brightness of the zodiacal light and other dim night phenomena. It is equipped with crossed polaroid filters which permit direct viewing of the solar disc and measurement of the polarization of the corona. It is used also to judge the horizon under zero-*g* conditions.

VOICE COMMUNICATIONS (Examples):

Affirmative	"Yes," or "That is correct."
All systems GO	"Everything is operating as planned. . . ."
Capcom	"Capsule communicator."
Capsep	"Capsule has separated."
Come in	"Please acknowledge."
Do you read?	"Are you receiving me?"
Five-by-five	"Loud and clear. . . ."
In the green	"Everything is operating perfectly. . . ."
Negative	"No," or "That is incorrect."
Over	"Switching back to you. . . ."
Out	"My transmission is complete; am ending communications. . . ."
Roger	"I understand."
Stand by one	"We're tied up; please wait. You're first on call. . . ."
Wilco	"Will comply."

VOLUME. The measure of space occupied by a body.

VORTEX GENERATOR. A movable or fixed surface—usually a series of sharp vertical fins—on any aerodynamic body that is used as a spoiler in the airflow to break down the airflow, and usually to effect a redistribution of the airflow over movable control surfaces.

VOSTOK BOOSTER. A two-stage liquid-propellant rocket booster with a total of six liquid propellant engines, clustering unknown. Total usable thrust 1,323,000 lbs. Orbital *payload* capacity in excess of 14,000 lbs.

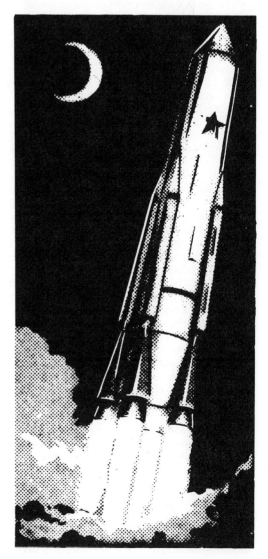

VOSTOK BOOSTER at launch. Four liquid-propellant engines in first stage burning with 1,056,000 lbs. thrust. Employed also for heavy satellite orbital shots

VOSTOK ORIENTATION. To properly orient the Vostok spaceship under manual control operation, the Russian cosmonaut employs an optical orientation device in order to determine the position of his spacecraft in relation to the earth. The optical device is installed in one of the Vostok viewports (there are five in the spacecraft); the device consists of two annular mirror-reflectors, a light filter, and a latticed glass. The rays traveling from the line of the horizon strike the first reflector and, passing through the glass of the viewport, reach the second reflector, which directs them through the latticed glass to the eyes of the cosmonaut. If the spacecraft's bearings in relation to the vertical axis are correct, the cosmonaut sees the horizon in the form of a circle in his field of vision. Through the central part of the viewport the cosmonaut sees the part of the earth's surface directly beneath his spacecraft. The position of the Vostok's longitudinal axis in relation to the direction of flight is determined by watching the "run" of the earth's surface in the pilot's field of vision. With co-ordinated use of the Vostok reaction control jets the cosmonaut can turn the Vostok in a direction ensuring that the line of the horizon is visible in the orientation system in the form of a concentric circle, and that the direction of the earth's "run" coincides with the course plotted on the latticed glass (the chart). This provides immediate proof of the correct orientation of the spacecraft. If necessary the cosmonaut's field of vision can be covered by a light filter or shutter. See **attitude; attitude control movements; attitude control system; reaction control jets; Vostoks.**

VOSTOKS. Soviet manned spaceships: first to orbit the earth unmanned; first to orbit the earth with animals and recover the animals unharmed; first to carry man into orbit; first to remain in orbit several days; and first to accomplish orbital rendezvous (distance of separation between Vostoks III and IV, 1.87 miles). Weight in excess of 10,000 lbs. (Vostok I was 10,416 lbs.; Vostok II was 10,408 lbs.). Approximate length 22 feet, approximate width 14 feet. In one-man configuration has life-support and power-supply system effective for 12-day orbital flight.

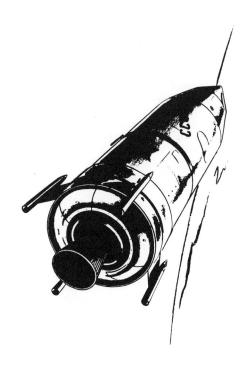

VOSTOK. Five-ton Soviet manned spacecraft in orbital rendezvous configuration

VOYAGER. Follow-on-project to **Mariner.** The first interplanetary-probe payloads scheduled to be boosted by the Saturn C-1 and C-1B boosters. The Voyager payloads are planned to weigh a minimum of from 2,400 to 3,000 lbs., and to orbit Mars or Venus. The orbiting vehicle will carry out observations and studies of the planet from a distance of several hundred miles, and then eject a capsule to land on the planet surface. During descent and after landing the capsule is to carry out extensive and detailed measurements. These data are transmitted to the orbiting vehicle, and relayed to the earth.

W

WALLOPS STATION. NASA research, development, and vehicle launch site on Virginia coast. Extensive work is being conducted at Wallops on man-in-space systems and vehicles.

WARNING LIGHT. A light on any control panel, board, console, or within a spacecraft or aircraft cabin, immediately visible to one or more persons, that signifies a condition of danger or imminent danger. An amber or yellow light usually denotes a non-critical malfunction, while a red light denotes a critical malfunction—such as overheating or dangerously low fuel supply.

WATER–CUSHION PRINCIPLE. A g-force protective system based on the demonstrated increased tolerance to g force of a man immersed in water. Forces of 13g have been withstood without difficulty for as long as 4 minutes when the test subject was immersed in a centrifuge water tank called the **sarcophagus.** The water-cushion principle is based on the Archimedes principle that "When a solid is immersed in a fluid, it loses a portion of its weight, and this portion is equal to the weight of the fluid which it displaces; that is, to the weight of its own bulk of the fluid." Early tests proved that under high-g forces the test subject could move his limbs without difficulty, because his proportional weight was well below normal weight under the onset of the g forces. Further improvement came by moving from supine to semi-supine position and placing a basic contour couch of balsa wood beneath the test subject. At a sustained force of 13g, the test subject was completely mobile as to limbs and extremities. No pain developed and the duration of each test run was limited only by the test subject's ability to breathe. Prior to the 13g runs at 4 minutes' duration, g-loading limits were 12g for 1 minute 45 seconds prior to blackout. Current tests are planned to exceed considerably the 13g/4-minute outer limit. See **positive-g tolerance; semi-supine position.**

WATER SUIT. A g-suit in which water is used in the interlining, thereby automatically approximating the required hydrostatic pressure-gradient under g forces. See **g-suit; pressure suit.**

WATER SYSTEM. Water-flow system for flame bucket beneath large rocket boosters, to spray water against steel and concrete during live booster firing. In Atlas launch stand, water-flow rate during firing is 35,000 gallons per minute. See **flame bucket.**

WAVEGUIDE. A system of material boundaries capable of guiding electromagnetic waves.

WEIGHT. The force with which an earthbound body is attracted toward the earth.

WEIGHTLESSNESS. The condition that exists when there is a lack of resistance to a body under the influence of gravity. A vehicle in orbit is weightless because it *falls* continually about the earth without any resistance to that fall. The arc of its flight matches—parallels approximately—the arc or the curve of the earth's surface. As fast as the vehicle falls (in response to gravity), the surface of the earth curves away beneath it. The capsule falls without resistance—and therefore is weightless. Under conditions of weightlessness, no acceleration, whether of gravity or other force, can be detected by an observer within the system in question. (Weightlessness can be produced within the atmosphere in aircraft flying a parabolic flight path.) (Illustrations, page 222.)

WEIGHTLESS REGURGITATION PHENOMENON. A condition encountered under zero-g tests that consists of regurgitation of part of the stomach contents when a slight blow, or steady pressure, is imparted to the abdomen. This particular reaction is observed most often in zero-g tests following the subject's drinking large volumes of fluids.

WESTFORD. An Air Force project using an Atlas-Agena B booster vehicle to place in circular orbit millions of fine wires ejected from the Agena B stage as the vehicle eases into orbit. The wires would be used for passive-reflector communications with earth-to-earth points.

222

WEIGHTLESSNESS in an aircraft flying a parabolic arc (*left*). Seven-day manned experiment (*right*) to determine what effects prolonged floating—a state in many ways similar to the weightlessness of space flight—has on the human body. The subject was suspended completely in water, and took his diet for the week through a straw. One unexpected result was softening of the bones.

WEIGHTLESSNESS. Profile of mission flown by fighter aircraft in parabolic arc to establish zero-*g* condition for 45 seconds

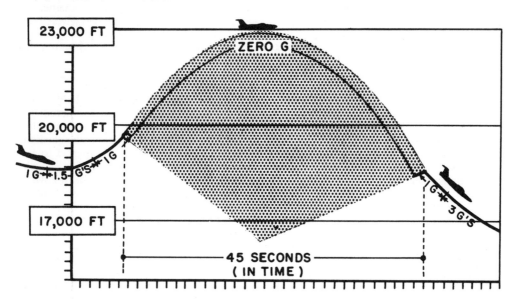

WET EMPLACEMENT. A launch emplacement that provides a deluge of water for cooling the flame bucket, rocket vehicle engines, and other equipment during the launch of the rocket vehicle. See **flame deflector; underdeck spray.**

WET START. The ignition of a liquid-rocket engine wherein the combustion is inhibited by water dilution of the fuel. This results in a slower buildup of thrust than the "dry start" and subjects the engine and airframe to less violent stresses.

WHIP ANTENNA. An antenna that is shaped and flexible, like a whip. Used widely in space-vehicle systems.

WHISTLER. A radio-frequency electromagnetic signal that sounds like a whistle; sometimes generated by lightning discharges.

WHITE ROOM. A specially constructed room near the top of a gantry service tower in which a manned spacecraft is sealed off from the elements, and the environment controlled to minimize the effects of humidity, dust, and other factors on the spacecraft components.

WINDBLAST. The effect of wind upon the face and body of a pilot who ejects from an aircraft into the open air at very high speeds. Windblast can be severe enough to tear limbs from their sockets, snap bones, kill a man instantly.

WINDOW. World War II popular name for metal foil strips dropped through the air to achieve maximum possible display on tracking radarscopes. See **chaff.**

WOBBLE PUMP. An emergency fuel pump for any fuel or fuel reservoir system of an aircraft or spacecraft that is operated by wobbling the handle or moving it back and forth.

WORKING FLUID. A fluid (gas or liquid) that converts one form of energy applied to it to another form of energy, or is the medium for the transfer of energy from one part to another. See **heat exchanger.**

WRIST MIRROR. A small rectangular or curving mirror worn on the wrist of an astronaut so that he can hold his arm in front of him in order to read instruments or study equipment in his spacecraft not otherwise visually accessible to him.

X

X-15. A stub-winged, rocket-powered hypersonic aerospace craft for advanced flight research. The X-15, able to fly at more than 4,000 mph, is a true aerospace vehicle by virtue of its ability to exceed 50 miles in altitude—that being the height regarded by the military services as qualifying the pilot as an astronaut who has completed a space flight.

X-20. Official designation for Dyna-Soar. See **Dyna-Soar.**

X-15 rocket-powered hypersonic plane, shown in high-speed glide without power

WINDBLAST

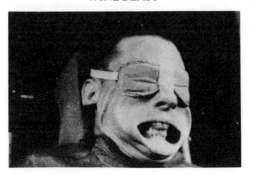

XLR. Experimental Liquid Rocket.

X-RAY. Electromagnetic radiation of very short wavelength, lying between the wavelength interval of 0.1 to 100 angstroms (between gamma rays and ultraviolet radiation). Also called "X-Radiation," "Roentgen Ray." X-rays penetrate various thicknesses of all solids and they act upon photographic plates in the same manner as light. Secondary X-rays are produced whenever X-rays are absorbed by a substance; in the case of absorption by a gas, this results in ionization.

X-TIME. The time remaining in a countdown prior to the launching of a rocket vehicle, according to the specific countdown schedule. See **T-time.**

Y

YAW. (1) The lateral rotational or oscillatory movement of an aircraft, spacecraft, rocket, or the like about a transverse axis. (2) The amount of this side-to-side movement, i.e., the angle of yaw.

YOKE. A control column in the form of a wheel, half-wheel, or similar shape; especially refers to a dual control column in an aircraft or spacecraft.

Z

ZENITH. See **spatial references.**

ZERO. Final moment of a countdown; for a booster vehicle, that moment when the countdown ends and booster ignition sequence for flight commences.

ZERO GRAVITY (Zero g). A condition in which a body falling under the influence of gravity experiences no resistance to its fall. See **weightlessness.**

ZERO HOUR CIRCLE. See **spatial references.**

ZERO–MISS GUIDANCE SYSTEM. Guidance system for Apollo lunar missions under development by MIT Instrumentation Laboratory. System will be totally integrated and will supply guidance and astrogation data throughout all phases of the lunar missions. The system involves an extraordinarily complex series of interrelationships with Apollo vehicle, communications systems, and crew control, varying with the specific mission. Inertial guidance is the basic element of the system; optical, radio, and radar links are integrated as prime navigational systems as well, especially for pre-established flight stages and for constant refinement of guidance information.

ZIP FUEL. A boron-based high-energy liquid fuel. See **exotic fuel.**

ZODIAC. A belt on the celestial sphere on which the moon, sun, and planets appear to move about the earth, the middle line of the belt being the ecliptic or the sun's path.

ZODIACAL BAND. A faintly luminous light band that appears on the celestial sphere, connecting the zodiacal light with Gegenschein, and caused by extension of the solar corona to distances beyond the orbit of the earth. See **Gegenschein.**

ZODIACAL LIGHT. "Planes" or "wings" of faint light extending on either side of the sun approximately in the plane of the ecliptic. This light is visible only after sunset or prior to sunrise, and is believed to be an extension of the outer solar atmosphere.

ZULU. Reference to a time reading that is based on Greenwich Mean Time (GMT). All manned flight and unmanned satellite operations are co-ordinated according to Zulu Time.

Line drawings by Fred L. Wolff.
All photos used through the courtesy of the following: NASA, *pp. 17, 23, 30, 43, 48, 50, 64, 65, 71, 72 bot., 85, 96, 97, 113, 121, 123, 125, 126, 135, 138, 140, 155, 158, 164, 171 bot., 186, 187, 189 left and bot., 200, 210, 222 left;* Official U.S. Air Force Photos, *pp. 18, 20, 21, 31, 39, 61, 63, 78, 87, 89, 91, 95 top, 101, 129, 130, 141, 146, 161, 171 top, 176, 179, 181, 194, 205, 212, 216, 217, 222 right;* General Electric, *p. 52;* Lockheed Missiles and Space Co., *pp. 55, 168;* The Martin Co., *pp. 68, 183, 191 top right, 192, 207;* Northrop, *p. 72 top;* Lockheed Propulsion Co., *p. 76 top;* Thiokol Chemical Corp., *p. 76 bot.;* Official U.S. Navy Photos, *pp. 81, 182, 198, 223;* McDonnell Aircraft Corp., *p. 86;* Aeronutronic Div., Ford Motor Co., *p. 94;* North American Aviation, *pp. 95 bot., 169;* American Museum of Natural History, *pp. 114, 132;* General Dynamics Corp., *p. 127;* Perkin-Elmer Corp., *p. 147;* Carl Byoir and Associates, Inc., *p. 151;* Republic Aviation Corp., *p. 153;* Boeing Airplane Co., *pp. 167, 191 bot. right;* Douglas Aircraft Corp., *p. 175;* American Telephone and Telegraph Co., *p. 185;* Hughes Aircraft Co., *p. 199.* The paintings on *pp. 16, 115, 189 top right, 191 left* are by Fred L. Wolff.